FINANCIAL ACCOUNTING PRINCIPLES WORKBOOK

V4.0

Lead Authors
Neville Joffe and Penny Parker

Contributors and Reviewers

Ronnie Carter, CPA
Patrick Henry Community College

Suryakant Desai, Ed.D., CPA, CFP
Dallas County Community College District

Cathy Duffy, Ed.D., M.Sc., B.Sc.
Champlain College

Dr. Regan Garey, D.B.A., M.B.A., B.S., B.A.
Lock Haven University

Sharon O'Reilly, M.B.A., B.A.
Gateway Technical College

Textbook ISBN: 978-1-926751-73-3
Workbook ISBN: 978-1-926751-74-0

Financial Accounting Principles Workbook, V4.0
Authors: Neville Joffe and Penny Parker
Publisher: AME Learning Inc.
Content Contributors and Developmental Editors:
        Kobboon Chotruangprasert/Graeme Gomes
Production Editors: Melody Yousefian
Copy Editor: Lisa McManus
Indexer: Elizabeth Walker
Typesetter: Paragon Prepress Inc.
Vice President and Publishing Manager: Linda Zhang
Cover Design: Bram Wigzell
Online Course Design & Production: AME Multimedia Team

2 3 4 MCRL 20 19 18

Printed in China

This workbook is written to provide accurate information on the covered topics.
It is not meant to take the place of professional advice.

For more information contact:

AME Learning Inc.
410-1220 Sheppard Avenue East
Toronto, ON, Canada M2K 2S5
Phone: 416.479.0200
Toll-free: 1.888.401.3881
E-mail: info@amelearning.com
Visit our website at: www.amelearning.com

Table of Contents

Chapter 1

FINANCIAL STATEMENTS: PERSONAL ACCOUNTING

LEARNING OBJECTIVES

LO **1**   Describe the purpose of accounting

LO **2**   Describe the balance sheet

LO **3**   Describe the income statement

LO **4**   Define an accounting period

LO **5**   Explain how the accounting equation works

LO **6**   Explain accrual-based accounting

LO **7**   Explain how to account for debt

LO **8**   Explain how to account for assets

LO **9**   Explain how to account for prepaid expenses

LO **10**   Define capital

LO **11**   Demonstrate how double entries are recorded in T-accounts

AMEENGAGE   *Access **ameengage.com** for integrated resources including tutorials, practice exercises, the digital textbook and more.*

Assessment Questions

AS-1 LO 1

Define accounting and describe the purpose of accounting.

_____

_____

_____

AS-2 LO 2

What is net worth?

_____

_____

_____

AS-3 LO 2

In simple terms, what are assets and liabilities?

_____

_____

AS-4 LO 3

What are revenues and expenses? Provide an example of each in your personal life.

_____

_____

_____

AS-5 LO 2

Explain the role of the balance sheet.

_____

_____

_____

AS-6 LO 3

Explain the role of the income statement.

_____

_____

_____

AS-7 LO 4

What are some advantages of using monthly accounting periods in your personal balance sheet?

_____

_____

_____

AS-8 LO 5

What is the accounting equation?

_____

_____

AS-9 LO 10

What is the equation for calculating ending net worth for a period?

_____

_____

AS-10 LO 3

Define surplus and deficit.

_____

_____

_____

_____

AS-11 LO 5

What is a T-account?

_____

_____

AS-12 LO 6

Explain accrual-based accounting.

_____

_____

_____

_____

AS-13 LO 6

Briefly describe the cash-based method of accounting.

_____

_____

_____

_____

AS-14 LO 7

True or False: When you borrow money, you have more cash but your net worth decreases.

_____

_____

AS-15 LO 7

True or False: When you pay off a loan, your cash decreases and your net worth increases.

_____

_____

AS-16 LO 8

True or False: Buying an asset has no impact on net worth.

_____

_____

AS-17 LO 9

What is a prepaid expense?

_____

_____

AS-18 LO 9

When an expense is initially prepaid, which accounts increase or decrease?

_____

_____

AS-19 `LO 9`

When does an expense need to be recorded under accrual-based accounting? What are the three possible timings the payment can be made for an expense?

_____

_____

_____

_____

_____

AS-20 `LO 10`

What is capital?

_____

_____

AS-21 `LO 11`

Where do the opening balances of the assets and liabilities normally appear on T-accounts?

_____

_____

_____

_____

Application Questions Group A

AP-1A `LO 2`

April Rose had the following financial data for the year ended December 31, 2018.

Cash	$6,000
Jewelry	10,000
Automobile	18,000
House	256,000
Bank Loan	45,000
Credit Card	5,000
Mortgage	140,000

Required

a) Calculate April Rose's total assets.

_____

_____

_____

_____

_____

b) Calculate April Rose's total liabilities.

_____

_____

_____

_____

AP-2A `LO 2 5`

Consider the following information for Julius Palanca.

Cash	$12,000
Jewelry	18,000
Automobile	22,000
House	161,000
Credit Card	5,000
Bank Loan	10,000
Mortgage	125,000

Required

a) Calculate Julius Palanca's total assets.

_____

_____

_____

b) Calculate Julius Palanca's total liabilities.

_____

_____

_____

_____

c) Calculate Julius Palanca's net worth.

_____

_____

_____

_____

_____

AP-3A LO 8

Darryl purchased a new laptop on January 1, 2018 worth $2,000. He paid the entire amount using cash. He also purchased a new cell phone worth $300 on account. How will these transactions affect Darryl's net worth?

_____

_____

AP-4A LO 3 6 10 11

The following information was taken from the personal records of Juliet Lahm on April 30, 2018.

Cash	$3,000
Jewelry	2,000
House	190,000
Mortgage	80,000
Net Worth	115,000

The following transactions occurred during the month of May 2018.

1. Earned monthly salary of $5,050
2. Paid $1,200 cash for utilities
3. Purchased an automobile worth $10,000 on account
4. Paid $600 cash for food expenses
5. Paid $400 cash for gas

Required

a) Complete the cash T-account to determine the ending balance of cash.

INCREASE		DECREASE
+	**CASH**	−
Opening Bal.		

b) Complete the personal income statement to determine the surplus or deficit for the period.

Personal Income Statement For the Month Ended May 31, 2018		

c) What is Juliet Lahm's net worth on May 31?

_____

_____

_____

_____

_____

AP-5A LO 2 5

A person has the following information with regard to his own balance sheet, but the liability section is missing.

Cash	$35,000
Automobile	58,000
House	100,000
Net Worth	55,000

Determine the total amount of liabilities.

_____

_____

_____

_____

_____

AP-6A LO 5

Calculate the missing amounts in the following table.

	Scenario 1	Scenario 2
Total Assets	$123,000	
Total Liabilities		$34,000
Net Worth	$94,000	$114,000

AP-7A `LO 5`

As of December 31, 2017, Maria Green had total assets of $40,000, and total liabilities of $15,000. As of December 31, 2018, Maria's total assets and liabilities increased to $50,000 and $30,000, respectively. How has Maria's net worth changed since the end of 2017?

_____

_____

_____

_____

_____

_____

AP-8A `LO 2 3 5 11`

The following information pertains to Darius Jakande's personal finances.

Opening Balances as at January 1, 2018	
Cash	$9,000
Contents of Home	6,000
Automobile	29,000
House	156,000
Unpaid Accounts	5,500
Bank Loan	60,000
Net Worth	134,500

The following transactions occurred during the month of January 2018.

1. Paid maintenance expense with $120 cash

2. Purchased new furniture worth $2,500 with cash

3. Paid credit card liability of $5,500 (Unpaid Accounts) in full

4. Paid telephone, electricity and water bills for January with $1,200 cash

5. Purchased $2,000 of groceries and goods for personal consumption with cash

6. Deposited $4,040 from salary earned during the month

Using the information provided, first record the opening balances in the T-accounts. Then, record the transactions for the month of January in the T-accounts and complete the calculations at the bottom of the table.

PERSONAL BALANCE SHEET
As at January 31, 2018

ASSETS	LIABILITIES

CASH
- INCREASE +
- DECREASE −
- Opening

CONTENTS OF HOME
- INCREASE +
- DECREASE −
- Opening

AUTOMOBILE
- INCREASE +
- DECREASE −
- Opening

HOUSE
- INCREASE +
- DECREASE −
- Opening

UNPAID ACCOUNTS
- DECREASE −
- INCREASE +
- Opening

BANK LOAN
- DECREASE −
- INCREASE +
- Opening

NET WORTH
NET WORTH
- DECREASE −
- INCREASE +
- Opening

Total Assets _____
Total Liabilities _____
Net Worth _____

PERSONAL INCOME STATEMENT
For the Month Ended Jan 31, 2018

REVENUE
- DECREASE −
- INCREASE +

LESS EXPENSES

ENTERTAINMENT EXPENSE
- INCREASE +
- DECREASE −

FOOD EXPENSE
- INCREASE +
- DECREASE −

INTEREST EXPENSE
- INCREASE +
- DECREASE −

MAINTENANCE EXPENSE
- INCREASE +
- DECREASE −

UTILITIES EXPENSE
- INCREASE +
- DECREASE −

Total Revenue _____
Less Total Expenses _____
Surplus (Deficit) _____

AP-9A LO 2 3 5 11

Alan Marshall is preparing his balance sheet and income statement for the month ended April 30, 2018. Use the following information to help him prepare his financial statements.

Opening Balances as at April 1, 2018

Cash	$5,000
Contents of Home	1,000
Automobile	4,000
House	280,000
Unpaid Accounts	10,000
Auto Loan	30,000
Net Worth	250,000

The following transactions occurred during the month of April.

1. Purchased new home furniture worth $2,000 using a credit card
2. Paid credit card bill with $3,000 cash
3. Paid utility bills of $800 for the month of April using a credit card
4. Purchased groceries and food for $2,500 using cash
5. Made a principal payment of $1,250 for the auto loan
6. Paid April's rent of $1,500 with cash
7. Deposited $4,050 from salary earned during the month

Using the information provided, first record the opening balances in the T-accounts. Then, record the transactions for the month of April in the T-accounts and complete the calculations at the bottom of the table.

PERSONAL BALANCE SHEET
As at April 30, 2018

ASSETS

INCREASE	DECREASE
+ CASH −	
Opening	

INCREASE	DECREASE
+ CONTENTS OF HOME −	
Opening	

INCREASE	DECREASE
+ AUTOMOBILE −	
Opening	

INCREASE	DECREASE
+ HOUSE −	
Opening	

LIABILITIES

DECREASE	INCREASE
− UNPAID ACCOUNTS +	
	Opening

DECREASE	INCREASE
− AUTO LOAN +	
	Opening

NET WORTH

DECREASE	INCREASE
− NET WORTH +	
	Opening

Total Assets _____

Total Liabilities _____ } _____

Net Worth _____

PERSONAL INCOME STATEMENT
For the Month Ended April 30, 2018

DECREASE	INCREASE
− REVENUE +	

LESS EXPENSES

INCREASE	DECREASE
+ ENTERTAINMENT EXPENSE −	

INCREASE	DECREASE
+ FOOD EXPENSE −	

INCREASE	DECREASE
+ INTEREST EXPENSE −	

INCREASE	DECREASE
+ MAINTENANCE EXPENSE −	

INCREASE	DECREASE
+ RENT EXPENSE −	

INCREASE	DECREASE
+ UTILITIES EXPENSE −	

Total Revenue _____

Less Total Expenses _____

Surplus (Deficit) _____

AP-10A LO 3 4

Tobias Kaufman is a senior administrator at a market research firm. In November, he received a salary increase from $3,500 per month to $4,000 per month. He would like to know how this has impacted his net worth. However, he has never prepared a personal balance sheet or an income statement that would help him calculate his net worth. Tobias gathered the following information to help him understand his financial position.

	September 30, 2018	October 31, 2018	November 30, 2018
Cash	$1,000	$2,150	$4,050
House	120,000	120,000	120,000
Bank Loan	400	350	300
Salary	3,500	3,500	4,000
Entertainment Expense	200	500	400
Food Expense	1,500	1,200	1,100
Insurance Expense	150	150	150
Utilities Expense	200	400	300
Miscellaneous Expense	175	50	100

Prepare Tobias Kaufman's income statement for the three months.

Tobias Kaufman Personal Income Statement For the Month Ending				
	September 30, 2018	October 31, 2018	November 30, 2018	Total

AP-11A LO 4 10

Jeff Winger is working at a law firm. His salary recently increased and he would like to keep track of his net worth. Jeff has gathered the following information. Assume the opening net worth for June 30 is $0.

	June 30, 2018	July 31, 2018	August 31, 2018
Cash	$2,500	$4,100	$6,300
Automobile	13,000	13,000	13,000
Credit Card Bills	1,000	800	500
Automobile Loan	12,000	11,500	11,000
Salary	4,300	4,900	4,900
Food Expense	290	500	100
Entertainment Expense	210	800	500
Rent Expense	1,300	1,300	1,300

Complete the table below.

	June 30, 2018	July 31, 2018	August 31, 2018
Opening Net Worth			
Surplus (Deficit)			
Closing Net Worth			

Analysis

Jeff notices that his cash has not increased by as much as his net worth has. Why is this the case?

_____

_____

_____

_____

_____

AP-12A LO 2 5

Using the opening balances provided in each balance sheet, enter the updated amounts for each transaction in the blank balance sheets labeled Answers.

a) Borrowed $4,000 from the bank

Opening Balances

Assets		Liabilities	
Cash	$5,000	Unpaid Accounts	$3,000
Investment	8,000	Bank Loan	0
Contents of Home	6,000	Automobile Loan	5,000
Automobile	20,000	Student Loan	6,000
House	280,000	Mortgage	250,000
		Total Liabilities	264,000
		Net Worth	55,000
Total Assets	$319,000	**Total Liabilities + Net Worth**	$319,000

Answers

b) Purchased $3,000 of investments in cash

Opening Balances

Assets		Liabilities	
Cash	$7,000	Unpaid Accounts	$3,000
Investment	8,000	Bank Loan	0
Contents of Home	6,000	Automobile Loan	5,000
Automobile	20,000	Student Loan	6,000
House	180,000	Mortgage	150,000
		Total Liabilities	164,000
		Net Worth	57,000
Total Assets	$221,000	**Total Liabilities + Net Worth**	$221,000

Answers

c) Paid $1,000 to reduce an outstanding automobile loan (principal portion)

Opening Balances

Assets		Liabilities	
Cash	$3,000	Unpaid Accounts	$3,000
Contents of Home	6,000	Bank Loan	0
Automobile	20,000	Automobile Loan	5,000
House	180,000	Student Loan	6,000
		Mortgage	150,000
		Total Liabilities	164,000
		Net Worth	45,000
Total Assets	$209,000	**Total Liabilities + Net Worth**	$209,000

Answers

d) Bought a motorcycle for $6,000, paid a $1,000 deposit with cash and borrowed $5,000 from the bank

Opening Balances

Assets		Liabilities	
Cash	$2,000	Unpaid Accounts	$3,000
Contents of Home	4,000	Bank Loan	1,000
Motorcycle	0	Student Loan	11,000
Automobile	20,000	Mortgage	150,000
House	180,000	**Total Liabilities**	165,000
		Net Worth	41,000
Total Assets	$206,000	**Total Liabilities + Net Worth**	$206,000

Answers

AP-13A LO 10

Timothy Hollister collected the following amounts in cash for the month of February 2018.

Salary paid by employer	$2,400
Winnings at the casino	$270
Gifts	$295
Performance bonus paid by employer	$450

Calculate Timothy's total revenue and total capital items for February 2018.

_____

_____

_____

AP-14A LO 5

Indicate whether the terms of the accounting equation will increase or decrease for each transaction by placing a "+" or "−" in the appropriate space. If a term is not changed by the transaction, leave the space blank. The first transaction has been completed for you.

Transaction	Assets	= Liabilities	+ Net Worth
1. Deposited salary earned	+		+
2. Purchased a new TV on credit			
3. Received a cash gift			
4. Purchased fuel for car on credit			
5. Made a loan payment including interest			
6. Received cash from a student loan			
7. Received a paycheck			

AP-15A LO 2 3 6 11

The following information is available from Anna Edison's financial records.

Opening Balances as at June 1, 2018

Cash	$18,000
Furniture	3,100
Valuables & Electronics	3,200
House	255,000
Student Loans	39,000
Family Loan	2,000
Mortgage	100,000
Net Worth	138,300

The following transactions took place during the month of June.

1. $350 was taken from the bank account for a car lease payment
2. Paid $1,000 cash against the student loans, which includes $140 of interest
3. Won a tablet worth $800 as a raffle prize
4. Made a mortgage payment of $2,000 with cash, which includes $400 of interest
5. $4,800 from salary earned was directly deposited to the bank account
6. A family member accepted $2,000 worth of jewelry as repayment of the family loan

Required

a) Using the information provided, first record the opening balances in the T-accounts, Then, record the transactions for the month of June in the T-accounts and complete the calculations at the bottom of the table.

279,300 **PERSONAL BALANCE SHEET** 279,300
As at June 30, 2018

ASSETS		LIABILITIES	
INCREASE	DECREASE	DECREASE	INCREASE
+ CASH –		– STUDENT LOANS +	
Opening $18,000	$350	$860	$39,000 Opening
$4,800	$1000		
	$2000		
$19,450			$38,140

INCREASE	DECREASE	DECREASE	INCREASE
+ FURNITURE –		– FAMILY LOAN +	
Opening $3,100		$350	$2,000 Opening
$3,100			$1,650

INCREASE	DECREASE	DECREASE	INCREASE
+ VALUABLES & ELECTRONICS –		– MORTGAGE +	
Opening $3,200 = $4,000		$1600	$100,000 Opening
$800 –			
$2,000 →			
$2,000			$98,400

		NET WORTH	
INCREASE	DECREASE	DECREASE	INCREASE
+ HOUSE –		– NET WORTH +	
Opening $255,000			$138,300 Opening
			$800
$255,000			$139,100

Total Assets	$558,600 / 279,300
Total Liabilities	$141,000
Net Worth	$143,010

INCOME STATEMENT
For the Month Ended June 30, 2018

REVENUE	
DECREASE	INCREASE
–	+
$800	$4,000

LESS EXPENSES

INCREASE	DECREASE
+ AUTOMOBILE EXPENSE –	

INCREASE	DECREASE
+ ENTERTAINMENT EXPENSE –	

INCREASE	DECREASE
+ GROCERIES EXPENSE –	

INCREASE	DECREASE
+ INTEREST EXPENSE –	
$140 $400	

INCREASE	DECREASE
+ TRAVEL EXPENSE –	

Total Revenue	$4,800
Less Total Expenses	890
Surplus (Deficit)	$3,910 –

Revenue – Expenses =   139,100 Net Worth
+ Surplus (3,910) =
$193,010

b) Complete the income statement for the month of June.

Income Statement For the Month Ended June 30, 2018		
Revenue		$4,800
Expenses		
Auto Expense	$350	
Interest Expense	$540	
Total Expenses		890
Surplus (deficit)		$3,910

c) Complete the personal balance sheet as at June 30, 2018.

Personal Balance Sheet As at June 30, 2018			
Assets		Liabilities	
Cash	$19,450	Student Loans	$38,140
Valuables & Electronics	2,000	Mortgage	98,400
Furniture	3,100	Total Liabilities	136,540
House	255,000	Net Worth	143,010
Total Assets		Total Liabilities + Net Worth	$279,550

AP-16A LO 5 11

Indicate whether assets, liabilities or net worth will increase or decrease and by how much, based on each transaction. The first one has been done for you. Always ensure the accounting equation is balanced.

Provide an explanation only if net worth is affected.

Transaction	Assets	Liabilities	Net Worth	Explanation
1. Purchased a new television for $700 on credit	+ 700	+ 700		
2. Received $2,000 in salary				
3. Paid $1,200 cash for one year of insurance				
4. Purchased a new $500 gaming console with cash				
5. Paid for groceries with $80 cash				
6. Paid $400 toward the car loan				
7. Paid $30 interest on the car loan				
8. Paid $600 toward unpaid bills				
9. Used one month of insurance (from #3)				

AP-17A LO 5 9 11

Indicate whether the account balances will increase or decrease and by how much, based on each transaction. The first one has been done for you. Always ensure the accounting equation is balanced.

Provide an explanation only if net worth is affected.

Transaction	Assets	= Liabilities	+ Net Worth	Explanation
1. Purchased a new television for $700 on credit	+ 700	+ 700		
2. Purchased $100 worth of gas on credit				
3. Made an $850 car loan payment				
4. Purchased a chandelier for $200 cash				
5. Prepaid three months of rent with $3,300 cash				
6. Received a cash gift of $500				
7. Used up one of three months of prepaid rent				
8. Paid interest of $50, in cash, on the car loan				
9. Received a phone bill for $110				

Analysis

The net worth account is only updated at the end of an accounting period. Revenue and expense accounts, and the net worth account, track changes in net worth during the period. For each transaction that affects net worth, determine whether a revenue, expense, or net worth is used to track the change.

_____
_____
_____
_____
_____
_____

AP-18A LO 2 5 9

On December 1, 2018, Shervin decided to track his finances. On this date, his assets and liabilities were as follows.

Cash	$14,000
Prepaid Rent	3,000
Prepaid Insurance	300
House	160,000
Contents of Home	19,000
Automobile	30,000
Student Loan	10,000
Unpaid Accounts	17,000
Bank Loan	25,000
Mortgage	120,000

Required

a) What is the value of his total assets?

_____

_____

_____

_____

_____

_____

b) What is the value of his total liabilities?

_____

_____

_____

_____

c) What is Shervin's net worth on December 1, 2018?

_____

_____

_____

_____

d) During the month of December, Shervin recognized $150 of prepaid expenses as an actual expense on the income statement. Determine the change in his cash account and net worth.

Transaction	Change in Cash	Change in Net Worth
Recognized $150 of prepaid expenses as actual expense		

AP-19A LO 5 8

Nick Miller wrote down his personal accounting information but some of it was destroyed.

Bicycle	$700
Automobile	3,000
Cash	800
Furniture	?
Net Worth	3,350
Overdue Rent	?
Television	500
Total Assets	6,100
Unpaid Bills	2,300

Required

a) How much is Nick's furniture worth?

_____

_____

_____

_____

b) How much rent does Nick owe?

_____

_____

_____

_____

Analysis

Nick has worked 80 hours at his job as a bartender and earned $1,900 but will not get paid for another two weeks. According to accrual-based accounting, has Nick's net worth increased? Why or why not?

_____

_____

_____

_____

AP-20A LO 5

State how the following transactions would affect net worth (increase, decrease, no change).

Transaction	Effect on Net Worth
Borrow cash	
Pay entertainment expense with cash	
Pay food expense with cash	
Buy assets with cash	
Charge home repairs expense on credit card	
Pay insurance expense with cash	
Pay loan principal with cash	
Purchase assets on account	
Receive salary	
Pay rent expense with cash	

AP-21A LO 2 3 6

Using the following chart, indicate whether there would be an increase, decrease or no change to cash and net worth for the transactions provided. The first transaction has been completed for you.

Transaction	Cash			Net Worth		
	Increase	Decrease	No Change	Increase	Decrease	No Change
Deposit salary earned	X			X		
Pay cash for food						
Purchase a new car						
Pay rent expense in advance						
Reduce student loan principal						
Buy a new computer with cash						
Obtain a bank loan						
Pay entertainment expenses						
Record cash earned from a part-time job						

AP-22A LO 10

Sofie Nilsson collected the following amounts in cash for the month of March 2018.

Full-time employment income	$1,200
Income from part-time job	$220
Rental income	$525

Calculate Sofie's total revenue and total capital items for March 2018.

_____

_____

_____

Application Questions Group B

AP-1B LO 3

Dana Shukrun was reviewing her records on December 31, 2018. Below is a list of items and their values.

Cash	$7,900
Computer	700
Automobile	19,100
House	255,000
Mortgage	150,000
Credit Card	4,600
Bank Loan	37,700

Required

a) Calculate Dana Shukrun's total assets.

b) Calculate Dana Shukrun's total liabilities.

AP-2B LO 2 3 5

John Bonham was performing a year-end review of his finances and came up with this list.

Cash	$13,200
Furniture	1,900
Automobile	21,900
House	210,000
Credit Card	4,600
Student Loan	11,400
Mortgage	100,000

Required

a) Calculate John Bonham's total assets.

b) Calculate John Bonham's total liabilities.

c) Calculate John Bonham's net worth.

AP-3B LO 2 5

Consider the following information.

Cash	$6,000
Automobile	50,000
Prepaid Insurance	3,000
Bank Loan	10,000
Unpaid Credit Card Bills	2,000
Net Worth	?

How much is the net worth?

_____

_____

_____

_____

_____

AP-4B LO 2 3 5 6 11

Christine Sutherland compiled the following information on May 31, 2018.

Cash	$2,100
Jewelry	3,000
House	186,200
Mortgage	171,800
Net Worth	19,500

The following transactions occurred during the month of June 2018.

1. Received $4,100 cash for her monthly salary
2. Paid $590 cash for maintenance on her car
3. Paid cash for telephone, water and electricity for $540
4. Purchased an automobile worth $10,600 on credit
5. Received $30 interest earned on bank deposits
6. Paid $320 for food with cash

Required

a) Use the T-account to calculate the ending balance of cash.

INCREASE	DECREASE
+ **CASH**	−

b) What is the surplus or deficit for the accounting period?

_____

_____

c) What is Christine Sutherland's net worth on June 30?

_____

_____

AP-5B LO 2 3 4 6

Toshiro's financial records show that his assets and net worth as of May 1, 2018 are as follows.

Cash	$6,000
Computer	4,000
Contents of Home	17,500
Automobile	20,000
House	137,500
Student Loan	?
Net Worth	113,000

Required

a) Toshiro wants to find out how much he owes for his student loan. Determine his total liabilities.

_____

_____

_____

_____

_____

_____

_____

b) During the month of May, Toshiro paid $2,000 for two months of rent in advance ($1,000 per month). Calculate the change in Toshiro's cash account and personal net worth.

Transaction	Change in Cash	Change in Net Worth
Prepaid two months rent		

AP-6B LO 5

Calculate the missing amounts in the following table.

	Scenario 1	Scenario 2
Total Assets	$125,900	
Total Liabilities		$33,200
Net Worth	$92,700	$117,100

AP-7B LO 1 4

As of December 31, 2017, Deena Balsdon had total assets of $42,800 and total liabilities of $16,700. As of December 31, 2018, Deena's total assets and liabilities increased to $48,900 and $26,100, respectively. Fill out the following table of account balances. How has Deena's net worth changed since 2017?

	As at December 31, 2017	As at December 31, 2018
Net Worth		

AP-8B LO 2 3 5 11

Alan Marshall is preparing his balance sheet and income statement for the month ended July 31, 2018. Use the following information to help him prepare his financial statements.

Opening Balances as at July 1, 2018

Cash	$4,400
Contents of Home	2,800
Automobile	4,800
House	287,900
Unpaid Accounts	8,500
Mortgage	239,300
Net Worth	52,100

The following transactions occurred during the month of July.

1. Purchased a $1,600 high-definition television using a credit card
2. Paid a telephone bill of $640 for the month of July using a credit card
3. Paid a credit card bill with cash for $3,300
4. Purchased $1,010 of groceries using cash
5. Paid July's utilities of $1,100 with cash
6. Made a principal payment of $1,100 for the mortgage
7. Deposited $4,700 of salary earned during the month
8. Earned $60 interest on a savings account

Using the information provided, first record the opening balances in the T-accounts. Then, record the transactions for the month of July in the T-accounts and complete the calculations at the bottom of the table.

PERSONAL BALANCE SHEET
As at July 31, 2018

ASSETS

INCREASE	DECREASE
+	**CASH**	–

Opening

INCREASE	DECREASE
+	**CONTENTS OF HOME**	–

Opening

INCREASE	DECREASE
+	**AUTOMOBILE**	–

Opening

INCREASE	DECREASE
+	**HOUSE**	–

Opening

LIABILITIES

DECREASE	INCREASE
–	**UNPAID ACCOUNTS**	+

Opening

DECREASE	INCREASE
–	**MORTGAGE**	+

Opening

NET WORTH

DECREASE	INCREASE
–	**NET WORTH**	+

Opening

Total Assets

Total Liabilities

Net Worth

PERSONAL INCOME STATEMENT
For the Month Ended July 31, 2018

REVENUE

DECREASE	INCREASE
–	+

LESS EXPENSES

INCREASE	DECREASE
+	**CLOTHING EXPENSE**	–

INCREASE	DECREASE
+	**FOOD EXPENSE**	–

INCREASE	DECREASE
+	**TELEPHONE EXPENSE**	–

INCREASE	DECREASE
+	**UTILITIES EXPENSE**	–

Total Revenue

Less Total Expenses

Surplus (Deficit)

AP-9B LO 2 3 5 6 11

The following information is available from Elaine Georgiu's financial records.

Opening Balances as at February 1, 2018

Cash	$34,000
Prepaid Insurance	3,500
Automobile	45,000
Boat	81,000
Unpaid Accounts	21,000
Automobile Loan	25,000
Net Worth	117,500

The following transactions took place during the month of February.

1. Purchased fuel for the boat with $85 cash
2. Earned $1,250 in wages and deposited it in a bank account
3. Purchased $420 of groceries on a credit card
4. Won $200 cash from a lottery
5. Paid $3,600 cash for credit card bills due
6. Paid $360 interest on credit card bill with cash
7. Booked a flight on credit for $900
8. Recognized one month of car insurance used up for $350

Using the information provided, first record the opening balances in the T-accounts. Then, record the transactions in the T-accounts and complete the calculations at the bottom of the table.

PERSONAL BALANCE SHEET
As at February 28, 2018

ASSETS

INCREASE   DECREASE

+   CASH   –

Opening

INCREASE   DECREASE

+ PREPAID INSURANCE –

Opening

INCREASE   DECREASE

+   AUTOMOBILE   –

Opening

INCREASE   DECREASE

+   BOAT   –

Opening

LIABILITIES

DECREASE   INCREASE

–   UNPAID ACCOUNTS   +

Opening

DECREASE   INCREASE

–   AUTOMOBILE LOAN   +

Opening

NET WORTH

DECREASE   INCREASE

–   NET WORTH   +

Opening

Total Assets

Total Liabilities

Net Worth

INCOME STATEMENT
For the Month Ended February 28, 2018

REVENUE

DECREASE   INCREASE

–   +

LESS EXPENSES

INCREASE   DECREASE

+ ENTERTAINMENT EXPENSE –

INCREASE   DECREASE

+   FOOD EXPENSE   –

INCREASE   DECREASE

+   FUEL EXPENSE   –

INCREASE   DECREASE

+   INSURANCE EXPENSE   –

INCREASE   DECREASE

+   INTEREST EXPENSE   –

INCREASE   DECREASE

+   TRAVEL EXPENSE   –

Total Revenue

Less Total Expenses

Surplus (Deficit)

Analysis

Elaine will be canceling her auto insurance with no cancellation fee incurred. Which accounts will be affected by the insurance cancellation? How will the balances change?

_____

_____

AP-10B LO 2 3 4

Ethan is a songwriter and composer. His income is based solely on royalties that he receives regularly. Ethan opted to use three months as his accounting period.

The following information pertains to income earned and expenses incurred from January 1, 2018 to March 31, 2018.

	January	February	March
Royalty Income	$12,000	$13,000	$10,000
Interest Expense	60	60	60
Food Expense	2,000	2,100	1,900
Maintenance Expense	350	500	180
Clothing Expense	900	1,500	0
Utilities Expense	300	500	0
Rent Expense	1,500	1,500	1,500
Miscellaneous Expense	15	50	5

Required

a) Prepare a personal income statement for each of the three months.

Ethan Personal Income Statement For the Period Ended March 31, 2018				
	January	February	March	Total

b) What amount should be added to Ethan's net worth on March 31, 2018?

_____

_____

_____

_____

AP-11B LO 2 3 4

Archie always prepares an income statement and balance sheet each month, but he has fallen behind. Assume the opening net worth for October 31, 2018 is $6,770. Luckily, he has kept track of his account balances as shown below.

	October 31, 2018	November 30, 2018
Cash	$2,500	$6,900
Entertainment Expense	500	250
Food Expense	280	270
Gasoline Expense	140	130
Prepaid Rent	4,200	2,800
Rent Expense	1,400	1,400
Salary	5,050	5,050
Unpaid Accounts	700	700
Automobile	3,500	3,500

Complete the table below.

	October 31, 2018	November 30, 2018
Opening Net Worth		
Surplus (Deficit)		
Closing Net Worth		

Analysis

Archie noticed that his net worth did not increase as much as his cash did during November. Why is this the case?

_____

_____

AP-12B LO 2 5

Using the opening balances provided in each balance sheet, enter the updated amounts for each transaction in the blank balance sheets labeled Answers.

a) Applied for and received a student loan of $5,700

Opening Balances

Assets		Liabilities	
Cash	$5,600	Unpaid Accounts	$2,500
Investment	8,400	Bank Loan	900
Contents of Home	6,200	Automobile Loan	4,800
Automobile	22,300	Student Loan	5,500
House	287,900	Mortgage	241,500
		Total Liabilities	255,200
		Net Worth	75,200
Total Assets	$330,400	**Total Liabilities + Net Worth**	$330,400

Answers

b) Purchased some furniture and jewelry for $5,000 cash

Opening Balances

Assets		Liabilities	
Cash	$8,200	Unpaid Accounts	$2,400
Investment	7,200	Bank Loan	200
Contents of Home	6,100	Automobile Loan	4,400
Automobile	22,900	Student Loan	6,200
House	272,300	Mortgage	242,200
		Total Liabilities	255,400
		Net Worth	61,300
Total Assets	$316,700	**Total Liabilities + Net Worth**	$316,700

Answers

c) Paid a portion of the principal of the automobile loan for $1,200

Opening Balances

Assets		Liabilities	
Cash	$4,500	Unpaid Accounts	$2,200
Contents of Home	5,500	Bank Loan	600
Automobile	19,000	Automobile Loan	4,200
House	290,000	Student Loan	6,800
		Mortgage	242,800
		Total Liabilities	256,600
		Net Worth	62,400
Total Assets	$319,000	**Total Liabilities + Net Worth**	$319,000

Answers

d) Bought a motorcycle for $7,100—paid a $1,400 deposit with cash and borrowed $5,700 from the bank

Opening Balances

Assets		Liabilities	
Cash	$5,000	Unpaid Accounts	$2,000
Contents of Home	6,700	Bank Loan	1,000
Motorcycle	0	Student Loan	11,000
Automobile	17,000	Mortgage	242,000
House	283,300	**Total Liabilities**	256,000
		Net Worth	56,000
Total Assets	$312,000	**Total Liabilities + Net Worth**	$312,000

Answers

AP-13B LO 10

Prisha Afsahani received the following amounts in cash for the month of November 2018.

Salary	$2,100
Gifts	$240
Winnings at the casino	$170
Performance bonus paid by employer	$460

Calculate Prisha's total revenue and total capital items for November 2018.

_____

_____

_____

_____

AP-14B LO 5

Indicate whether the terms of the accounting equation will increase or decrease for each transaction by placing a "+" or "−" in the appropriate space. If a term is not changed by the transaction, leave the space blank. The first transaction has been completed for you.

Transaction	Assets	= Liabilities	+ Net Worth
1. Deposited salary earned	+		+
2. Purchased a new bicycle on credit			
3. Purchased groceries on credit			
4. Borrowed money from the bank			
5. Purchased a ring for $200 cash			
6. Received a cash gift			
7. Made a loan payment with interest			

AP-15B LO 2 3 5 11

The following information is available from Drew Bernard's financial records.

Opening Balances as at September 1, 2018

Cash	$1,500
Automobile	9,400
Boat	18,000
Instruments	7,600
House	415,000
Student Loans	67,000
Unpaid Accounts	8,500
Mortgage	250,000
Net Worth	126,000

The following transactions took place during the month of September.

1. Purchased a piano worth $900 using cash
2. Put $720 worth of food expenses on a credit card
3. Purchased an $800 guitar on credit
4. Received a cash inheritance of $45,000
5. Paid off unpaid accounts with $9,570 cash
6. Received $50 interest on the bank account

Using the information provided, first record the opening balances in the T-accounts. Then, record the transactions in the T-accounts and complete the calculations at the bottom of the table.

PERSONAL BALANCE SHEET
As at September 30, 2018

ASSETS		LIABILITIES	

ASSETS

INCREASE	DECREASE
+ CASH –	
Opening	

INCREASE	DECREASE
+ AUTOMOBILE –	
Opening	

INCREASE	DECREASE
+ BOAT –	
Opening	

INCREASE	DECREASE
+ INSTRUMENTS –	
Opening	

INCREASE	DECREASE
+ HOUSE –	
Opening	

LIABILITIES

DECREASE	INCREASE
– STUDENT LOANS +	
	Opening

DECREASE	INCREASE
– UNPAID ACCOUNTS +	
	Opening

DECREASE	INCREASE
– MORTGAGE +	
	Opening

NET WORTH

DECREASE	INCREASE
– NET WORTH +	
	Opening

Total Assets _____

Total Liabilities _____   }_____

Net Worth _____

INCOME STATEMENT
For the Month Ended September 30, 2018

REVENUE

DECREASE	INCREASE
–	+

LESS EXPENSES

INCREASE	DECREASE
+ ENTERTAINMENT EXPENSE –	

INCREASE	DECREASE
+ GROCERIES EXPENSE –	

INCREASE	DECREASE
+ INTEREST EXPENSE –	

INCREASE	DECREASE
+ MAINTENANCE EXPENSE –	

Total Revenue _____

Less Total Expenses _____

Surplus (Deficit) _____

AP-16B LO 5 11

Indicate whether assets, liabilities or net worth will increase or decrease and by how much, based on each transaction. The first one has been done for you. Always ensure the accounting equation is balanced.

Provide an explanation only if net worth is affected.

	Assets	= Liabilities	+ Net Worth	Explanation
1. Purchased a new television for $700 on credit	+ 700	+ 700		
2. Won $700 in a lottery				
3. Deposited $2,800 in salary				
4. Purchased furniture for $400 in cash				
5. Transferred $500 from a checking account to a savings account				
6. Paid $150 for concert tickets with a credit card				
7. Paid $200 cash for utilities				
8. Paid $1,500 toward the mortgage				
9. Paid $1,100 toward unpaid bills				

AP-17B LO 5 11

The following information is available from Lily's financial records.

Opening Balances as at November 1, 2018

Cash	$18,000
Furniture	3,100
Valuables & Electronics	3,200
House	255,000
Student Loans	39,000
Mortgage	100,000
Family Loan	2,000
Net Worth	138,300

Indicate whether the account balances will increase or decrease and by how much, based on each transaction. Always ensure the accounting equation is balanced.

	Assets	= Liabilities	+ Net Worth	Explanation
1. Purchased $1,600 worth of new bedroom furniture with cash				
2. Won a tablet worth $800 as a raffle prize				
3. $350 was taken from the bank account for a car rental payment				
4. A family member accepted $2,000 worth of jewelry as repayment for the family loan				
5. Made a $2,000 mortgage payment with cash, including $400 of interest				
6. Paid $1,000 towards the student loans with cash, including $140 of interest				
7. Salary earned of $4,800 was directly deposited to the bank account				

Analysis

The net worth account is only updated at the end of an accounting period. Revenue and expense accounts and the net worth account track changes in net worth during the period. For each transaction that affects net worth, determine whether a revenue, expense, or net worth is used to track the change.

AP-18B LO 2 3

Consider the following financial information of Pete Griphin.

Automobile	$66,000
Boat	55,000
Automobile Loan	50,000
Cash	14,500
Coin Collection	1,200
Cottage	84,000
House and Property	510,000
Prepaid House Insurance	8,500
Mortgage Principal	450,000
Trailer	4,000

Required

a) Calculate Pete's total assets.

---

b) Calculate Pete's total liabilities.

---

c) Calculate Pete's net worth.

Analysis

Pete makes payments against his liabilities and updates all of his account balances at the end of each month. Which account balances will change at the end of the month? Which will increase and which will decrease?

_____

_____

_____

_____

AP-19B LO 5 6 7 8

Jess Day stored her personal accounting information in the computer but some of it was deleted by accident.

Appliances	$1,100
Cell Phone	500
Family Loan	?
Jewelry	800
Net Worth	4,500
Unpaid Bills	350
Automobile	5,000

Required

a) What are Jess' total assets?

_____

_____

b) What is the amount of Jess' family loan?

_____

_____

_____

_____

Analysis

Jess works as a teacher. She has agreed to work as a substitute during one day next week for extra wages. According to accrual-based accounting, has Jess' net worth increased? Why or why not?

_____

_____

_____

_____

_____

_____

AP-20B LO 5 6 9

Dex had the following transactions during the month of May.

1. Purchased a new laptop for $1,200 cash
2. Put $1,600 of car repairs on his credit card
3. Spent $80 on a steak dinner with his sister and paid with his credit card
4. Prepaid his son's nanny $850 cash for future services
5. Received a salary of $5,500

How have these transactions affected Dex's net worth?

_____

_____

_____

_____

_____

Analysis

Has Dex's cash changed the same amount as his net worth? Why or why not?

_____

_____

_____

_____

_____

AP-21B LO 2 3 6 11

On June 1, 2018, Joey had $3,100 in cash (including his bank account). The following transactions took place for the month of June.

1. Returned a newly purchased cell phone to the store for $150 cash
2. Purchased a new laptop for $1,200 cash
3. Bought a concert ticket for $90 cash
4. Received wages of $3,200 for the month
5. Spent $300 cash on food for the month
6. Received monthly utility bills of $310, due July 21
7. Received interest on a savings account of $35

Required

a) What is the balance of cash on June 30?

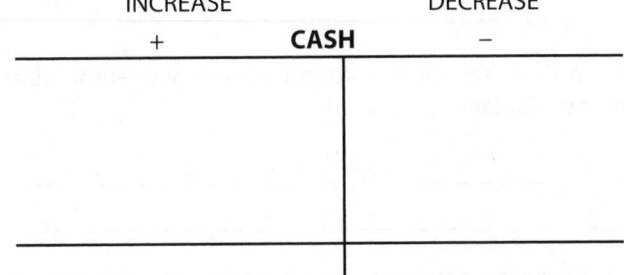

b)   Prepare a personal income statement for Joey for June.

Personal Income Statement		
For the Month Ended June 30, 2018		
Revenue		
Expenses		
Surplus (Deficit)		

Analysis

Joey purchased his car using 0% financing. This means there is no interest on the loan. What is the effect on net worth after each car payment? Would the effect be any different if the loan had interest? Explain.

_____

_____

_____

_____

AP-22B LO 5

Lucia has total assets of $35,000 and total liabilities of $20,000. She owns a few pieces of gold jewelry that were originally purchased for $1,000 total. She recently purchased some additional jewelry for $3,000 cash. Which account balances will change from this transaction and by how much? Use the accounting equation to check your answer.

_____

_____

_____

_____

_____

Analysis

Lucia wants to increase her net worth so she decides to purchase a new automobile by getting a bank loan. Has her net worth changed as expected? Explain.

_____

_____

_____

AP-23B LO 2 3 5 6

Jed Mosley had the following financial data for the year ended December 31, 2018.

Automobile	$6,500
Checking Account	1,100
Credit Card Bill	2,100
Electronics	1,000
Furniture	2,000
Hydro Bill	120
Phone Bill	150
Savings Account	10,000

Required

a) Calculate Jed's total assets.

_____

_____

_____

_____

_____

_____

_____

b) Calculate Jed's total liabilities.

_____

_____

_____

_____

Analysis

Jed realized he has a rent payment coming up on January 1, 2017 that will cover January's rent. Should this be included in December's financial data? Explain.

_____

_____

_____

_____

_____

_____

_____

Case Study

CS–1 LO 2 3 5 6 7 8 9 10 11

After taking the first part of this financial accounting course, you excitedly tell a friend what you have learned. You tell him about assets, liabilities and net worth and how they increase and decrease in value with every financial transaction. Your friend decides to start getting organized and apply accounting principles to his personal finances. He compiles everything that he thinks is important and calculates his net worth. He then asks you to look over what he has done to make sure it is correct. His important financial items are listed below, along with his version of the T-account records.

1. He had $950 in his bank account at the beginning of the month.
2. He had a $1,200 balance on his credit card at the beginning of the month.
3. He estimates that he had about $3,000 worth of "stuff" in his apartment at the beginning of the month (TV, sound system, computer and furniture).
4. He deposited his salary of $1,500.
5. He paid in advance for three months of rent with $1,350 cash.
6. He paid $600 to pay off a portion of the credit card bill.
7. He purchased a new video game system for $350 with his credit card.
8. He bought $120 worth of food with cash.
9. He got hired at a second job. He will start next month and will earn $800 per month.
10. He spent $250 cash on movies, stage plays and Dave and Buster's.
11. He lived in his apartment for one of the three months he already paid for (see #5).

+	CASH		–	
1.	950	5.	1,350
4.	1,500	6.	600
		8.	120
		10.	250
Total	**$130**		

–	UNPAID ACCOUNTS		+	
6.	600	2.	1,200
		7.	350
		Total	**$950**

–	NET WORTH		+	
5.	1,350	3.	3,000
8.	120	4.	1,500
10.	250	7.	350
		9.	800
		Total	**$3,930**

Required

a) What are some immediate problems that you see with what your friend has prepared?

_____

_____

_____

_____

_____

b)   With all the problems you see, your friend asks you to show him what the correct records should look like. Use the templates at the end of this problem to record the transactions.

_____

_____

After showing your friend the corrected version, he asks a number of questions.

c)   Why did you use all of these accounts when I only used three (Cash, Unpaid Accounts and Net Worth)?

_____

_____

_____

_____

_____

d)   Why is the $3,000 worth of "stuff" not considered net worth?

_____

_____

_____

_____

e)   I was having trouble figuring out how to record my second job which I start next month. They are going to be paying me $800 a month! I figured it will increase my net worth, but I didn't know where else to put it. I knew it couldn't be cash, because they haven't paid me yet. What did you do with it and why?

_____

_____

_____

f)   What did you do with my rent? Shouldn't the entire $1,350 decrease my net worth? And what would happen if I did it my way?

_____

_____

_____

_____

_____

_____

_____

g)   I forgot to tell you that the $600 credit card payment included $30 of interest. I didn't think it mattered since the total payment amount is the same. This won't change anything, right?

_____

_____

h) You may have noticed that I am running low on cash. Any suggestions on how I can raise more cash?

_____

_____

_____

_____

_____

_____

_____

_____

i) This is very useful and I would like to do this more often. I can do it this weekend, then two weeks
from now once I finish my exams, then probably not for another month after that. I'm going on a well-
deserved vacation after my exams, so I won't be around to look after it. Do you think this will work out
well?

_____

_____

_____

_____

_____

_____

_____

_____

_____

_____

_____

_____

_____

_____

_____

_____

_____

j) Using the information provided, record the transactions in the T-accounts and complete the calculations
at the bottom of the personal balance sheet and income statement (on the next page).

PERSONAL BALANCE SHEET

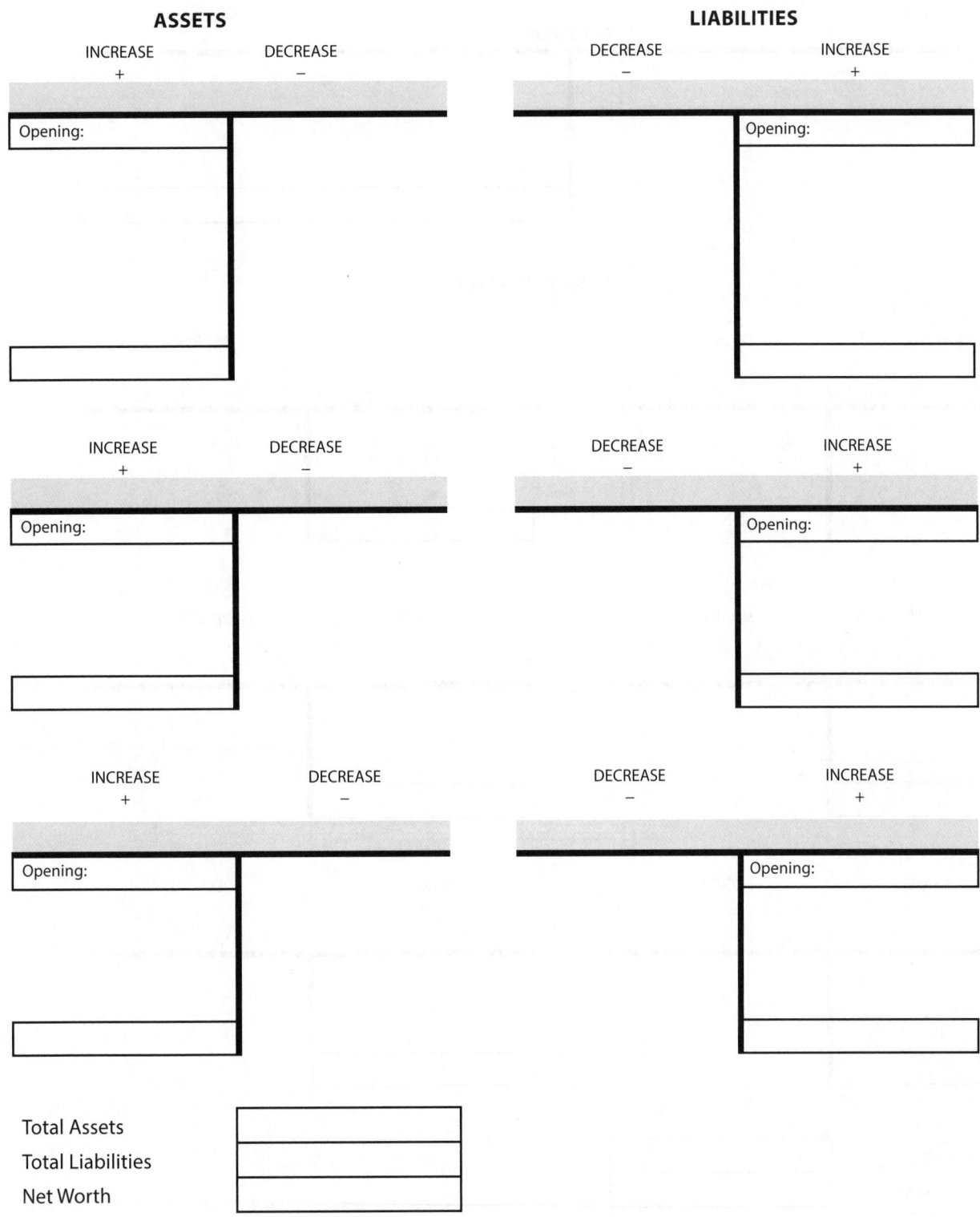

| | | ASSETS | | | | LIABILITIES | |

ASSETS

INCREASE +	DECREASE −
Opening:	

INCREASE +	DECREASE −
Opening:	

INCREASE +	DECREASE −
Opening:	

LIABILITIES

DECREASE −	INCREASE +
	Opening:

DECREASE −	INCREASE +
	Opening:

DECREASE −	INCREASE +
	Opening:

Total Assets	
Total Liabilities	
Net Worth	

PERSONAL INCOME STATEMENT

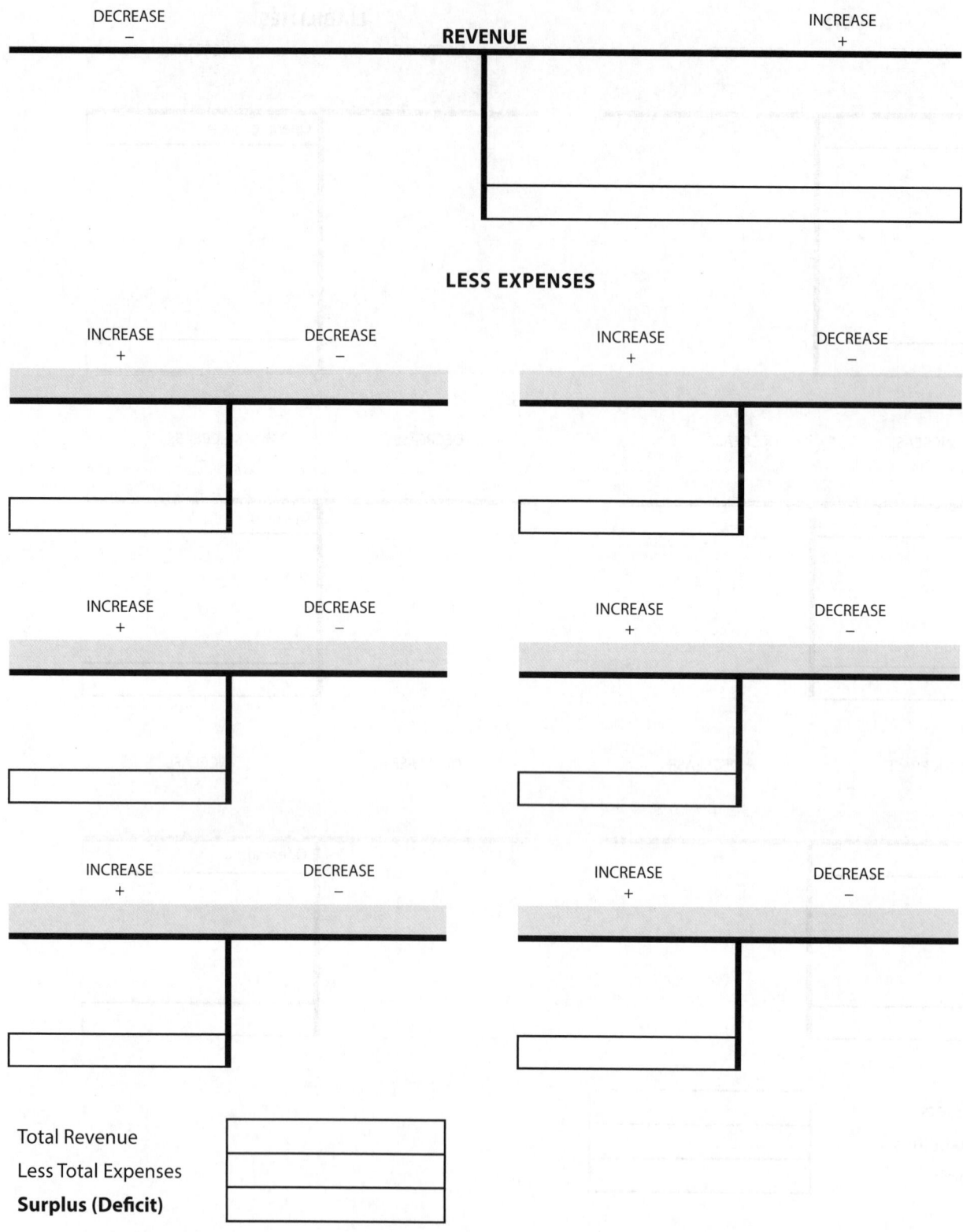

| DECREASE
– | REVENUE | INCREASE
+ |

LESS EXPENSES

| INCREASE
+ | DECREASE
– | | INCREASE
+ | DECREASE
– |

| INCREASE
+ | DECREASE
– | | INCREASE
+ | DECREASE
– |

| INCREASE
+ | DECREASE
– | | INCREASE
+ | DECREASE
– |

Total Revenue

Less Total Expenses

Surplus (Deficit)

Chapter 2

LINKING PERSONAL ACCOUNTING TO BUSINESS ACCOUNTING

LEARNING OBJECTIVES

LO 1 List the differences between personal accounts and business accounts

LO 2 Describe the three main types of businesses

LO 3 Record revenue based on the concept of accruals

LO 4 Record expenses based on the concept of accruals

LO 5 Record business transactions in T-accounts

LO 6 Identify the four required financial statements and prepare three financial statements

LO 7 Describe ethics relating to financial statement reporting

AMEENGAGE *Access **ameengage.com** for integrated resources including tutorials, practice exercises, the digital textbook and more.*

Assessment Questions

AS-1 LO 1

Net worth in personal accounting is similar to which item in accounting for businesses?

AS-2 LO 1

What is equity?

AS-3 LO 1

What is the formula for calculating the ending owner's equity balance?

AS-4 LO 1

Describe owner's contributions and owner's withdrawals and explain how they affect the balance sheet.

AS-5 LO 2

List the three main types of businesses.

AS-6 LO 2

Describe what a service business does. Provide two examples of service businesses.

_____

_____

_____

AS-7 LO 2

Describe what a merchandising business does. Provide an example of a merchandising business.

_____

_____

_____

AS-8 LO 2

Describe what a manufacturing business does. Provide two examples of a manufacturing business.

_____

_____

_____

AS-9 LO 3

What does it mean to _recognize_ revenue?

_____

_____

AS-10 LO 3

Describe the three different times cash can be received from a customer related to earning revenue.

_____

_____

_____

AS-11 LO 3

What is the entry to record revenue if a customer pays _when_ the service is delivered?

_____

_____

AS-12 LO 3

What is the entry to record revenue if a customer pays _after_ the service is delivered?

_____

_____

AS-13 LO 3

What is the entry if a customer pays _before_ the service is delivered?

_____

_____

AS-14 LO 3

What type of account is unearned revenue?

_____

_____

AS-15 LO 4

Give three examples of expenses that businesses commonly prepay.

_____

_____

_____

AS-16 LO 4

Describe the three different times cash can be paid to a supplier related to an expense.

_____

_____

_____

_____

AS-17 LO 4

What does it mean to _incur_ an expense?

_____

_____

AS-18 LO 4

What is the entry to record an expense if a company pays _when_ the expense is incurred?

_____

_____

AS-19 LO 4

What is the entry to record an expense if a company pays _after_ the expense is incurred?

_____

_____

_____

AS-20 LO 4

What is the entry if a company pays _before_ the expense is incurred?

_____

_____

_____

AS-21 LO 6

In what order are the assets of a business listed? Explain.

_____

_____

_____

AS-22 LO 6

In what order are the liabilities of a business listed? Explain.

_____

_____

_____

AS-23 LO 6

What are the three categories on the statement of cash flows?

_____

_____

_____

AS-24 LO 6

On the statement of cash flows, where would cash received from customers be reported, and is it an inflow or outflow of cash?

_____

_____

_____

AS-25 LO 7

What factors can lead a person to commit fraud?

_____

_____

Application Questions Group A

AP-1A LO 1 3 4

For each transaction, indicate whether the total assets (A), liabilities (L) or owner's equity (OE) increased (+), decreased (−) or did not change (o) by placing the symbol in the appropriate column.

	A	L	OE
1. Paid salaries for current month			
2. Purchased equipment on credit			
3. Purchased furniture using cash			
4. Made an additional investment into the business			
5. Received payment for services to be provided next month			
6. Made partial payment for equipment purchased on credit			
7. Billed customers for services performed			
8. Withdrew cash for personal use			
9. Received payment from customers already billed			
10. Received bills for utilities to be paid next month			

AP-2A LO 1 3 4

The given transactions were completed by Juliet's Delivery Services during May 2018. Indicate the effects of each transaction by placing the appropriate letter in the space provided.

A   Increase in asset, decrease in another asset
B   Increase in asset, increase in liability
C   Increase in asset, increase in owner's equity
D   Decrease in asset, decrease in liability
E   Decrease in asset, decrease in owner's equity

_____ Received cash for providing delivery services
_____ Paid amount owing that was outstanding to a creditor
_____ Invested additional cash in the business
_____ Paid advertising expense with cash
_____ Billed customers for delivery services on account
_____ Purchased office furniture on account
_____ Paid rent for the month
_____ Received cash from customers on account
_____ Received cash in advance for services to be provided in the next month
_____ Owner withdrew cash for personal use

AP-3A LO 6

Organize the following asset and liability accounts in the order they are likely to appear in a balance sheet.

Assets	Liabilities
Accounts Receivable	Notes Payable
Cash	Accounts Payable
Equipment	Unearned Revenue
Prepaid Expenses	

AP-4A LO 3 4

Simpson Moving had the following transactions during the month. Indicate whether assets, liabilities or owner's equity will increase or decrease and by how much, based on each transaction. Provide an explanation only if equity is affected. The first entry has been done for you. Always ensure the accounting equation is balanced.

	Assets =	Liabilities +	Owner's Equity	Explanation
1. Paid $200 cash for maintenance expense	−200		−200	Paid for maintenance expense
2. The owner invested $4,000 cash in the business				
3. Paid $2,400 cash for one year of insurance				
4. Received a telephone bill for $150, which will be paid later				
5. Purchased equipment worth $1,000 on account				
6. Provided services and collected $4,200 cash				
7. Paid $500 toward the bank loan				
8. Paid $50 interest related to the bank loan				
9. Paid $700 of accounts payable				

AP-5A LO 3 4 5

Dry Cleanest offers extensive dry cleaning services. Riya Kapoor started this company one year ago. The opening balances of the accounts on August 1, 2018 are shown below.

Cash	$980
Accounts Receivable	620
Prepaid Expenses	300
Machinery	3,800
Accounts Payable	1,020
Notes Payable	0
Kapoor, Capital	4,680

Required

a) Indicate whether assets, liabilities or owner's equity will increase or decrease and by how much, based on each transaction during August. Provide an explanation only if equity is affected. The first one has been done for you. Always ensure the accounting equation is balanced.

	Assets =	Liabilities +	Owner's Equity	Explanation
1. Borrowed $10,000 from the bank	+10,000	+10,000		
2. Purchased machinery for $7,300 cash				
3. Billed clients $2,950 for completed services, which is due in 30 days				
4. Paid $130 cash for regular maintenance on the machine				
5. Collected $1,300 from clients who owed money				
6. Paid $3,000 in advance for four months of rent				
7. Recorded $1,600 of cash sales for the month				
8. Paid $700 owed to a supplier				

b) Based on the information provided, first record the opening balances in the T-accounts. Then, record the transactions for the month of August in the T-accounts, and complete the bottom of the table.

Dry Cleanest
Balance Sheet
As at August 31, 2018

ASSETS		LIABILITIES	

ASSETS

INCREASE   DECREASE
+   **CASH**   –

Opening

INCREASE   DECREASE
+ ACCOUNTS RECEIVABLE –

Opening

INCREASE   DECREASE
+   **PREPAID EXPENSES**   –

Opening

INCREASE   DECREASE
+   **MACHINERY**   –

Opening

LIABILITIES

DECREASE   INCREASE
–   **ACCOUNTS PAYABLE**   +

Opening

DECREASE   INCREASE
–   **NOTES PAYABLE**   +

Opening

OWNER'S EQUITY

DECREASE   INCREASE
–   **KAPOOR, CAPITAL**   +

Opening

INCREASE   DECREASE
+ KAPOOR, WITHDRAWALS –

Total Assets   _____
Total Liabilities   _____
Owner's Equity   _____   _____

Dry Cleanest
Income Statement
For the Month Ended August 31, 2018

REVENUE

DECREASE   INCREASE
–   **SERVICE REVENUE**   +

LESS EXPENSES

INCREASE   DECREASE
+   **INSURANCE EXPENSE**   –

INCREASE   DECREASE
+   **MAINTENANCE EXPENSE**   –

INCREASE   DECREASE
+   **SALARIES EXPENSE**   –

INCREASE   DECREASE
+   **UTILITIES EXPENSE**   –

Total Revenue   _____
Less Total Expenses   _____
Net Income (Loss)   _____

Analysis

The owner of Dry Cleanest wants to withdraw cash from the business, but she does not want the net income to fall below $4,000. What is the maximum amount of cash she can withdraw in order to keep net income above $4,000? Explain.

_____

_____

_____

_____

AP-6A LO 1 6

Alex Limbo is the owner of Double Duplicator. The following is a list of Double Duplicator's accounts and balances as at March 31, 2018.

Cash	$4,700
Limbo, Capital	2,000
Accounts Payable	5,000
Unearned Revenue	2,000
Prepaid Insurance	2,300
Notes Payable	10,000
Automobile Loan	18,000
Prepaid Rent	5,000
Automobile	25,000

Prepare a balance sheet as at March 31, 2018, using the above information.

AP-7A LO 6

Alex Papanov operates a construction company as a sole proprietorship called Papanov Construction. Alex is creating some financial records for the company for the end of April 2018, and has come up with the following account balances.

Accounts Payable	$750
Accounts Receivable	350
Notes Payable	5,000
Cash	11,250
Storage Warehouse	36,200
Tools and Equipment	7,900
Vehicle	13,800

Prepare the balance sheet as at April 30, 2018, for Papanov Construction.

AP-8A LO 5

Paul Stiles runs a small landscaping business. During the month of July 2018, he had the following transactions. For each transaction, provide the appropriate T-account name and fill in the amount.

1. Earned service revenue from a client and received $600 cash

2. Paid $150 cash for fuel for the lawn cutting equipment

3. Purchased a new lawn mower for $700 and will pay for it next month

4. Went to the bank and took out a $3,000 loan

AP-9A LO 5

Brad Picton operates a consulting business. During the month of December 2018, he had the following transactions. For each transaction, provide the appropriate T-account name and fill in the amount.

1. Invested $4,000 cash into the business

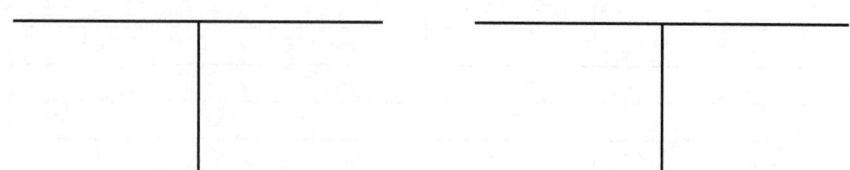

2. Paid $1,400 cash for a one-year insurance policy

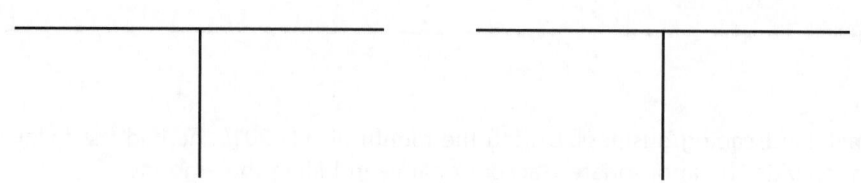

3. Received a $300 bill for utilities, which will be paid next month

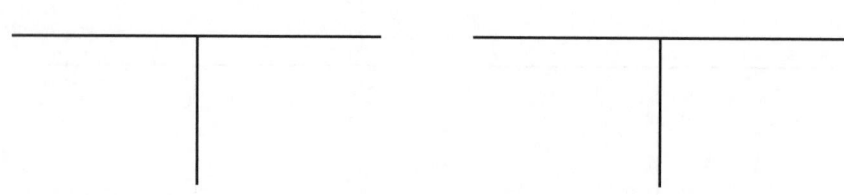

4. A customer paid $500 cash for work that was completed last month

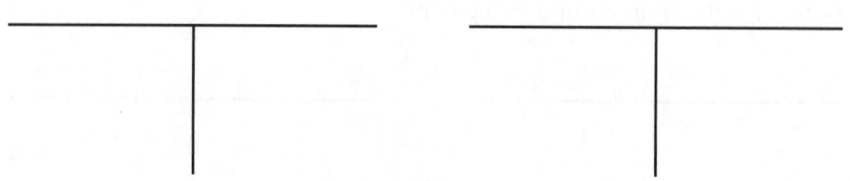

AP-10A LO 6

Isabela Paloma owns a painting business called Paloma Painters. She has recorded all the transactions for the month of July 2018. The balances of the accounts are shown below.

Account	Balance
Accounts Payable	$1,000
Accounts Receivable	500
Cash	1,500
Equipment	10,000
Maintenance Expense	100
Notes Payable	5,000
Paloma, Capital	3,750
Paloma, Withdrawals	1,400
Prepaid Insurance	1,200
Rent Expense	200
Service Revenue	5,200
Telephone Expense	150
Travel Expense	300
Unearned Revenue	400

Required

a) Using the information provided, prepare the income statement for Paloma Painters for the month of July.

b) Prepare the statement of owner's equity for Paloma Painters for the month of July. Isabela did not make any investments in the business during the month.

c) Prepare the balance sheet for Paloma Painters as at July 31, 2018.

AP-11A LO 1 3 4 5

Jessica Holmes recently started her own shoe repair business. Transactions for the first month of operations (June 2018) are as follows.

1.   Jessica invested $10,000 cash in the business
2.   Paid two months of rent for $1,000 in advance
3.   Purchased store equipment worth $3,000 with cash
4.   Incurred business registration expenses, paid with $600 cash
5.   Paid travel expenses with $1,100 cash
6.   Received $2,300 cash from customers for shoe repair services performed during the month
7.   Provided shoe repair services worth $1,200 on account
8.   Paid $1,300 salary to an assistant
9.   Borrowed $3,000 cash from the bank
10. Received $800 in bills for electricity, water and telephone, to be paid next month
11. Jessica withdrew $500 cash for personal purposes
12. Received $200 owing from a customer for service provided earlier this month

Record the above transactions on the T-account worksheet.

Holmes Shoe Repair
Balance Sheet
As at June 30, 2018

ASSETS

INCREASE	DECREASE
+ **CASH**	–

Opening

INCREASE	DECREASE
+ **ACCOUNTS RECEIVABLE**	–

Opening

INCREASE	DECREASE
+ **PREPAID RENT**	–

Opening

INCREASE	DECREASE
+ **EQUIPMENT**	–

Opening

LIABILITIES

DECREASE	INCREASE
– **ACCOUNTS PAYABLE**	+

Opening

DECREASE	INCREASE
– **NOTES PAYABLE**	+

Opening

OWNER'S EQUITY

DECREASE	INCREASE
– **HOLMES, CAPITAL**	+

Opening

INCREASE	DECREASE
+ **HOLMES, WITHDRAWALS**	–

Opening

Total Assets _____

Total Liabilities _____

Owner's Equity _____

Holmes Shoe Repair
Income Statement
For the Month Ended June 30, 2018

REVENUE

DECREASE	INCREASE
– **SERVICE REVENUE**	+

LESS EXPENSES

INCREASE	DECREASE
+ **REGISTRATION & LICENSES EXPENSE** –	

INCREASE	DECREASE
+ **RENT EXPENSE**	–

INCREASE	DECREASE
+ **SALARIES EXPENSE**	–

INCREASE	DECREASE
+ **TELEPHONE & UTILITIES EXPENSE** –	

INCREASE	DECREASE
+ **TRAVEL EXPENSE**	–

Total Revenue _____

Less Total Expenses _____

Net Income (Loss) _____

AP-12A LO 1 3 4 5

Sheila Abney opened a dormitory locator business called Room Finders near a college campus. During the first month of operations, June 2018, Sheila had the following transactions.

1. Invested $10,000 of personal funds to start the business
2. Incurred travel expenses for $650, which will be paid later
3. Paid $700 cash for maintenance expense
4. Received $5,000 cash for services provided to clients
5. Paid $650 for the on account purchase in transaction 2
6. Paid three months of office rent in advance, in the amount of $1500
7. Incurred $300 of utilities expense, which will be paid next month
8. Received $1,000 cash from a customer for services to be provided in two months
9. Provided $1,200 in services for a customer who will pay later
10. Recognized one month of office rent that was prepaid
11. Sheila withdrew $1,000 cash for personal use
12. Purchased a second-hand car worth $10,000 for business use with cash
13. Received $700 from the customer owing for the service provided earlier this month

Prepare a T-account worksheet.

Room Finders
Balance Sheet
As at June 30, 2018

ASSETS		
INCREASE	DECREASE	
+	–	
Opening		

LIABILITIES		
DECREASE	INCREASE	
–	+	
	Opening	

INCREASE	DECREASE
+	–
Opening	

DECREASE	INCREASE
–	+
	Opening

INCREASE	DECREASE
+	–
Opening	

DECREASE	INCREASE
–	+
	Opening

INCREASE	DECREASE
+	–
Opening	

OWNER'S EQUITY		
DECREASE	INCREASE	
–	+	
	Opening	

INCREASE	DECREASE
+	–

Room Finders
Income Statement
For the Month Ended June 30, 2018

REVENUE		
DECREASE	INCREASE	
–	+	

LESS EXPENSES

INCREASE	DECREASE
+	–

INCREASE	DECREASE
+	–

INCREASE	DECREASE
+	–

INCREASE	DECREASE
+	–

INCREASE	DECREASE
+	–

Total Assets _____

Total Liabilities _____ } _____

Owner's Equity _____

Total Revenue _____

Less Total Expenses _____

Net Income (Loss) _____

AP-13A LO 1 3 4 5

John Cheng Communications is a public relations firm. On April 30, 2018, the firm had the following ending balances.

Cash	$20,000
Prepaid Rent	10,000
Equipment	25,000
Accounts Payable	8,000
Capital	47,000

During the month of May, the company completed the following transactions.

1. Purchased $800 of office equipment on account
2. Paid $6,000 to reduce the amount owing to a supplier
3. Received $5,000 cash from customers for services rendered
4. Paid May's utility bill with $700 cash
5. Purchased a computer worth $1,500 on account
6. Received a bill for $1,000 to be paid in July for advertisements during the month of May
7. Paid May's salaries with $1,900 cash
8. Withdrew $3,000 cash for personal use
9. Recognized $2,000 rent for May (which was prepaid)
10. Received $4,000 cash in advance for a contract to be completed in three months

Prepare the T-account worksheet.

Note: The ending balances for the month of April are the opening balances for the month of May.

Cheng Communications
Balance Sheet
As at May 31, 2018

ASSETS		LIABILITIES	
INCREASE	DECREASE	DECREASE	INCREASE
+	−	−	+
Opening			Opening

INCREASE	DECREASE
+	−
Opening	

INCREASE	DECREASE
+	−
Opening	

DECREASE	INCREASE
−	+
	Opening

DECREASE	INCREASE
−	+
	Opening

OWNER'S EQUITY

DECREASE	INCREASE
−	+
	Opening

INCREASE	DECREASE
+	−

Total Assets

Total Liabilities

Owner's Equity

Cheng Communications
Income Statement
For the Month Ended May 31, 2018

REVENUE	
DECREASE	INCREASE
−	+

LESS EXPENSES

INCREASE	DECREASE
+	−

INCREASE	DECREASE
+	−

INCREASE	DECREASE
+	−

INCREASE	DECREASE
+	−

INCREASE	DECREASE
+	−

Total Revenue

Less Total Expenses

Net Income (Loss)

AP-14A LO 1 3 4 5

On December 1, 2018, Sheila Ann established City Laundry. During the first month, the following transactions occurred.

1. Sheila Ann deposited $15,000 into City Laundry's bank account
2. Bought tables and chairs worth $1,000 with cash
3. Received and paid a utilities bill for $1,200 in cash
4. Purchased washers and dryers worth $4,000; paid $2,000 cash with the remainder due in 30 days
5. Purchased two additional dryers worth $1,100 from Marky Distributors, on account
6. Received $4,000 cash for laundry services provided for the first half of the month
7. Paid $900 cash for a one-year insurance policy
8. Paid $1,000 cash for this month's rent
9. Paid the amount owing to Marky Distributors
10. Provided $3,500 of laundry services during the second half of the month for customers who will pay at a later date
11. Paid employee salaries of $1,400
12. Sheila withdrew $2,000 cash for personal use
13. Recorded first month's insurance expense of $75
14. Collected $3,000 cash from customers as payment on their accounts
15. Received $2,000 cash in advance for services to be provided next year

Prepare the T-account worksheet.

| City Laundry Balance Sheet As at December 31, 2018 | City Laundry Income Statement For the Month Ended December 31, 2018 |

City Laundry
Balance Sheet
As at December 31, 2018

ASSETS

INCREASE +	DECREASE −
Opening	

INCREASE +	DECREASE −
Opening	

INCREASE +	DECREASE −
Opening	

INCREASE +	DECREASE −
Opening	

LIABILITIES

DECREASE −	INCREASE +
	Opening

DECREASE −	INCREASE +
	Opening

OWNER'S EQUITY

DECREASE −	INCREASE +
	Opening

INCREASE −	DECREASE +

Total Assets	_____
Total Liabilities	_____ } _____
Owner's Equity	_____

City Laundry
Income Statement
For the Month Ended December 31, 2018

REVENUE

DECREASE −	INCREASE +

LESS EXPENSES

INCREASE +	DECREASE −

INCREASE +	DECREASE −

INCREASE +	DECREASE −

INCREASE +	DECREASE −

INCREASE +	DECREASE −

INCREASE +	DECREASE −

Total Revenue	_____
Less Total Expenses	_____
Net Income (Loss)	_____

AP-15A LO 1 3 4 5

On April 1, 2018, Aaron Ragan established a business to manage rental properties. He had the following transactions during its first month of operations.

1. Owner invested $20,000 cash into the business from his personal savings; amount was deposited into the business' bank account
2. Purchased $1,000 office equipment on account
3. Received $5,000 cash for managing rental properties for a client
4. Purchased furniture worth $350 on account
5. Paid a utilities bill of $400 for the month in cash
6. Used a bank loan to purchase office furniture for $5,000
7. Paid $500 cash to reduce the amount of the bank loan principal
8. Paid rent for the month with $1,800 cash
9. Paid office staff salaries with $1,500 cash
10. Withdrew $1,000 cash for personal use
11. Provided $2,000 worth of services for a customer on account

Prepare the T-account worksheet.

Ragan Properties
Balance Sheet
As at April 30, 2018

ASSETS

INCREASE	DECREASE
+	−
Opening	

INCREASE	DECREASE
+	−
Opening	

INCREASE	DECREASE
+	−
Opening	

LIABILITIES

DECREASE	INCREASE
−	+
	Opening

DECREASE	INCREASE
−	+
	Opening

OWNER'S EQUITY

DECREASE	INCREASE
−	+
	Opening

INCREASE	DECREASE
+	−

Total Assets	_____	
Total Liabilities	_____	} _____
Owner's Equity	_____	

Ragan Properties
Income Statement
For the Month Ended April 30, 2018

REVENUE

DECREASE	INCREASE
−	+

LESS EXPENSES

INCREASE	DECREASE
+	−

INCREASE	DECREASE
+	−

INCREASE	DECREASE
+	−

INCREASE	DECREASE
+	−

INCREASE	DECREASE
+	−

Total Revenue	_____
Less Total Expenses	_____
Net Income (Loss)	_____

AP-16A LO 1 3 4 5 6

Edward James decided to start his own car rental business after graduation, called James' Rent-A-Car. He recorded these transactions during the first month of operations (January 2018).

1. Edward invested $20,000 cash in the business
2. Borrowed $20,000 from the bank
3. Paid $35,000 cash for a new car to be used in the business
4. Paid the principal of the bank loan with $2,000 cash
5. Paid for $800 of maintenance expense with cash
6. Paid monthly salaries for personnel with $1,000 cash
7. Paid miscellaneous expenses with $300 cash
8. Received $8,000 in cash for service revenue for the month
9. Received a utilities bill for the month for $600, payable next month
10. Paid monthly interest on the bank loan with $200 cash
11. Paid $1,500 of insurance for the next five months in advance
12. Edward withdrew $1,000 cash for personal use
13. Received $3,000 cash from customers for services to be provided next month

Required

a) Prepare the T-account worksheet.

James' Rent-A-Car
Balance Sheet
As at January 31, 2018

ASSETS			LIABILITIES		
INCREASE	DECREASE		DECREASE	INCREASE	
+ CASH −			− ACCOUNTS PAYABLE +		
Opening				Opening	

INCREASE	DECREASE
+ PREPAID INSURANCE −	
Opening	

DECREASE INCREASE
− UNEARNED REVENUE +
Opening

DECREASE INCREASE
− NOTES PAYABLE +
Opening

INCREASE	DECREASE
+ AUTOMOBILE −	
Opening	

OWNER'S EQUITY

DECREASE INCREASE
− JAMES, CAPITAL +
Opening

INCREASE DECREASE
+ JAMES, WITHDRAWALS −

Total Assets _____
Total Liabilities _____ }
Owner's Equity _____ _____

James' Rent-A-Car
Income Statement
For the Month Ended January 31, 2018

REVENUE
DECREASE INCREASE
− SERVICE REVENUE +

LESS EXPENSES

INCREASE DECREASE
+ INTEREST EXPENSE −

INCREASE DECREASE
+ MAINTENANCE EXPENSE −

INCREASE DECREASE
+ MISCELLANEOUS EXPENSE −

INCREASE DECREASE
+ RENT EXPENSE −

INCREASE DECREASE
+ SALARIES EXPENSE −

INCREASE DECREASE
+ UTILITIES EXPENSE −

Total Revenue _____
Less Total Expenses _____
Net Income (Loss) _____

69

b)   Prepare the income statement for the month of January.

c)   Prepare the statement of owner's equity for the month of January.

d)   Prepare the balance sheet as at January 31, 2018.

AP-17A LO 1 3 4 5 6

Lina D'Amico is the owner of Lina's Computer Services. The balance sheet of Lina's Computer Services on February 28, 2018, is shown below.

Lina's Computer Services Balance Sheet As at February 28, 2018			
Assets		**Liabilities**	
Cash	$4,000	Accounts Payable	$3,000
Prepaid Insurance	3,000	Notes Payable	0
Furniture and Equipment	25,000	**Total Liabilities**	3,000
		Owner's Equity	
		D'Amico, Capital	29,000
Total Assets	$32,000	**Total Liabilities + Owner's Equity**	$32,000

During March, the business engaged in the following transactions.

1. Borrowed $20,000 from bank
2. Purchased computer equipment for $5,000 cash
3. Performed services for a customer and received $4,000 cash
4. Purchased furniture for $1,000 on credit
5. Paid $1,500 to a supplier for the amount owed
6. Paid the following expenses in cash: salaries, $1,000; rent, $1,500; and interest, $200
7. Received a $900 utilities bill, due next month
8. Withdrew $3,500 cash for personal use
9. Received $1,000 cash in advance for services to be completed next month

Required

a) Prepare the T-account worksheet.

Note: The ending balance for the month of February is the opening balance for the month of March.

Lina's Computer Services
Balance Sheet
As at March 31, 2018

ASSETS

INCREASE	DECREASE
+	–
Opening	

INCREASE	DECREASE
+	–
Opening	

INCREASE	DECREASE
+	–
Opening	

LIABILITIES

DECREASE	INCREASE
–	+
	Opening

DECREASE	INCREASE
–	+
	Opening

DECREASE	INCREASE
–	+
	Opening

OWNER'S EQUITY

DECREASE	INCREASE
–	+
	Opening

INCREASE	DECREASE
+	–

Total Assets _____

Total Liabilities _____ }

Owner's Equity _____ _____

Lina's Computer Services
Income Statement
For the Month Ended March 31, 2018

REVENUE

DECREASE	INCREASE
–	+

LESS EXPENSES

INCREASE	DECREASE
+	–

INCREASE	DECREASE
+	–

INCREASE	DECREASE
+	–

INCREASE	DECREASE
+	–

INCREASE	DECREASE
+	–

INCREASE	DECREASE
+	–

Total Revenue _____

Less Total Expenses _____

Net Income (Loss) _____

b) Prepare the income statement for the month of March.

c) Prepare the statement of owner's equity for the month of March.

d) Prepare the balance sheet as at March 31, 2018.

AP-18A LO 7

Over the summer, you were hired by your uncle as an accounting intern for his landscaping company, which operates as a sole proprietorship. While working as an intern, you discovered that Sandra, the company's only accountant, has been using the company's money to pay for some of her personal expenses. Sandra recorded these personal expenses in the company's books as business expenses. Sandra told you that she needed the money to pay the hospital bills of her sick child. She also requested that you do not tell your uncle about her actions because she is simply borrowing this money and will try to pay the company back in about a year. Because you were hired for only three months, there is no way for you to know whether Sandra will in fact return the money. While your uncle is a great landscaper, he has very limited accounting knowledge and thus does not know how to check Sandra's accounting work. He generally trusts Sandra because of her college degree in accounting.

Analyze Sandra's actions using the fraud triangle as the framework. Discuss whether you should reveal Sandra's actions to your uncle and why or why not.

AP-18A

Application Questions Group B

AP-1B `LO 1 3 4`

For each of the given transactions, determine the effect on owner's equity by placing an "X" in the space provided.

	Effect on Owner's Equity		
	Increase	**Decrease**	**No Effect**
1. Invested money in the business			
2. Purchased equipment on account			
3. Paid one third of the amount owing for the purchase of equipment			
4. Received cash for the services rendered			
5. Paid salaries for the month			
6. Withdrew cash for personal use			
7. Paid monthly rent			
8. Additional investment by the owner			
9. Provided services for a customer who will pay in two months			
10. Acquired land using cash			

AP-2B `LO 1 3 4`

For the following transactions, indicate in the last two columns the two accounts related to each transaction.

	Account 1	**Account 2**
1. Invested cash in the business		
2. Purchased service vehicle for business use		
3. Collected cash for services provided today		
4. Provided services this week on credit		
5. Paid operating expenses in cash		
6. Received a bill for operating expenses incurred this week		
7. Received a loan from the bank		
8. Collected cash from a customer for services provided previously		
9. Paid monthly salaries to employees with cash		
10. Incurred operating expenses this week, to be paid next month		
11. Paid cash for expenses incurred previously		
12. Received cash in advance for the service to be performed next month		

AP-3B `LO 1 2`

Match each term with the appropriate description.

A   Merchandising
B   Service
C   Manufacturing
D   Accounts Receivable
E   Cash

_____   A law firm is an example of this type of business.
_____   This account represents the amount owed to the business by its customers for services preformed earlier.
_____   This type of business buys goods to resell to customers.
_____   An automaker is an example of this type of business.
_____   This is the most liquid asset.

AP-4B LO 3 4

Focus In had the following transactions during the month. Indicate whether assets, liabilities or owner's equity will increase or decrease and by how much, based on each transaction. Provide an explanation only if equity is affected. Always ensure the accounting equation is balanced.

	Assets =	Liabilities +	Owner's Equity	Explanation
1. The owner invested $10,000 into the business	+10,000		+10,000	Owner investment
2. Paid $3,300 cash for three months rent				
3. Borrowed $5,000 worth from the bank				
4. Purchased furniture for $2,500 on account				
5. Paid $700 cash for advertising				
6. Provided services and received $2,300 cash				
7. Paid $400 for the furniture purchased earlier				
8. The owner withdrew $2,500 for personal use				
9. Used up one month of rent				

AP-5B LO 3 4 5

Vu's Auto Repair is a new business owned by Sam Vu, that started operations on April 1, 2018.

Required

a) Indicate whether assets, liabilities or owner's equity will increase or decrease and by how much, based on each transaction during April. Provide an explanation only if equity is affected. The first one has been done for you. Always ensure the accounting equation is balanced.

	Assets =	Liabilities +	Owner's Equity	Explanation
1. Sam invested $8,000 cash into the business	+8,000		+8,000	
2. Sam invested $2,500 worth of equipment into the business				
3. Purchased tools and supplies for $6,030 on credit				
4. Paid 12 months of insurance in advance at $250/month				
5. Made cash sales of $4,420 during the month				
6. Received a utility bill for $370 for the month, which will be paid later				
7. Paid wages to employees of $5,800				
8. Sam withdrew $2,000 cash from the business				
9. Recorded one month of insurance used up				
10. Received $2,000 cash for services to be provided in two months				

b)   Record the transactions in the T-accounts.

| Vu's Auto Repair Balance Sheet As at April 30, 2018 | | Vu's Auto Repair Income Statement For the Month Ended April 30, 2018 |

ASSETS

INCREASE	DECREASE
+ **CASH**	−
Opening	

INCREASE	DECREASE
+ **PREPAID INSURANCE**	−
Opening	

INCREASE	DECREASE
+ **TOOLS AND SUPPLIES**	−
Opening	

INCREASE	DECREASE
+ **EQUIPMENT**	−
Opening	

LIABILITIES

DECREASE	INCREASE
− **ACCOUNTS PAYABLE**	+
	Opening

DECREASE	INCREASE
− **UNEARNED REVENUE**	+
	Opening

DECREASE	INCREASE
− **NOTES PAYABLE**	+
	Opening

OWNER'S EQUITY

DECREASE	INCREASE
− **VU, CAPITAL**	+
	Opening

INCREASE	DECREASE
− **VU, WITHDRAWALS**	+

REVENUE

DECREASE	INCREASE
− **SERVICE REVENUE**	+

LESS EXPENSES

INCREASE	DECREASE
+ **INSURANCE EXPENSE**	−

INCREASE	DECREASE
+ **SALARIES EXPENSE**	−

INCREASE	DECREASE
+ **UTILITIES EXPENSE**	−

INCREASE	DECREASE
+	−

Total Assets _____

Total Liabilities _____ } _____

Owner's Equity _____

Total Revenue _____

Less Total Expenses _____

Net Income (Loss) _____

c) Complete the income statement for the month of April.

d) Complete the statement of owner's equity for the month of April.

e) Complete the balance sheet as at April 30, 2018.

AP-6B LO 6

Maya's Music offers music lessons to the public for all age groups. Maya Matlin is trying to assess her business by analyzing her balance sheet. Here are the accounts and balances of Maya's Music on October 31, 2018.

Accounts Payable	$1,250
Notes Payable	55,000
Building	120,000
Cash	8,150
Instruments	21,650
Prepaid Insurance	3,600
Supplies	280
Unearned Revenue	1,000

Prepare the balance sheet as at October 31, 2018 for Maya's Music.

Analysis

Maya thinks her business is doing well because her capital is so high. Is the balance sheet a useful tool to analyze performance? What other information is needed to assess whether Maya's Music has been performing well or not? Explain.

AP-7B LO 6

Some numbers are missing from the following balance sheet and statement of cash flows of Caldwell Enterprises.

Caldwell Enterprises Balance Sheet As at August 31, 2018			
Assets		**Liabilities**	
Cash	a)	Accounts Payable	$18,000
Accounts Receivable	15,000	Notes Payable	5,000
Office Supplies	3,000	**Total Liabilities**	b)
Furniture	10,000	**Owner's Equity**	
		Caldwell, Capital	c)
Total Assets	$35,100	**Total Liabilities + Owner's Equity**	d)

Caldwell Enterprises Statement of Cash Flows For the Month Ended August 31, 2018		
Cash Flow from Operating Activities		
Cash Received from Customers	$13,450	
Cash Paid to Employees	(6,000)	
Cash Paid for Interest	(50)	
Net Cash Provided by Operating Activities		e)
Cash Flow from Investing Activities		
Cash Payments for Furniture Purchase	(10,000)	
Net Cash Used by Investing Activities		f)
Cash Flow from Financing Activities		
Cash Received from Bank Loan	5,000	
Cash Withdrawal by Owner	(1,000)	
Net Cash Provided by Financing Activities		g)
Net Increase in Cash		h)
Cash Balance, August 1, 2018		i)
Cash Balance, August 31, 2018		j)

Required

Calculate the missing numbers for the following balances.

a) Cash balance in the balance sheet: _____

b) Total liabilities: _____

c) Caldwell, capital: _____

d) Total liabilities + owner's equity: _____

e) Net cash provided by operating activities: _____

f) Net cash used by investing activities: _____

g) Net cash provided by financing activities: _____

h) Net increase in cash: _____

i) Cash balance, August 1, 2018: _____

j) Cash balance, August 31, 2018: _____

AP-8B LO 5

Macy Stewart operates a nail and spa business. For the month of May 2018, she had the following transactions. For each transaction, provide the appropriate T-account name and fill in the amount.

1. Received a deposit of $400 from a wedding party for a spa treatment to be done next month

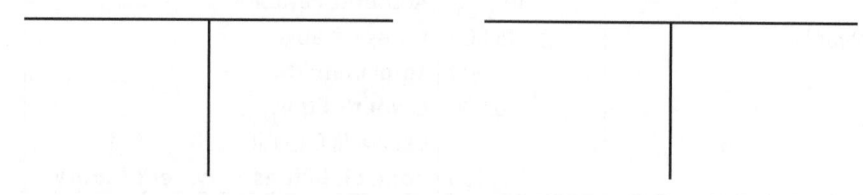

2. Took $800 from the business for personal use

3. Performed a manicure/pedicure for a client and charged her $100; the client will pay next month

4. Received and paid the telephone bill for $150

AP-9B LO 5

Stacy Dixon operates a small accounting business. During the month of October 2018, she had the following transactions. For each transaction, provide the appropriate T-account name and fill in the amount.

1. Provided services to a client and billed him $1,200; the client paid immediately with cash

2. Paid $80 for the telephone bill that was received and recorded last month

3. Paid $800 of the bank loan principal.

4. Provided services to a client and billed her $900; the client will pay next month

AP-10B LO 6

Faiyaz Dhawan Architects has recorded all the transactions for the month of March 2018. The balances of all the accounts are shown below. During the month, Faiyaz invested an extra $2,000 into the business.

Account	Balance
Accounts Payable	$3,500
Accounts Receivable	6,700
Cash	8,500
Equipment	18,000
Insurance Expense	700
Maintenance Expense	400
Notes Payable	7,500
Prepaid Rent	3,600
Dhawan, Capital	17,650
Dhawan, Withdrawals	2,600
Salaries Expense	5,200
Service Revenue	16,400
Travel Expense	1,400
Unearned Revenue	800
Utilities Expense	750

Required

a) Using the accounts and balances, prepare the income statement for Faiyaz Dhawan Architects for the month of March.

b) Prepare the statement of owner's equity for the month of March.

c) Prepare the balance sheet as at March 31, 2018.

AP-11B LO 1 3 4 5

Brenda Darby recently started her own consulting business, and completed these transactions during the first month of operations (May 2018).

1. Brenda invested $10,700 cash in the business
2. Purchased store furniture for $4,000 cash
3. Paid $1,100 cash for two months of insurance in advance
4. Incurred business registration expenses, paid with $640 cash
5. Paid travel expenses with $1,200 cash
6. Received $2,300 cash from clients for consulting services provided during the month
7. Borrowed $3,800 cash from the bank
8. Paid salary to an assistant with $790 cash
9. Received bills of $900 for May's electricity, water and telephone, to be paid next month
10. Brenda withdrew $700 cash for personal purposes
11. Received $1,000 cash for a consulting service to be completed next month

Record the above transactions in the T-account worksheet.

Darby Consulting
Balance Sheet
As at May 31, 2018

ASSETS			LIABILITIES		
INCREASE	DECREASE		DECREASE	INCREASE	
+	CASH	–	–	ACCOUNTS PAYABLE	+
Opening				Opening	

INCREASE	DECREASE		DECREASE	INCREASE	
+	PREPAID INSURANCE	–	–	UNEARNED REVENUE	+
Opening				Opening	

INCREASE	DECREASE		DECREASE	INCREASE	
+	FURNITURE	–	–	NOTES PAYABLE	+
Opening				Opening	

OWNER'S EQUITY

DECREASE	INCREASE	
–	DARBY, CAPITAL	+
	Opening	

INCREASE	DECREASE	
+	DARBY, WITHDRAWALS	–

Total Assets _____
Total Liabilities _____ } _____
Owner's Equity _____

Darby Consulting
Income Statement
For the Month Ended May 31, 2018

REVENUE		
DECREASE	INCREASE	
–	SERVICE REVENUE	+

LESS EXPENSES

INCREASE	DECREASE	
+	REGISTRATION EXPENSE	–

INCREASE	DECREASE	
+	SALARIES EXPENSE	–

INCREASE	DECREASE	
+	TRAVEL EXPENSE	–

INCREASE	DECREASE	
+	UTILITIES EXPENSE	–

Total Revenue _____
Less Total Expenses _____
Net Income (Loss) _____

AP-12B `LO` `1 3 4 5`

Deep Drains is a plumbing company that started operations in February 2017. The company is fully owned by Emma Reno. Consider the following opening balances as of February 1, 2018.

Cash	$13,200
Prepaid Rent	5,700
Prepaid Insurance	4,000
Property, Plant & Equipment	38,200
Accounts Payable	3,300
Notes Payable	11,300
Reno, Capital	46,500

The following transactions were completed during the month of February.

1. Purchased plane tickets for business travel with $1,140 cash
2. Paid $3,300 cash to reduce the balance of accounts payable
3. Purchased equipment worth $3,400 with a bank loan
4. The owner invested $6,700 additional cash in the company
5. Paid $850 cash for registration expenses
6. Received a bill for $590 for utilities used during the month; the bill was immediately paid with cash
7. Earned revenue and received $10,000 cash
8. Recognized prepaid rent as an expense for $1,110
9. Paid interest for the month of February with $50 cash
10. Paid monthly salaries with $4,100 cash
11. The owner withdrew $2,500 cash from the business to pay for personal expenses
12. Received $2,000 cash in advance for services to be rendered in three months

Using the information provided, first record the opening balances in the T-accounts. Then, record the transactions for the month of February in the T-accounts and complete the bottom of the table.

Deep Drains
Balance Sheet
As at February 28, 2018

ASSETS

INCREASE	DECREASE
+ CASH	−
Opening	

INCREASE	DECREASE
+ PREPAID RENT	−
Opening	

INCREASE	DECREASE
+ PREPAID INSURANCE	−
Opening	

INCREASE	DECREASE
+ EQUIPMENT	−
Opening	

LIABILITIES

DECREASE	INCREASE
− ACCOUNTS PAYABLE	+
	Opening

DECREASE	INCREASE
− UNEARNED REVENUE	+
	Opening

DECREASE	INCREASE
− NOTES PAYABLE	+
	Opening

OWNER'S EQUITY

DECREASE	INCREASE
− RENO, CAPITAL	+
	Opening

INCREASE	DECREASE
+ RENO, WITHDRAWALS	−

Total Assets _____

Total Liabilities _____ } _____

Owner's Equity _____

Deep Drains
Income Statement
For the Month Ended February 28, 2018

REVENUE

DECREASE	INCREASE
− SERVICE REVENUE	+

LESS EXPENSES

INCREASE	DECREASE
+ INTEREST EXPENSE	−

INCREASE	DECREASE
+ REGISTRATION EXPENSE	−

INCREASE	DECREASE
+ RENT EXPENSE	−

INCREASE	DECREASE
+ SALARIES EXPENSE	−

INCREASE	DECREASE
+ UTILITIES EXPENSE	−

INCREASE	DECREASE
+ TRAVEL EXPENSE	−

Total Revenue _____

Less Total Expenses _____

Net Income (Loss) _____

AP-13B LO 1 3 4 5

Candace Harris Legal is a law firm. On July 31, 2018, the firm had the following ending balances.

Cash	$18,500
Prepaid Insurance	9,200
Property, Plant & Equipment	22,300
Accounts Payable	8,100
Harris, Capital	41,900

During the month of August, the company completed the following transactions.

1. Purchased $1,000 of office equipment on account
2. Received $4,600 cash from customers for services rendered
3. Paid $4,900 owing to a supplier
4. Paid a $570 utilities bill for August with cash
5. Purchased a computer on account for $1,420
6. Paid August's salaries with $3,600 cash
7. Received a $1,150 advertising bill to be paid in September for advertisements during the month of August
8. Performed services worth $2,000 for customers on account
9. Withdrew $3,200 cash for personal use
10. Recognized $1,700 insurance for August (which was prepaid)
11. Received $1,500 cash for legal services to be done next month
12. Collected all the balances owing from customers for services performed earlier

Using the information provided, first record the opening balances in the T-accounts. Then, record the transactions for the month of August in the T-accounts and complete the bottom of the table.

Candace Harris Legal
Balance Sheet
As at August 31, 2018

ASSETS		LIABILITIES	

ASSETS

INCREASE	DECREASE
+	CASH	−

Opening

+ ACCOUNTS RECEIVABLE −

INCREASE	DECREASE

Opening

+ PREPAID INSURANCE −

INCREASE	DECREASE

Opening

+ EQUIPMENT −

INCREASE	DECREASE

Opening

LIABILITIES

− ACCOUNTS PAYABLE +

DECREASE	INCREASE

Opening

− UNEARNED REVENUE +

DECREASE	INCREASE

Opening

OWNER'S EQUITY

− HARRIS, CAPITAL +

DECREASE	INCREASE

Opening

+ HARRIS, WITHDRAWALS −

INCREASE	DECREASE

Total Assets _____

Total Liabilities _____

Owner's Equity _____ } _____

Candace Harris Legal
Income Statement
For the Month Ended August 31, 2018

REVENUE

− SERVICE REVENUE +

DECREASE	INCREASE

LESS EXPENSES

+ ADVERTISING EXPENSE −

INCREASE	DECREASE

+ INSURANCE EXPENSE −

INCREASE	DECREASE

+ SALARIES EXPENSE −

INCREASE	DECREASE

+ UTILITIES EXPENSE −

INCREASE	DECREASE

Total Revenue _____

Less Total Expenses _____

Net Income (Loss) _____

AP-14B LO 1 3 4 5

Christine Jacob is a financial planning consultant. During the month of February 2018, she completed the following transactions.

1. Christine invested $8,000 cash in the business
2. Paid $1,400 cash for office rent for the month of February
3. Received $6,500 from a client for services rendered
4. Paid $500 cash for gas
5. Paid $700 cash to Helpful Entrepreneur for consulting services
6. Purchased office equipment worth $900 on account
7. Owner withdrew $2,500 cash for personal use
8. Donated $800 cash to the American Red Cross
9. Provided $2,000 worth of services for a client who paid on account
10. Made partial payment of $500 on the equipment that was purchased on account
11. Received $500 cash for services to be provided next month
12. Collected $1,000 cash from a client who owed for services provided earlier in the month

Prepare the T-account worksheet.

Christine Jacob Financial Planning
Balance Sheet
As at February 28, 2018

ASSETS		LIABILITIES	

INCREASE + / **DECREASE −**

Opening

INCREASE + / **DECREASE −**

Opening

INCREASE + / **DECREASE −**

Opening

LIABILITIES

DECREASE − / INCREASE +

Opening

DECREASE − / INCREASE +

Opening

DECREASE − / INCREASE +

OWNER'S EQUITY

DECREASE − / INCREASE +

Opening

INCREASE + / DECREASE −

INCREASE + / DECREASE −

Total Assets _____

Total Liabilities _____

Owner's Equity _____ } _____

Christine Jacob Financial Planning
Income Statement
For the Month Ended February 28, 2018

REVENUE	

DECREASE − / INCREASE +

LESS EXPENSES

INCREASE + / DECREASE −

INCREASE + / DECREASE −

INCREASE + / DECREASE −

INCREASE + / DECREASE −

INCREASE + / DECREASE −

INCREASE + / DECREASE −

INCREASE + / DECREASE −

Total Revenue _____

Less Total Expenses _____

Net Income (Loss) _____

AP-15B LO 1 3 4 5

Troy Dale, a graphic designer, opened his own business on March 1, 2018. During the month, he completed the following transactions related to his professional practice.

1. Transferred $30,000 cash from personal bank account to the business account
2. Provided services for $3,000 cash
3. Purchased office and computer equipment worth $8,000 on account, which will be paid next month
4. Paid $1,100 cash for meals and entertainment
5. Paid insurance expense with $800 cash
6. Performed services for clients for $4,000 on account
7. Paid $600 cash for miscellaneous expenses
8. Received a utilities bill of $1,000, to be paid next month
9. Paid $1,200 cash for office rent for the month of March
10. Paid $1,000 salary to his assistant
11. Collected 50% of the balance owing from clients for services performed earlier this month
12. Received $1,000 cash for services to be performed in three months

Prepare the T-account worksheet.

Dale Design
Balance Sheet
As at March 31, 2018

ASSETS

INCREASE	DECREASE
+	−
Opening	

INCREASE	DECREASE
+	−
Opening	

INCREASE	DECREASE
+	−
Opening	

LIABILITIES

DECREASE	INCREASE
−	+
	Opening

DECREASE	INCREASE
−	+
	Opening

OWNER'S EQUITY

DECREASE	INCREASE
−	+
	Opening

INCREASE	DECREASE
+	−

Total Assets _____

Total Liabilities _____

Owner's Equity _____ } _____

Dale Design
Income Statement
For the Month Ended March 31, 2018

REVENUE

DECREASE	INCREASE
−	+

LESS EXPENSES

INCREASE	DECREASE
+	−

INCREASE	DECREASE
+	−

INCREASE	DECREASE
+	−

INCREASE	DECREASE
+	−

INCREASE	DECREASE
+	−

INCREASE	DECREASE
+	−

Total Revenue _____

Less Total Expenses _____

Net Income (Loss) _____

AP-16B LO 1 3 4 5 6

Ella Kates founded Health-Plus Clinic as a medical clinic that started operations in January 2017. Consider the following opening balances as of January 1, 2018.

Cash	$15,000
Prepaid Rent	6,000
Prepaid Insurance	5,000
Equipment	30,000
Accounts Payable	3,000
Notes Payable	10,000
Kates, Capital	43,000

The following transactions occurred during the month of January.

1. Purchased plane tickets with $1,500 cash; the plane tickets are to attend a business conference
2. Paid $3,000 cash to reduce the balance of accounts payable
3. The owner invested $5,000 additional cash in the company
4. Purchased $4,000 worth of equipment with a bank loan
5. Paid $1,000 cash for maintenance expenses
6. Earned $15,000 revenue from patients on a cash basis
7. Received a $900 bill for utilities used during the month; a check was issued to pay the bill immediately
8. Recognized $2,000 of prepaid rent as an expense
9. Paid $100 interest for the month with cash
10. Paid $4,000 in monthly salaries to all medical practitioners and clinic personnel
11. Received $2,000 cash from one of its clients for services to be provided in March
12. The owner withdrew $2,000 cash from the business to pay for personal expenses

Required

a) Prepare the T-account worksheet.

Health-Plus Clinic
Balance Sheet
As at January 31, 2018

ASSETS		LIABILITIES	
INCREASE	DECREASE	DECREASE	INCREASE
+	−	−	+
Opening			Opening

INCREASE	DECREASE	DECREASE	INCREASE
+	−	−	+
Opening			Opening

INCREASE	DECREASE	DECREASE	INCREASE
+	−	−	+
Opening			Opening

INCREASE	DECREASE	**OWNER'S EQUITY**	
+	−	DECREASE	INCREASE
Opening		−	+
			Opening

INCREASE	DECREASE
+	−

Total Assets _____

Total Liabilities _____

Owner's Equity _____ } _____

Health-Plus Clinic
Income Statement
For the Month Ended January 31, 2018

REVENUE	
DECREASE	INCREASE
−	+

LESS EXPENSES

INCREASE	DECREASE
+	−

INCREASE	DECREASE
+	−

INCREASE	DECREASE
+	−

INCREASE	DECREASE
+	−

INCREASE	DECREASE
+	−

INCREASE	DECREASE
+	−

Total Revenue _____

Less Total Expenses _____

Net Income (Loss) _____

b) Prepare the income statement for the month of January.

c) Prepare the statement of owner's equity for the month of January.

d) Prepare the balance sheet as at January 31, 2018.

AP-17B LO 1 3 4 5 6

Helga Stiles operates a hairstyling company. The opening balances from Helga's Hairstyling's financial records on March 1, 2018 are shown below.

Cash	$18,000
Equipment	4,300
Supplies	1,200
Building	140,000
Accounts Payable	3,600
Notes Payable	100,000
Stiles, Capital	59,900

The following transactions took place during the month of March.

1. $5,000 cash was taken from the bank account for a bank loan payment
2. Paid down a portion of the accounts payable with $1,000 cash
3. Recorded cash sales of $5,500
4. Received a delivery of supplies for $2,000; invoice is due in 30 days
5. Received a bill of $650 for maintenance on equipment, which will be paid next month
6. Paid salaries to employees with $1,500 cash
7. Withdrew $2,000 cash from the business
8. Provided services worth $2,000 for clients on account
9. Received $1,500 cash in advance of service to be done next month
10. Collected $1,000 of the amount owing from clients

Required

a) Record the transactions in the T-accounts.

Helga's Hairstyling
Balance Sheet
As at March 31, 2018

ASSETS

INCREASE	DECREASE
+ CASH –	
Opening	

INCREASE	DECREASE
– ACCOUNTS RECEIVABLE +	
Opening	

INCREASE	DECREASE
+ SUPPLIES –	
Opening	

INCREASE	DECREASE
+ EQUIPMENT –	
Opening	

INCREASE	DECREASE
+ BUILDING –	
Opening	

LIABILITIES

DECREASE	INCREASE
– ACCOUNTS PAYABLE +	
	Opening

DECREASE	INCREASE
– UNEARNED REVENUE +	
	Opening

DECREASE	INCREASE
– NOTES PAYABLE +	
	Opening

OWNER'S EQUITY

DECREASE	INCREASE
– STILES, CAPITAL +	
	Opening

INCREASE	DECREASE
+ STILES, WITHDRAWALS –	

Total Assets _____

Total Liabilities _____ }
Owner's Equity _____ _____

Helga's Hairstyling
Income Statement
For the Month Ended March 31, 2018

REVENUE

DECREASE	INCREASE
– SERVICE REVENUE +	

LESS EXPENSES

INCREASE	DECREASE
+ MAINTENANCE EXPENSE –	

INCREASE	DECREASE
+ SALARIES EXPENSE –	

INCREASE	DECREASE
+ TELEPHONE EXPENSE –	

INCREASE	DECREASE
+ UTILITIES EXPENSE –	

Total Revenue _____

Less Total Expenses _____

Net Income (Loss) _____

b)   Complete the income statement for the month of March.

c)   Complete the statement of owner's equity for the month of March.

d)   Complete the balance sheet as at March 31, 2018.

AP-18B LO 7

After facing a financial shortage, Antonio, the owner of a toy manufacturer, decided to apply for a bank loan for his business. The bank requested important reports, including the company's financial statements, to review. To maximize his chance of getting the bank loan approved, Antonio suppressed a product safety report stating that the material used to manufacture the company's new toys can be harmful if children bite on them. Additionally, he asked the accountant to re-classify some expenses as assets in order to show a higher net income figure to the bank.

Required

a) Discuss whether Antonio is behaving in an ethical manner by omitting the product safety report and re-classifying expenses as assets.

b) Discuss whether Antonio and the bank share any common interests.

Case Study

CS-1 LO 1 3 4 5

Granyard Clockworks is a service company that repairs damaged watches and clocks. The company is owned by Maurice Granyard. Maurice is fully liable for all activities of the business. In the most recent month (May 2018), Granyard Clockworks had the following transactions.

1. Maurice deposited $40,000 of additional cash into the business
2. Borrowed $15,000 in cash from the bank
3. Paid $3,500 cash for May's rent
4. Paid $6,000 in salaries for May
5. Performed services and earned $18,000 in cash
6. Incurred telephone expenses of $500 (to be paid next month)
7. Performed services for a client for $3,000 on account
8. Prepaid insurance for one year in the amount of $11,000
9. Incurred maintenance expense of $1,000 (paid on account)
10. Maurice withdrew $5,000 from the business for personal use
11. Received $2,000 cash for repair services to be done in July
12. Collected 80% of the $3,000 amount owing from a client for services performed earlier this month

As at April 30, 2018, the ending account balances for Granyard Clockworks were as follows.

Cash	$50,000
Accounts Receivable	12,000
Prepaid Insurance	800
Equipment	40,000
Accounts Payable	2,000
Notes Payable	60,000
Granyard, Capital	40,800

Required

a) Complete the T-account worksheets for May 2018.

Granyard Clockworks
Balance Sheet
As at May 31, 2018

Granyard Clockworks
Income Statement
For the Month Ended May 31, 2018

ASSETS		LIABILITIES		REVENUE	

ASSETS

INCREASE	DECREASE
+	CASH	–

Opening

INCREASE	DECREASE
–	ACCOUNTS RECEIVABLE	+

Opening

INCREASE	DECREASE
+	PREPAID INSURANCE	–

Opening

INCREASE	DECREASE
+	EQUIPMENT	–

Opening

LIABILITIES

DECREASE	INCREASE
–	ACCOUNTS PAYABLE	+

Opening

DECREASE	INCREASE
–	UNEARNED REVENUE	+

Opening

DECREASE	INCREASE
–	NOTES PAYABLE	+

Opening

OWNER'S EQUITY

DECREASE	INCREASE
–	GRANYARD, CAPITAL	+

Opening

INCREASE	DECREASE
+	GRANYARD, WITHDRAWALS	–

REVENUE

DECREASE	INCREASE
–	REVENUE	+

LESS EXPENSES

INCREASE	DECREASE
+	MAINTENANCE EXPENSE	–

INCREASE	DECREASE
+	RENT EXPENSE	–

INCREASE	DECREASE
+	SALARIES EXPENSE	–

INCREASE	DECREASE
+	TELEPHONE EXPENSE	–

INCREASE	DECREASE
+		–

Total Assets _____

Total Liabilities _____

Owner's Equity _____

Total Revenue _____

Less Total Expenses _____

Net Income (Loss) _____

b) If Maurice Granyard sells all of the business' assets for cash and pays off the company's debts, what is the remaining amount? What does it represent?

_____

_____

_____

Notes

Chapter 3

THE ACCOUNTING FRAMEWORK

LEARNING OBJECTIVES

LO 1 Describe the users of accounting information

LO 2 Describe the fields of accounting

LO 3 Compare the different forms of business organization

LO 4 Identify the objective, constraints and qualitative characteristics of financial information

LO 5 List and apply basic accounting assumptions and principles

LO 6 Explain the importance of ethics in accounting

AMEENGAGE™ *Access **ameengage.com** for integrated resources including tutorials, practice exercises, the digital textbook and more.*

——————— Assessment Questions ———————

AS-1 LO 1

What is an internal user? What do internal users use financial information for?

_____

_____

_____

AS-2 LO 1

What is an external user? What do external users use financial information for?

_____

_____

_____

AS-3 LO 2

Briefly define financial accounting.

_____

_____

_____

AS-4 LO 2

Briefly define managerial accounting.

_____

_____

_____

AS-5 `LO` `2`

Jessica works full-time as a management accountant for a manufacturing company. Does Jessica practice public or private accounting? Which accounting designation is likely to be the best fit for her job?

AS-6 `LO` `2`

Working for an audit firm, Pablo audits many clients' accounting records. Does Pablo practice public or private accounting? Which accounting designation does Pablo need to have?

AS-7 `LO` `3`

What is a sole proprietorship? What is the title of a sole proprietorship's equity section?

AS-8 `LO` `3`

Explain the concept of unlimited liability.

AS-9 `LO` `3`

What is a partnership?

AS-10 `LO` `3`

What are the four types of partnerships that can be created?

AS-11 `LO` `3`

What is the difference between a general partnership and a limited partnership?

AS-12 `LO 3`

Describe a corporation.

_____

_____

_____

_____

AS-13 `LO 3`

What is a nonprofit organization?

_____

_____

_____

AS-14 `LO 3`

Provide three examples of nonprofit organizations.

_____

_____

AS-15 `LO 4`

Briefly define and explain GAAP. Which organization has the legal authority to develop US GAAP?

_____

_____

_____

_____

_____

AS-16 `LO 4`

What is IFRS and which forms of organization can adhere to it?

_____

_____

_____

_____

_____

_____

AS-17 `LO 4`

Describe the cost constraint.

_____

_____

_____

AS-18 LO 4

Describe the materiality constraint.

_____

_____

_____

AS-19 LO 4

Describe the conservatism constraint.

_____

_____

_____

AS-20 LO 4

Describe the consistency constraint.

_____

_____

_____

AS-21 LO 4

What are the four qualitative characteristics of effective and useful information?

_____

_____

_____

AS-22 LO 4

Describe the characteristic of relevance.

_____

_____

_____

AS-23 LO 4

Describe timeliness. Which characteristic is timeliness a component of?

_____

_____

_____

AS-24 LO 4

Describe the characteristic of reliability.

_____

_____

_____

AS-25 LO 4

What is verifiability? Which characteristic is verifiability a component of?

_____

_____

AS-26 LO 4

Describe the characteristic of understandability.

_____

_____

AS-27 LO 4

What is faithful representation? Which characteristic is faithful representation a component of?

_____

_____

AS-28 LO 4

What is neutrality? Which characteristic is neutrality a component of?

_____

_____

AS-29 LO 4

Describe the characteristic of comparability.

_____

_____

AS-30 LO 4

What is a trade-off? Provide an example of a commonly discussed trade-off of qualitative characteristics.

_____

_____

_____

AS-31 LO 5

Describe the business entity assumption.

_____

_____

_____

AS-32 LO 5

Describe the going concern assumption.

_____

_____

_____

AS-33 `LO 5`

Describe the monetary unit assumption.

_____

_____

AS-34 `LO 5`

Describe the time period assumption.

_____

_____

AS-35 `LO 5`

Describe the principle of measurement.

_____

_____

AS-36 `LO 5`

Describe the principle of revenue recognition.

_____

_____

_____

AS-37 `LO 5`

Describe the principle of expense recognition.

_____

_____

AS-38 `LO 5`

Describe the principle of disclosure.

_____

_____

AS-39 `LO 6`

List two ethical standards for accountants.

_____

_____

_____

AS-40 `LO 6`

What is the name of the Act that the United States Congress passed in 2002 to prevent accounting practices from fraudulent activities?

_____

_____

Application Questions Group A

AP-1A LO 1

Identify whether the following users of accounting information are internal or external users by marking an "X" in the appropriate category.

	Internal	External
Lenders		
Suppliers		
Salespeople		
Customers		
Business owners		
Accountants		
Government agencies		
Purchasing managers		
Press and media		
Production managers		

AP-2A LO 3

Match each form of an organization with the appropriate description.

A	Sole Proprietorship
B	Partnership
C	Corporation
D	Nonprofit Organization

_____ This type of organization usually does not have an identifiable owner.

_____ There are four types. Some owners have limited liability, while others have unlimited liability.

_____ A business operated by a single owner.

_____ This type of business often elects a board of directors.

AP-3A LO 5

Match each of the following assumptions and principles to the appropriate description in the table below.

- Business entity assumption
- Going concern assumption
- Monetary unit assumption
- Time period assumption
- Revenue recognition
- Measurement

Term (fill in)	Description
	accounting takes place over specific fiscal periods
	sales must be recorded when ownership of a good transfers from the seller to the buyer
	assumes that a business will continue to operate into the foreseeable future
	financial reports should be expressed in a single currency
	accounting for a business must be kept separate from the personal affairs of its owner or any other business
	purchases must be recorded at their values on the date of purchase

AP-4A LO 4

Hawkton Publishing Corporation is a publisher of math textbooks. The company is a large, well-known, publicly traded corporation with thousands of stockholders. It produces financial statements on an annual basis. The most recent financial statements (for the year ended December 31, 2018) showed comparative balances for 2018 and 2017. The 2018 balances were derived using accrual-based accounting whereas the 2017 balances were derived using cash-based accounting.

Which characteristic(s) of information did Hawkton fail to represent? Explain.

_____
_____
_____
_____
_____
_____
_____
_____

AP-5A LO 5

Alton Floral is a new company that operates in the gardening industry. The owner of the company has decided not to hire an accountant but instead maintain the accounting records on his own. He has included his newly hired employees as assets on the balance sheet in the account "Human Resources." He has valued them based on the amount of their future salaries on the balance sheet. Also, the financial statements are not supported by notes explaining some of the figures.

Which of the basic accounting principles and/or assumptions has Alton Floral violated? Explain.

_____
_____
_____
_____
_____

AP-6A LO 4

Suppose that a company has changed its policy for depreciation from one year to the next. An employee in the accounting department addressed this change with the owner. The employee asked the owner why the accounting policy was changed and why the reason for the change was not disclosed in the notes to the financial statements. The owner replied, "GAAP gives you the option to use a different depreciation method from one year to the next. We are not required to explain our choices." Is the owner's statement correct? Explain.

_____
_____
_____
_____
_____
_____
_____

AP-7A LO 5

Heggy Company, a privately owned corporation, manufactures cell phone accessories. It relies on GAAP to prepare its financial statements. The company is doing well and is planning to expand its product line. Assume you are a newly hired accountant for Heggy and you are reviewing the company's financial statements.

The company recently purchased machinery as part of its expansion strategy. After a long negotiation, Heggy's purchasing department was able to purchase the machinery for $700,000, well below the market value of $740,000. The machinery has been recorded in Heggy's books at $740,000.

Also, Heggy Company paid $15,000 for the cost of the plant's insurance for the upcoming year and expensed the whole amount. Heggy believes that this is an effective cost-saving strategy in the long run as it will avoid the extra bookkeeping associated with updating the prepaid insurance account.

Has Heggy Company violated any principles of GAAP? Explain.

AP-8A LO 5

Tasai Corporation is an American manufacturer of wings for commercial aircrafts. Tasai is a large company famous for the unique design of its wings. You are appointed as its audit manager.

As you go through the income statement, you notice that the company has set aside one line item under revenue. The line item shows an amount of 800,000 in Brazilian currency (reals). The notes related to this item indicate that the company completed a project in Brazil, and due to the large amount of foreign exchange loss, the company decided to report the figure in reals. The accounting department thinks this practice is permitted under GAAP as long as it is clearly explained in the notes.

You also note that this year's travel expense is significantly larger than last year's. As part of the audit procedures, you examine travel documents and invoices and realize that one of the owners included his personal travel expenses as part of his business-related travels. In addition, Tasai Corporation has changed one of its accounting policies and disclosed the nature, impact and reason of this change in the notes.

As the audit manager, discuss if any accounting assumptions or principles have been violated.

AP-9A LO 4

Sood Supplies sells electronic components to computer manufacturers. Sood Supplies' financial statements are issued on an annual basis for a large number of users, such as investors and the bank. The financial reporting of the company is based on GAAP.

Prior to the issuance of the current year's financial statements, the head of engineering and the accounting manager discussed the amount of warranty expense that should be recognized for the year. The head of engineering believes that only 2% of sales needs to be calculated as a provision for the warranty expense, while the accounting manager believes that 6% of sales should be recorded as an expense. The accounting manager argues that the 6% is estimated based on historical trends of the company and the industry; however, the engineering department claims that its new method of quality assurance will reduce future warranty expenses. The engineering department could not submit any documents to support the claim. Eventually, the accounting manager decided to use the 2% calculation.

Do you believe any of the accounting constraints or qualitative characteristics have been violated by Sood Supplies? Explain.

AP-10A LO 4

Identify the qualitative characteristic of financial information that has been violated in each of the following scenarios.

a) Thorn Company has reported several gains for the period, but has not provided any explanation or proof of how they occurred.

b) Due to recent layoffs, Monte Carlo Ltd. was not able to complete and issue its 2017 financial statements and accompanying notes. The information was instead included with the 2018 financial report in the following year.

c) To value inventory, Toland and Sons uses a different accounting policy in the current year compared to last year. There is no justification for the change in the accounting policy in the notes to the financial statements.

d) Eris Laboratories used many uncommon medical terms and scientific language in the notes to the financial statements. This language was not explained anywhere else.

e) A bank decided not to grant a loan to Mida Ltd. after a customer filed a substantial lawsuit. Mida Ltd. did not include any mention of the lawsuit in the financial statements or in the notes to the financial statements.

AP-11A LO 4 5

Identify the accounting principle or constraint that has been violated in each of the following scenarios.

a) Bill Co. purchased a two-year insurance policy and expensed the entire amount in the period of purchase.

___

b) Charlie Co. listed inventory at its market value of $31,000 on the balance sheet, even though it was purchased for $20,000.

___

c) Percy Co. did not include the details of its property, plant and equipment, even though this information is relevant to the users.

___

d) Fred Co. made a sale on the last day of the accounting period. The customer paid for the item in the following month, so this sale was included in the next period's financial statements.

___

e) George Co. has plans to restructure its operations next year and will sell off about half of the business. This information was not included in the notes to the financial statements because it does not affect the current financial information.

___

f) Ron Co. applied a certain accounting policy that allowed the company to report higher assets and net income. A different accounting policy was available that would have resulted in a lower balance of assets and net income.

___

g) Ginny Co. changed the accounting policy used to value property, plant and equipment after using a different policy for 10 years. There was no justification for the change.

___

AP-12A LO 5

For each of the following transactions that pertain to Jackson Lawn Care in July, identify the best course of action that properly follows GAAP principles.

a) Jackson Lawn Care needed to purchase a new lawn mower to replace the old, defective one. The full retail price of the new lawn mower, according to the supplier, was $1,750. Jackson Lawn Care negotiated a price of $1,500 and paid cash on July 1. A friend of the company's owner offers to pay the company $1,000 for the lawn mower after the company uses it for one year. At what value should the lawn mower be recorded in Jackson Lawn Care's books as of the purchase date?

___

b) In addition to providing lawn maintenance services, Jackson Lawn Care sells items related to lawn care. The government recently announced that one of the pesticides that the company sells will be banned due to its adverse environmental effect. The reduction in the inventory value due to the ban is material. Should the company disclose the information?

___

c) On July 25, a client prepaid $200 cash for Jackson Lawn Care to mow his lawn in August. In which month should the company recognize this revenue?

_____

_____

d) Due to a high demand of the company's services, Jackson Lawn Care had to hire a temporary worker for a special project. On June 20, the worker signed a contract to work for Jackson Lawn Care during July 15 – 30. The worker successfully completed the project at the end of July and will be paid her wages on August 5. In which month should the company recognize the worker's wages expenses?

_____

_____

_____

AP-13A LO 6

Lanying is a senior accountant who recently agreed to give a professional review of the financial statements of Baker Consulting Inc. Lanying is a friend of the president of this company and has an outstanding loan to the company. Baker Consulting Inc. is having cash flow issues, which may force it to lay off some employees, but the owner has assured Lanying that everything is under control and that the company is about to land several large sales contracts. He also explained that if the financial statements revealed any issues, the company would lose potential customers and suppliers. After some discussion, Lanying decided to issue a positive opinion of the financial statements and not disclose any issues. Has Lanying violated any ethical standards of accounting? Discuss.

_____

_____

_____

_____

_____

_____

_____

_____

_____

_____

_____

_____

_____

_____

_____

_____

_____

Application Questions Group B

AP-1B LO 1 2 3

Jaun and Camilla share the ownership of a consulting business called PumpIT Solutions. In addition to hiring a few IT consultants, they also hired Dev and Kathy as accountants. Kathy is responsible for preparing financial statements under US GAAP for external auditors, the government and the bank that the company is borrowing money from. (Juan and Camilla share unlimited liability for the business' debts, and also share the business' profits.) Dev is responsible for preparing specialized reports to assist Juan, Camilla, the marketing manager and the IT consultants in making business decisions.

Required

a) Identify all important internal users of PumpIT Solutions' accounting information.

b) Identify all important external users of PumpIT Solutions' accounting information.

c) For Dev and Kathy, indicate which field of accounting (financial or managerial) each of them works in and whether they practice public or private accounting.

d) Indicate whether PumpIT Solutions is organized as a sole proprietorship, partnership, corporation or nonprofit organization.

AP-2B LO 4

Match each of the following characteristics of financial information to the appropriate description in the table below.

- Relevance
- Reliability
- Understandability
- Comparability
- Timeliness
- Verifiability

Term (fill in)	Description
	information is free from material error and bias
	a component of relevance
	the financial statements of a company should be prepared in a similar way year after year
	a component of reliability
	financial information can be comprehended by users with a reasonable knowledge of the business
	all information for decision-making is present in the financial statements

AP-3B LO 4 5

Match each of the following constraints and principles to the appropriate description in the table below.

- Conservatism
- Expense recognition
- Consistency
- Materiality
- Disclosure

Term (fill in)	Description
	The accountant should exercise the option that results in a lower balance of assets, lower net income or a higher balance of debt.
	This prevents people from changing accounting methods for the sole purpose of manipulating figures on the financial statements.
	The costs of doing business must be recorded in (or matched to) the same accounting period as the revenues they helped to generate.
	Any and all information that affects the full understanding of a company's financial statements must be included with the financial statements.
	This refers to the significance of information to users. The more significant a piece of information is means that it could influence or change a user's decision.

AP-4B LO 4

Reflex Sports Inc. is a manufacturer of sports equipment for children. It relies on GAAP to prepare its financial statements. The nature of its accounting transactions can be quite complex at times. However, the financial statements have no additional notes to support them. The company also does not keep all invoices on record to back up expense amounts reported on the financial statements. Which characteristic(s) of information did Reflex Sports fail to represent? Explain.

_____

_____

_____

_____

AP-5B LO 5

Mackenzie Attire is currently preparing its annual financial statements for the past fiscal year. The company uses cash-based accounting. The company's policy includes receiving payment for its services well before the service is performed. The owner recently purchased a fish tank for his home and the transaction included a decrease to Mackenzie Attire's equity (an expense was recorded in the income statement). The value of inventory is adjusted annually to be stated at fair value. Which of the basic accounting principles and/or assumptions has Mackenzie Attire violated? Explain.

_____

_____

_____

_____

_____

_____

_____

_____

AP-6B LO 5

IMORI is large, publicly traded construction company. IMORI has entered into a three-year construction contract with Siano Company. Siano paid upfront for the full value of the contract, and IMORI has recorded the entire amount as revenue immediately. Explain the accounting principle that has been violated.

_____

_____

_____

_____

_____

AP-7B LO 5

Blossoma Inc. is a private supplier of organic beauty products. The company prepares its financial statements in compliance with GAAP. Due to recent economic difficulties, Blossoma Inc. had to file for bankruptcy. The company's property, plant and equipment are listed on the balance sheet at what they could be sold for, which is lower than their original purchase price. Has Blossoma Inc. violated any of the basic accounting principles and/or assumptions? Explain.

_____

_____

_____

_____

_____

AP-8B LO 4 5

Team Toro Inc, a unionized company, is in the business of planning and hosting events for various colleges and universities. Its services include a wide range of activities, such as decor and design, accommodation for guests and catering. At the end of the year, prior to issuing its financial statements, the head of the accounting department discovered that the union is planning to go on a legal strike at the beginning of next year. After discussing the matter with the board members, the accounting manager decides not to disclose this issue since the strike will happen next year and this year's financial statements are not affected. In addition, the accounting manager thinks the disclosure may have an unnecessary negative impact on the company's financial position and reputation in the market. Discuss whether any accounting principles or qualitative characteristics have been violated.

_____

_____

_____

_____

_____

_____

_____

AP-9B LO 4 5

Imzy Company is a small, private company that relies on GAAP to prepare financial statements. During the year, the company has experienced a number of tax disputes with the government. This issue was not included in the notes to the financial statements, as the bookkeeper believes this type of tax dispute is common for a small business. In addition, the bookkeeper does not keep purchase invoices because he thinks the costs of holding all those receipts outweighs the benefits for a small company. Explain whether any accounting principles or qualitative characteristics have been violated by the bookkeeper.

_____

_____

_____

_____

_____

_____

_____

_____

AP-10B LO 4

Identify the qualitative characteristic that describes each of the following scenarios.

a) Titus Group presented its financial information in a way that allowed informed users to comprehend the meaning of the information.

_____

b) Hunt Manufacturing included references to source documents to explain where certain financial figures originated from.

_____

c) Arloc Games Company uses the same accounting methods each year when preparing the financial statements.

_____

d) Crypt Technologies reported all financial information that could have an impact on the decisions of the users of the financial statements.

_____

AP-11B LO 4 5

Identify the accounting principle or constraint that describes each of the following scenarios.

a) Pangea Construction recorded revenue for a five-year construction contract evenly over the five years.

_____

b) Athena Spa has committed to opening a second location in the next eight months. Details regarding this expansion were included in the financial information.

_____

c) Zeus Electric used the same accounting policy for depreciation as last year, even though it could have reported a higher net income by switching to a different method.

_____

d) Neptune Water Supply grouped small assets such as pens, staplers and notepads together as office supplies because the cost of separating them outweighed the benefits.

_____

e) Hermes Athletics had its land appraised at $60,000. The land was listed on the balance sheet at $50,000, which was the price originally paid for it.

_____

f) Hera Consulting prepaid cash for its annual insurance policy. The amount was expensed on a monthly basis as it was used up.

_____

AP-12B LO 4

The accountant for GYC Consultants is facing an important accounting decision. The company recently incurred a material transaction that can be accounted for in three different ways (options A, B and C). The effect on the company's net income and total assets for each option is shown below. Under GAAP, which option should GYC's accountant choose to account for the transaction and why?

Effect on	Option A	Option B	Option C
Net Income	+$5,200	+$4,100	+$4,600
Total Assets	+$1,100	+$900	+$1,000

_____
_____
_____
_____
_____

AP-13B LO 6

Marcus is the senior accountant for a small accounting firm. He is currently performing the year-end audit of Le Jardin Inc., a manufacturer of high quality furniture. After Marcus met with Le Jardin's CEO in a restaurant, the CEO noticed that Le Jardin's financial records, which were provided to Marcus, were scattered on the ground. The CEO was extremely disappointed because the records were meant for internal use only. Which ethical standard did Marcus violate? Explain.

_____

119

Case Study

CS-1 LO  4 5

Gordon is the majority owner of Gordon House Restaurant (GHR), a publicly traded chain of family restaurants. The company is owned by hundreds of stockholders, who expect timely, reliable and accurate financial statements. GHR produces financial statements periodically. It is now June 15, 2018. The accountant has prepared the financial statements for the eight-month period ended May 31, 2018. The previous financial statements covered a one-year period.

GHR was recently sued by another company, the details of which are not disclosed in the financial statements. The court proceedings have not yet ended. However, as of May 31, 2018, it was believed that GHR is very likely to lose the case and pay a significant amount in damages to the plaintiff.

Also consider the following additional information.

- Cash disbursements are not supported by additional source documents
- GHR has recognized revenue in a different accounting period than the costs associated with producing that revenue

Required

a) Which of the four qualitative characteristics of financial information has GHR failed to apply? Explain.

_____

_____

_____

_____

_____

_____

_____

_____

_____

_____

_____

b) Which of the assumptions and principles of accounting has GHR violated? Explain.

_____

_____

_____

_____

_____

_____

_____

_____

_____

Chapter 4

THE ACCOUNTING CYCLE: JOURNALS AND LEDGERS

LEARNING OBJECTIVES

LO 1   Distinguish between debits and credits

LO 2   Describe the accounting cycle

LO 3   Explain how to analyze a transaction

LO 4   Record transactions in the general journal

LO 5   Post journal entries to the general ledger

LO 6   Prepare a trial balance

LO 7   Describe ethics and internal controls relating to recording and posting transactions

AMEENGAGE™   *Access **ameengage.com** for integrated resources including tutorials, practice exercises, the digital textbook and more.*

Assessment Questions

AS-1 LO 1

What does the term debit refer to?

_____

_____

AS-2 LO 1

True or False: A credit will always be an increase to any account.

_____

_____

AS-3 LO 1

Which three types of accounts use the debit side of the T-account to increase their value?

_____

_____

AS-4 LO 1

Which three types of accounts use the credit side of the T-account to increase their value?

_____

_____

AS-5 LO 1

What is the normal balance of an asset?

_____

_____

AS-6 LO 1

What is the normal balance of a liability?

_____

_____

AS-7 LO 5

Explain the purpose of a chart of accounts.

_____

_____

_____

AS-8 LO 2 3 4 5 6

List and describe the first four steps of the accounting cycle.

_____

_____

_____

_____

AS-9 LO 4

In the accounting cycle, what is the purpose of creating journals?

_____

_____

AS-10 LO 5

In the accounting cycle, what is the purpose of the general ledger?

_____

_____

AS-11 LO 6

In the accounting cycle, what is the purpose of the trial balance?

_____

_____

AS-12 LO 4

In the journal, what information is entered in the PR (posting reference) column?

_____

_____

AS-13 LO 5

What is the relationship between the closing balance and the opening balance for an asset?

_____

_____

_____

AS-14 LO 6

If the trial balance balances, were all transactions correctly recorded? Explain.

_____

_____

AS-15 LO 6

If an error is found in a journal entry that has already been prepared and posted to the general ledger, how should the error be corrected?

_____

_____

AS-16 LO 7

Does using a computerized accounting information system automatically mean that accounting information is reliable and accurate? Explain.

_____

_____

_____

_____

_____

_____

_____

_____

_____

_____

_____

_____

_____

_____

_____

Application Questions Group A

AP-1A LO 1 3

Esteem Fitness provides fitness services for its customers. During June 2018, Esteem Fitness had the following transactions.

Jun 1   Sold one-month memberships to customers for $4,500 on account
Jun 3   Received a telephone bill for $250, which will be paid next month
Jun 6   Paid an employee's salary of $1,200
Jun 10   Received $3,000 cash from customers paying in advance for upcoming one-year memberships
Jun 15   Paid $6,000 cash in advance for six months of rent
Jun 20   Received a $10,000 loan from the bank
Jun 26   Purchased equipment with $8,000 cash

Complete the table to analyze each transaction.

	Account Name	Category	Increase or Decrease	Debit or Credit
Jun 1				
Jun 3				
Jun 6				
Jun 10				
Jun 15				
Jun 20				
Jun 26				

AP-2A LO 1 3

Have-a-Bash, owned by Finn Tymes, provides party planning services. During October 2018, Have-a-Bash had the following transactions.

Oct 1   Finn invested $5,000 cash into the business

Oct 2   Planned a party for a customer and received $900 cash

Oct 4   Received a $500 utilities bill, which will be paid later

Oct 10   Paid $200 cash for maintenance for the month

Oct 12   Paid $400 towards the bank loan principal

Oct 18   Received cash from a customer who owed $1,100

Oct 22   Paid the utilities bill received earlier

Oct 28   Paid $3,000 cash in advance for office rent

Complete the table to analyze each transaction.

	Account Name	Category	Increase or Decrease	Debit or Credit
Oct 1				
Oct 2				
Oct 4				
Oct 10				
Oct 12				
Oct 18				
Oct 22				
Oct 28				

AP-3A LO 1

For the following list of accounts, indicate which side of the T-account causes an increase or decrease. The first account has been done for you.

Account Title	Debit	Credit
Cash	Increase	Decrease
Advertising Expense		
Service Revenue		
Unearned Revenue		
Accounts Receivable		
Accounts Payable		
Owner's Capital		
Owner's Withdrawals		
Prepaid Rent		
Rent Expense		

AP-4A LO 3 4

Kick-off Sports Training helps train children in various sporting activities. During May 2018, the following transactions took place.

May 3   Received a maintenance bill for $500, which will be paid next month
May 3   Received $2,750 cash for training services provided
May 4   Borrowed $4,000 cash from the bank
May 4   Received $220 from a customer who owed money on training services already provided
May 10   Prepaid $1,200 cash for insurance for one year
May 10   Paid telephone expenses of $150 for the month with cash
May 11   Paid $700 cash to reduce the amount owed to a supplier
May 15   Paid $25 interest on the bank loan

Prepare the journal entries for the transactions.

Date	Account Title and Explanation	PR	Debit	Credit

AP-5A LO 3 4

Rejuvenation Spa is a sole proprietorship owned by Claire Sawyer. During the month of July 2018, the following transactions took place.

July 3	Provided services to a customer on account worth $3,600
July 4	Borrowed $2,000 cash from the bank
July 6	Provided services to a customer and received $2,400 in cash
July 10	Received a telephone bill for $250, which will be paid later
July 11	Paid $600 cash to reduce the amount owed to a supplier
July 15	Collected $1,800 cash from customers owing on account
July 20	Paid the telephone bill from July 10
July 21	Paid a portion of the bank loan principal with $1,500 cash
July 31	Paid salaries for the month with $1,600 cash
July 31	Purchased equipment for $1,900, which will be paid later

Prepare the journal entries for the above transactions.

Date	Account Title and Explanation	PR	Debit	Credit

AP-6A LO 3 4

Noel Dy opened an automobile repair shop. The following transactions occurred during the month of March 2018.

Mar 1   Noel Dy invested $10,000 cash and $8,000 worth of equipment in the business
Mar 3   Paid $1,000 cash to rent the shop space
Mar 5   Purchased $1,200 worth of shop tools using cash
Mar 7   Received $2,000 cash for repair work done for MJ Gonzales
Mar 8   Purchased $1,000 worth of shop tools from Adrian Cruz on account
Mar 15 Paid half of the amount due to Adrian Cruz with cash
Mar 18 Paid $200 cash to a local publication for advertising
Mar 19 Paid salaries with $1,000 in cash
Mar 20 Noel Dy withdrew $1,500 cash for personal use
Mar 29 Bought $1,000 worth of chairs and tables for the shop on account
Mar 31 Noel Dy personally invested additional equipment worth $5,000 for business use
Mar 31 Received $3,000 cash from various customers for repairs done on their automobiles

Prepare journal entries for the above transactions.

Date	Account Title and Explanation	PR	Debit	Credit
March 1	Cash / ~~Equipment~~		10,000	
	Equipment		8,000	
	Capital			18,000
March 3	~~Cash~~ Rent Expense		1,000	
	~~Rent~~ Cash			1,000
March 5	Equipment		1,200	
	Cash			1,200
March 7	Cash		2,000	
	Service Revenue			2,000
March 8	Equipment		1,000	
	Accounts payable			1,000
March 15	Accounts Payable		1,000	
	Cash			500
March 18	Advertising Expense		200	
	Cash			200
March 19	Salary Expense		1,000	
	Cash			1,000
March 20	Owner's w/drawal		1,500	
	Cash			1,500

Date	Account Title and Explanation	PR	Debit	Credit
March 31	Equipment		1,000	
	Accounts Payable			1,000
March 31	Cap Capital		5,000	
	Equipment			5,000
March 31	Servi Cash		3,000	
	Service Revenue			3,000

AP-7A LO 3 4 5 6

Thomas Topology provides surveying services to construction companies and municipalities. The company is owned and operated by Thomas Edwards. The closing balances at the end of March 2018 and the chart of accounts are shown below.

Thomas Topology Balance Sheet As at March 31, 2018			
Assets		**Liabilities**	
Cash	$22,000	Accounts Payable	$10,500
Accounts Receivable	9,000	Unearned Revenue	4,500
Equipment	8,000	Notes Payable	6,000
		Total Liabilities	21,000
		Owner's Equity	
		Edwards, Capital	18,000
Total Assets	$39,000	**Total Liabilities and Owner's Equity**	$39,000

Account Description	Account #
ASSETS	
Cash	101
Accounts Receivable	105
Prepaid Insurance	110
Equipment	120
LIABILITIES	
Accounts Payable	200
Unearned Revenue	210
Notes Payable	215
OWNER'S EQUITY	
Edwards, Capital	300
Edwards, Withdrawals	310

Account Description	Account #
REVENUE	
Service Revenue	400
EXPENSES	
Insurance Expense	515
Interest Expense	520
Rent Expense	540
Salaries Expense	545
Telephone Expense	550
Travel Expense	555

During the month of April, Thomas Topology had the following transactions.

Apr 1   Purchased office equipment on account worth $7,000

Apr 2   Received $25,000 cash for services provided

Apr 3   Paid $1,000 cash for April's rent

Apr 4   Prepaid $1,200 for insurance for one year

Apr 10   Paid $200 cash to reduce the balance of accounts payable

Apr 14   Paid $8,000 cash for employee's salaries

Apr 22   Received a telephone bill for $250, which will be paid next month

Apr 24   Recorded travel expenses for $8,000 to be paid next month

Apr 30   Paid $4,550 to bank for the bank loan principal and interest; interest was $50 and the remainder was principal

Required

a) Prepare the journal entries for the month of April.

Date	Account Title and Explanation	PR	Debit	Credit

Date	Account Title and Explanation	PR	Debit	Credit

b) Post the journal entries to the ledger accounts.

Account:						GL No:	
Date	Description	PR	DR	CR	Balance	

Account:						GL No:	
Date	Description	PR	DR	CR	Balance	

Account:						GL No:	
Date	Description	PR	DR	CR	Balance	

Account:					GL No:	
Date	Description	PR	DR	CR	Balance	

Account:					GL No:	
Date	Description	PR	DR	CR	Balance	

Account:					GL No:	
Date	Description	PR	DR	CR	Balance	

Account:					GL No:	
Date	Description	PR	DR	CR	Balance	

Account:					GL No:	
Date	Description	PR	DR	CR	Balance	

Account:					GL No:	
Date	Description	PR	DR	CR	Balance	

Account:					GL No:	
Date	Description	PR	DR	CR	Balance	

Account:					GL No:	
Date	Description	PR	DR	CR	Balance	

Account:					GL No:	
Date	Description	PR	DR	CR	Balance	

Account:					GL No:	
Date	Description	PR	DR	CR	Balance	

Account:					GL No:	
Date	Description	PR	DR	CR	Balance	

Account:					GL No:	
Date	Description	PR	DR	CR	Balance	

Account:					GL No:	
Date	Description	PR	DR	CR	Balance	

c)   Prepare a trial balance at the end of April.

AP-8A LO 3 4 5 6

High Flying Biplane provides sightseeing tours in vintage biplanes. The company is owned by Sky Bridges. The closing balances at the end of May 2018 and the chart of accounts are shown below.

High Flying Biplane Balance Sheet As at May 31, 2018			
Assets		**Liabilities**	
Cash	$8,000	Accounts Payable	$8,200
Accounts Receivable	6,000	Unearned Revenue	3,200
Prepaid Insurance	1,200	Notes Payable	20,000
Equipment	60,000	**Total Liabilities**	31,400
		Owner's Equity	
		Bridges, Capital	43,800
Total Assets	$75,200	**Total Liabilities and Owner's Equity**	$75,200

Account Description	Account #
ASSETS	
Cash	101
Accounts Receivable	105
Prepaid Insurance	110
Equipment	120
LIABILITIES	
Accounts Payable	200
Interest Payable	205
Unearned Revenue	210
Notes Payable	215
OWNER'S EQUITY	
Bridges, Capital	300
Bridges, Withdrawals	310

Account Description	Account #
REVENUE	
Service Revenue	400
EXPENSES	
Advertising Expense	500
Insurance Expense	515
Interest Expense	520
Telephone Expense	550

During the month of June, High Flying Biplane had the following transactions.

Jun 1   The owner invested $5,000 cash into the business
Jun 2   Received $1,500 cash for tours that will be provided in August
Jun 3   Received an advertising bill for $400, which will be paid next month
Jun 4   Paid the telephone bill with $200 cash
Jun 10   Provided tours worth $2,400 to a customer who will pay next month
Jun 14   Purchased equipment with $4,000 cash
Jun 20   Received payments totaling $1,600 from customers paying their accounts
Jun 22   Paid $900 towards accounts payable
Jun 24   Paid $1,000 towards the bank loan principal
Jun 30   The owner withdrew $1,200 cash for personal use

Required

a)   Prepare the journal entries for the month of June.

Date	Account Title and Explanation	PR	Debit	Credit

b)   Post the journal entries to the ledger accounts.

Account:					GL No:	
Date	Description	PR	DR	CR	Balance	

Account:					GL No:	
Date	Description	PR	DR	CR	Balance	

Account:					GL No:	
Date	Description	PR	DR	CR	Balance	

Account:					GL No:	
Date	Description	PR	DR	CR	Balance	

Account:					GL No:	
Date	Description	PR	DR	CR	Balance	

Account:					GL No:	
Date	Description	PR	DR	CR	Balance	

Account:					GL No:	
Date	Description	PR	DR	CR	Balance	

Account:					GL No:	
Date	Description	PR	DR	CR	Balance	

Account:					GL No:	
Date	Description	PR	DR	CR	Balance	

Account:					GL No:	
Date	Description	PR	DR	CR	Balance	

Account:					GL No:	
Date	Description	PR	DR	CR	Balance	

Account:					GL No:	
Date	Description	PR	DR	CR	Balance	

Account:					GL No:	
Date	Description	PR	DR	CR	Balance	

Account:					GL No:	
Date	Description	PR	DR	CR	Balance	

Account:					GL No:	
Date	Description	PR	DR	CR	Balance	

c)   Prepare a trial balance at the end of June.

AP-9A LO 6

Micro Company, owned by Steven Upton, showed these accounts and their corresponding normal balances on May 31, 2018.

Account Title	Balance
Upton, Capital	$23,500
Insurance Expense	900
Accounts Payable	15,500
Service Revenue	8,900
Equipment	34,500
Supplies Expense	3,000
Cash	6,400
Salaries Expense	4,000
Rent Expense	3,000
Upton, Withdrawals	3,000
Utilities Expense	1,300
Notes Payable	10,200
Prepaid Insurance	2,000

Prepare Micro Company's trial balance at May 31, 2018.

AP-10A LO 6

Home Circus is owned by Laura Roberts and provides acrobatic entertainment at children's parties and other events. Its complete general ledger for March 2018 is shown below.

Account: Cash						GL No: 101	
Date	**Description**	**PR**	**DR**	**CR**	**Balance**	
Mar 1	Opening Balance				7,800	DR
Mar 1		J1		1,800	6,000	DR
Mar 2		J1	2,900		8,900	DR
Mar 3		J1		1,440	7,460	DR
Mar 10		J1		10	7,450	DR
Mar 10		J1		780	6,670	DR
Mar 20		J1	2,600		9,270	DR
Mar 22		J1	800		10,070	DR
Mar 24		J1		710	9,360	DR
Mar 31		J1		2,000	7,360	DR

Account: Accounts Receivable						GL No: 105	
Date	**Description**	**PR**	**DR**	**CR**	**Balance**	
Mar 1	Opening Balance				2,460	DR
Mar 22		J1		800	1,660	DR

Account: Prepaid Insurance						GL No: 110	
Date	**Description**	**PR**	**DR**	**CR**	**Balance**	
Mar 1	Opening Balance				0	DR
Mar 1		J1	1,800		1,800	DR

Account: Office Supplies						GL No: 115	
Date	**Description**	**PR**	**DR**	**CR**	**Balance**	
Mar 1	Opening Balance				640	DR
Mar 4		J1	250		890	DR

Account: Equipment						GL No: 120	
Date	**Description**	**PR**	**DR**	**CR**	**Balance**	
Mar 1	Opening Balance				10,500	DR
Mar 20		J1		2,600	7,900	DR

Account: Accounts Payable | | | | | | **GL No: 200**

Date	Description	PR	DR	CR	Balance	
Mar 1	Opening Balance				2,900	CR
Mar 4		J1		250	3,150	CR
Mar 24		J1	710		2,440	CR

Account: Unearned Revenue | | | | | | **GL No: 210**

Date	Description	PR	DR	CR	Balance	
Mar 1	Opening Balance				1,800	CR

Account: Notes Payable | | | | | | **GL No: 215**

Date	Description	PR	DR	CR	Balance	
Mar 1	Opening Balance				5,100	CR
Mar 10		J1	780		4,320	CR

Account: Roberts, Capital | | | | | | **GL No: 300**

Date	Description	PR	DR	CR	Balance	
Mar 1	Opening Balance				11,600	CR

Account: Roberts, Withdrawals | | | | | | **GL No: 310**

Date	Description	PR	DR	CR	Balance	
Mar 31		J1	2,000		2,000	DR

Account: Service Revenue | | | | | | **GL No: 400**

Date	Description	PR	DR	CR	Balance	
Mar 2		J1		2,900	2,900	CR

Account: Office Supplies Expense | | | | | | **GL No: 520**

Date	Description	PR	DR	CR	Balance	
Mar 10		J1	10		10	DR

Account: Rent Expense | | | | | | **GL No: 540**

Date	Description	PR	DR	CR	Balance	
Mar 3		J1	1,440		1,440	DR

Prepare a trial balance. Place the accounts in the order shown in the general ledger.

AP-11A LO 1 6

A part-time bookkeeper for Wombat Tours has created the trial balance at the end of the year and cannot get it to balance.

Wombat Tours Trial Balance December 31, 2018		
Account Title	**DR**	**CR**
Accounts Payable	$3,150	
Accounts Receivable	2,350	
Advertising Expense		$2,100
Notes Payable		5,200
Sharpe, Capital		6,170
Cash	6,200	
Interest Expense	560	
Maintenance Expense	240	
Office Supplies		1,600
Sharpe, Withdrawals		2,300
Prepaid Insurance	1,200	
Equipment	13,500	
Rent Expense	6,200	
Salaries Expense	5,300	
Service Revenue		25,800
Telephone Expense	450	
Unearned Revenue	1,680	
Total	**$40,830**	**$43,170**

All the entries have been journalized and posted to the general ledger properly, and all the accounts should have normal balances.

Recreate the trial balance for Wombat Tours so that the accounts are listed in the order they would typically appear in a chart of accounts, and ensure that debits equal credits.

AP-12A LO 3 4

Greg Carlin is the owner of Carlin Consulting. During the month of April 2018, he had the following transactions.

Apr 1   Greg invested $5,000 cash and equipment valued at $3,000 into the business

Apr 3   Provided consulting services to a customer; the customer paid $1,000 now and will pay $1,500 later

Apr 6   Received a loan from the bank for $6,000

Apr 8   Paid $1,300 for utilities for the month

Apr 17   Purchased equipment with $4,000 cash

Apr 20   Paid employee salaries with $2,100 cash

Apr 22   Provided consulting services to a customer on account for $1,600

Apr 28   Received the balance owing from the customer on April 3

Record the transactions in the journal.

Date	Account Title and Explanation	PR	Debit	Credit

Date	Account Title and Explanation	PR	Debit	Credit

AP-13A LO 6

On June 23, 2018, the bookkeeper for Henson Company discovered an error in the journal entries. On June 2, equipment was purchased on account for $9,000; however, it was recorded in the journals and ledgers for $90,000. Prepare the entries to correct this error.

Date	Account Title and Explanation	PR	Debit	Credit

AP-14A LO 6

On November 22, 2018, the bookkeeper for Fraggle Company discovered an error in the journal entries. On November 16, an entry was made for the cash purchase of office supplies for $550 that incorrectly debited equipment. Prepare the entries to correct this error.

Date	Account Title and Explanation	PR	Debit	Credit

AP-15A LO 7

Xavier works as an accountant for O'Hara Travel Services. He prepared the trial balance at the end of the period and discovered that it did not balance. The total debit balance was significantly larger than the total credit balance. Xavier believes that Mrs. O'Hara, the company's owner, would be happy if the net income figure was higher so that she can show the lender that the company is very profitable. Therefore, Xavier decides to balance the debit and credit sides by increasing the service revenue account balance, and therefore increasing the credit side of the trial balance. Did Xavier behave in an ethical manner? Explain.

Application Questions Group B

AP-1B LO 1 3

Perfect Party is owned by Candace Rodriguez and provides party planning services. During April 2018, Perfect Party had the following transactions.

Apr 1   The owner invested $5,800 cash into the business
Apr 4   Planned a party for a customer for $740; the customer will pay later
Apr 6   Paid $600 cash for rent for the month
Apr 8   Received a $370 telephone bill, which will be paid later
Apr 15   Paid $300 towards the bank loan principal
Apr 19   Received cash from a customer who owed $840
Apr 27   Paid the telephone bill received earlier

Complete the table to analyze each transaction.

	Account Name	Category	Increase or Decrease	Debit or Credit
Apr 1				
Apr 4				
Apr 6				
Apr 8				
Apr 15				
Apr 19				
Apr 27				

AP-2B LO 1 3

Bendari Tutoring Services had the following transactions for the month of November 2018.

Nov 1   Purchased supplies for $100 on account
Nov 4   Received $4,200 cash from clients as payment for tutoring
Nov 9   Received a telephone bill in the mail for $150
Nov 16   Paid an employee's salary of $3,500 in cash
Nov 25   Collected $500 from clients who owed money for previous services

Complete the table to analyze each transaction.

	Account Name	Category	Increase or Decrease	Debit or Credit
Nov 1				
Nov 4				
Nov 9				
Nov 16				
Nov 25				

AP-3B LO 1

For the accounts listed below, determine if the normal balance is a debit or a credit. Also, indicate if a debit or a credit will decrease the account balance.

	Normal Balance	Decrease
Cash		
Accounts Receivable		
Accounts Payable		
Notes Payable		
Owner's Capital		
Service Revenue		
Insurance Expense		
Prepaid Insurance		
Equipment		
Unearned Revenue		
Owner's Withdrawals		
Salaries Expense		
Office Supplies		

AP-4B LO 3 4

HomeStyle provides interior design solutions for residential and commercial spaces. During the month of July 2018, the following transactions took place.

Jul 3   Provided services to a customer and received $3,100 cash

Jul 4   Borrowed $2,500 from the bank

Jul 6   Provided services worth $2,800 to a customer on account

Jul 10   Received the utilities bill for $240, which will be paid later

Jul 11   Paid $690 cash to reduce the balance of accounts payable

Jul 15   Collected $1,900 cash from customers owing on account

Jul 20   Paid $2,600 towards the bank loan principal

Jul 21   Paid the amount owing from July 10

Jul 27   Paid salaries of $1,700 for the month with cash

Jul 31   Purchased equipment worth $3,100, which will be paid later

Prepare the journal entries for the above transactions.

Date	Account Title and Explanation	PR	Debit	Credit

Date	Account Title and Explanation	PR	Debit	Credit

AP-5B LO 3 4

Tracts of Land provides surveying services to construction companies and municipalities. During the month of February 2018, Tracts of Land had the following transactions.

Feb 1   Purchased equipment worth $8,200, which will be paid later

Feb 2   Provided services worth $20,200 to a customer on account

Feb 3   Paid $1,900 cash for February's utilities

Feb 4   Paid $1,600 for four months of insurance coverage

Feb 10   Paid $2,000 cash to reduce the balance of accounts payable

Feb 14   Paid $6,600 cash for a monthly maintenance contract

Feb 22   Received a bill for $5,800 in travel expenses to be paid next month

Feb 24   Received an advertising bill for $400, which will be paid next month

Feb 28   Paid $2,730 to the bank to reduce the bank loan principal; interest was $30 and the remainder was principal

Prepare the journal entries for the transactions.

Date	Account Title and Explanation	PR	Debit	Credit

AP-6B LO 3 4

Cherry Consulting Firm is owned by Ron Cherry and offers consulting services for small businesses. During June 2018, the following transactions occurred.

Jun 2   Received a deposit of $3,000 from a customer for services to be provided in the future
Jun 3   Paid a $495 utility bill that was received and recorded last month
Jun 8   Charged $1,400 in travel costs to a credit card
Jun 17   Paid $1,000 cash to reduce the bank loan; of that amount, $75 is interest and the remainder is principal
Jun 19   Ron withdrew $2,100 cash from the business for personal use
Jun 28   Paid $4,900 for salaries for the month

Prepare the journal entries for the above transactions.

Date	Account Title and Explanation	PR	Debit	Credit

AP-7B LO 3 4 5 6

Lowe Consulting provides advice and resources to entrepreneurs starting their own businesses. The company is a sole proprietorship owned by Leslie Lowe. The closing balances at the end of August 2018 and the chart of accounts are shown below.

Lowe Consulting Balance Sheet As at August 31, 2018			
Assets		**Liabilities**	
Cash	$7,200	Accounts Payable	$3,400
Accounts Receivable	2,300	Unearned Revenue	1,400
Office Supplies	850	Notes Payable	5,600
Equipment	11,500	**Total Liabilities**	10,400
		Owner's Equity	
		Lowe, Capital	11,450
Total Assets	$21,850	**Total Liabilities and Owner's Equity**	$21,850

Account Description	Account #
ASSETS	
Cash	101
Accounts Receivable	105
Prepaid Insurance	110
Office Supplies	115
Equipment	120
LIABILITIES	
Accounts Payable	200
Unearned Revenue	210
Notes Payable	215
OWNER'S EQUITY	
Lowe, Capital	300
Lowe, Withdrawals	310

Account Description	Account #
REVENUE	
Service Revenue	400
EXPENSES	
Insurance Expense	515
Interest Expense	520
Office Supplies Expense	530
Rent Expense	540

During the month of September, Lowe Consulting had the following transactions.

Sep 1	Paid $1,800 cash in advance for a one-year insurance policy
Sep 2	Received $1,900 cash for services provided
Sep 3	Paid $1,350 cash for September's rent
Sep 4	Purchased office supplies on account worth $250
Sep 10	Paid $960 towards the bank loan principal and $40 of interest on the loan
Sep 20	Received $2,200 cash from a customer booking consulting services in advance
Sep 22	Collected $850 from a customer paying their account
Sep 24	Paid $600 towards accounts payable
Sep 30	The owner withdrew $1,600 cash for personal use

Required

a) Prepare the journal entries for the month of September.

Date	Account Title and Explanation	PR	Debit	Credit

Date	Account Title and Explanation	PR	Debit	Credit

b) Post the journal entries to the ledger accounts.

Account: **GL No:**

Date	Description	PR	DR	CR	Balance

Account: **GL No:**

Date	Description	PR	DR	CR	Balance

Account: **GL No:**

Date	Description	PR	DR	CR	Balance

Account: **GL No:**

Date	Description	PR	DR	CR	Balance

Account:					GL No:	
Date	Description	PR	DR	CR	Balance	

Account:					GL No:	
Date	Description	PR	DR	CR	Balance	

Account:					GL No:	
Date	Description	PR	DR	CR	Balance	

Account:					GL No:	
Date	Description	PR	DR	CR	Balance	

Account:					GL No:	
Date	Description	PR	DR	CR	Balance	

Account:					GL No:	
Date	Description	PR	DR	CR	Balance	

Account:					GL No:	
Date	Description	PR	DR	CR	Balance	

Account:						GL No:	
Date	Description	PR	DR	CR	Balance		

Account:						GL No:	
Date	Description	PR	DR	CR	Balance		

Account:						GL No:	
Date	Description	PR	DR	CR	Balance		

Account:						GL No:	
Date	Description	PR	DR	CR	Balance		

c) Prepare a trial balance at the end of September.

AP-8B LO 3 4 5 6

Sokatoa, owned by Hiromi Nakata, had the following transactions for the month of July 2018.

Jul 1   Purchased a new machine with $12,000 cash

Jul 5   Provided services worth $10,000 to clients who will pay later

Jul 12   Hiromi withdrew $5,000 cash from the business

Jul 19   Received a maintenance bill for $1,100, which will be paid later

Jul 31   Got a loan from the bank for $25,000

Required

a)   Prepare the journal entries for the month of July.

Date	Account Title and Explanation	PR	Debit	Credit

b)   Post the journal entries to the ledger accounts.

Account: Cash   **GL No: 101**

Date	Description	PR	DR	CR	Balance	
	Opening Balance				31,800	DR

Account: Accounts Receivable   **GL No: 105**

Date	Description	PR	DR	CR	Balance	
	Opening Balance				5,000	DR

Account: Machine   GL No: 120

Date	Description	PR	DR	CR	Balance	
	Opening Balance				6,000	DR

Account: Accounts Payable   GL No: 200

Date	Description	PR	DR	CR	Balance	
	Opening Balance				3,500	CR

Account: Notes Payable   GL No: 215

Date	Description	PR	DR	CR	Balance	
	Opening Balance				0	CR

Account: Nakata, Capital   GL No: 300

Date	Description	PR	DR	CR	Balance	
	Opening Balance				39,300	CR

Account: Nakata, Withdrawals   GL No: 310

Date	Description	PR	DR	CR	Balance	

Account: Sales Revenue   GL No: 400

Date	Description	PR	DR	CR	Balance	

Account: Maintenance Expense   GL No: 520

Date	Description	PR	DR	CR	Balance	

Account: Salaries Expense   GL No: 540

Date	Description	PR	DR	CR	Balance	

c)   Prepare a trial balance at the end of July.

Analysis

Explain how the general ledger is similar to the T-accounts used in earlier chapters.

_____

_____

_____

_____

AP-9B LO 1 6

The following are the accounts of DRAM Company and their corresponding normal balances on October 31, 2018.

Account	Balance
David, Capital	$20,400
Accounts Payable	13,200
Insurance Expense	1,000
Service Revenue	6,800
Equipment	30,500
Supplies Expense	2,900
Cash	5,700
Salaries Expense	4,100
David, Withdrawals	3,100
Rent Expense	2,200
Telephone Expense	1,200
Notes Payable	11,700
Prepaid Rent	1,400

Prepare DRAM Company's trial balance for the month ended October 31, 2018.

AP-10B LO 6

The following account balances were taken from Macro Company's general ledger on February 28, 2018.

Account	Balance
Chalmers, Capital	$10,050
Accounts Payable	13,000
Prepaid Expenses	5,000
Interest Payable	825
Vehicle	32,000
Computer Equipment	19,000
Salary Expense	31,000
Unearned Revenue	8,000
Depreciation Expense	1,700
Rent Expense	2,400
Cash	15,275
Service Revenue	74,500

Prepare Macro Company's trial balance.

Analysis

The accountant at Macro Company was worried that he may have recorded some entries incorrectly in the journal, but upon seeing that the trial balance is in balance, he assumed that he must have done everything correctly. Is his assumption correct? Explain.

_____

_____

_____

_____

AP-11B LO 1

Indicate whether increases and decreases in the following groups of accounts correspond to debits or credits.

	Increase	Decrease
Liabilities		
Owner's Equity		
Expenses		
Owner's Withdrawals		
Revenues		
Assets		

Analysis

What is a normal balance? Provide an example.

_____

_____

_____

AP-12B LO 3 4

Helen Long owns and operates Long Landscaping, which provides landscaping and gardening services. During the month of August 2018, she had the following transactions.

Aug 1   Provided services to a customer who paid $800 cash

Aug 3   Paid $1,000 to the bank to repay a bank loan; of that amount, $100 was interest

Aug 6   Received a maintenance bill for $500, which will be paid later

Aug 8   Paid $1,600 for a one-year insurance policy

Aug 17   Paid $2,200 for rent for the month

Aug 20   Provided services to a customer for $1,300 and the customer will pay later

Aug 22   Paid the maintenance bill received on August 6

Aug 28   Received payment from the customer from August 20

Record the transactions in the journal.

Date	Account Title and Explanation	PR	Debit	Credit

Date	Account Title and Explanation	PR	Debit	Credit

AP-13B LO 6

On August 16, 2018, the bookkeeper for Reliable Administration discovered that an entry was made on August 9, to pay for a one-year insurance policy for $1,800; however, accounts payable was used instead of cash. Prepare the entries to correct this error.

Date	Account Title and Explanation	PR	Debit	Credit

AP-14B LO 6

On February 21, 2018, the bookkeeper for Balsdon Consulting discovered that an entry was made on February 6 to pay for repairs expense with $800 cash; however, rent expense was debited. Prepare the entries to correct this error.

Date	Account Title and Explanation	PR	Debit	Credit

AP-15B LO 7

Sassy Salon is a small hair salon with only three employees—two hairdressers, and an accountant who also acts as the receptionist, cashier, and performs other miscellaneous tasks to keep the salon operational. Sassy Salon uses a computerized accounting system, where the accountant is supposed to enter each credit card and cash receipt transaction as soon as a customer pays. Based on the accountant's input, the computerized accounting system automatically prepares journal entries, posts the entries to ledgers and prepares a trial balance at the end of the period. Sometimes, the amount of cash on hand at the end of the period is not the same as the cash balance reported by the computerized accounting system. This is mostly due to the accountant forgetting to input a transaction or making other mistakes, especially when the salon is busy and the amount of work is overwhelming. When there is a discrepancy, the accountant always has a difficult time locating the error and explaining the discrepancy to the business owner. Therefore, the accountant proposes to the owner that rather than inputting each sales transaction separately, she will wait until the end of the period to count the amount of cash on hand and enter sales transactions based on that amount. By doing so, there will never be a discrepancy. It also reduces the amount of work for the accountant, which allows her to focus on servicing customers. Should the owner approve the accountant's proposed change? Why or why not?

Case Study

CS-1 LO 1 2 3 4 5 6 7

Renu Mawani has been operating her own interior design business called Mawani Interiors for a couple of years. The following transactions occurred in March 2018.

Mar 2	Paid cash of $2,000 for March's office rental
Mar 3	Renu invested $7,000 cash into the business
Mar 4	Purchased equipment on account for $8,000
Mar 6	Received $2,800 cash from a client that owed the company for last month's services
Mar 8	Purchased office supplies using $370 cash
Mar 10	Paid $6,900 cash for a consulting invoice received and recorded last month
Mar 13	Completed work for a client and the client paid $2,900 cash
Mar 15	Prepaid $1,800 cash for a one-year insurance policy
Mar 16	Completed work for a client, who will pay $3,200 next month
Mar 20	Discovered that an error was made on the transaction recorded on Mar 4; the equipment cost $8,800, not $8,000
Mar 23	Received a $6,000 cash deposit from a client for work to be completed in the next few months
Mar 29	Received utility bills for $410 to be paid next month
Mar 29	Signed a notes payable to borrow $12,000 from the bank
Mar 30	Renu withdrew $3,000 cash for personal use
Mar 31	Paid $18,000 cash for employee salaries

Required

a) Below is the list of account names that the company uses and their respective opening account balances as at the beginning of March. For each of the accounts, identify the account category (assets, liabilities, owner's capital, owner's withdrawals, revenue or expenses) and input the opening account balance in the debit or credit column based on the side of its normal balance. The answers have been filled in for the accounts payable account as an example. Be sure to total both the debit and credit sides. (Hint: If all your answers are correct, the total debit will be equal to the total credit.)

Account Name	Balance	Account Category	Debit	Credit
Accounts Payable	6,900	Liabilities		6,900
Accounts Receivable	5,400			
Cash	2,200			
Equipment	11,600			
Mawani, Capital	12,500			
Mawani, Withdrawals	0			
Notes Payable	0			
Office Supplies	200			
Prepaid Insurance	0			
Insurance Expense	0			
Rent Expense	0			
Salaries Expense	0			
Service Revenue	0			
Unearned Revenue	0			
Utilities Expense	0			
Total				

b) Identify the steps in the accounting cycle that need to be done repeatedly during the accounting period before the trial balance can be prepared at the end of the accounting period.

_____

_____

_____

_____

c) Record all of March's transactions in the journal and post them to the ledger. The account number can be found on the top right corner of each account's ledger.

Date	Account Title and Explanation	PR	Debit	Credit

Date	Account Title and Explanation	PR	Debit	Credit

Account:						GL No:	
Date	Description	PR	DR	CR	Balance	

Account:						GL No:	
Date	Description	PR	DR	CR	Balance	

Account:					GL No:
Date	Description	PR	DR	CR	Balance

Account:					GL No:
Date	Description	PR	DR	CR	Balance

Account:					GL No:
Date	Description	PR	DR	CR	Balance

Account:					GL No:
Date	Description	PR	DR	CR	Balance

Account:					GL No:
Date	Description	PR	DR	CR	Balance

Account:					GL No:
Date	Description	PR	DR	CR	Balance

Account:					GL No:	
Date	**Description**	**PR**	**DR**	**CR**	**Balance**	

Account:					GL No:	
Date	**Description**	**PR**	**DR**	**CR**	**Balance**	

Account:					GL No:	
Date	**Description**	**PR**	**DR**	**CR**	**Balance**	

Account:					GL No:	
Date	**Description**	**PR**	**DR**	**CR**	**Balance**	

Account:					GL No:	
Date	**Description**	**PR**	**DR**	**CR**	**Balance**	

Account:					GL No:	
Date	**Description**	**PR**	**DR**	**CR**	**Balance**	

Account:					GL No:	
Date	**Description**	**PR**	**DR**	**CR**	**Balance**	

d) Prepare the trial balance.

e) In order to improve the efficiency of the accounting process, Renu is considering recording transactions directly to the ledger and eliminating the use of a journal. Would it be ethical to do so? Explain.

_____

_____

_____

_____

_____

_____

_____

_____

_____

_____

_____

_____

_____

_____

_____

_____

_____

_____

_____

_____

Notes

Chapter 5

THE ACCOUNTING CYCLE: ADJUSTMENTS

LEARNING OBJECTIVES

LO 1 Describe the purpose of adjustments

LO 2 Prepare adjusting entries for accrued revenue

LO 3 Prepare adjusting entries for accrued expenses

LO 4 Prepare adjusting entries for unearned revenue

LO 5 Prepare adjusting entries for prepaid expenses

LO 6 Prepare adjusting entries for depreciation

LO 7 Prepare an adjusted trial balance

LO 8 Describe ethics and internal controls relating to adjusting entries

AMEENGAGE™ Access **ameengage.com** for integrated resources including tutorials, practice exercises, the digital textbook and more.

———— Assessment Questions ————

AS-1 LO 1

What is an accounting period?

_____

_____

AS-2 LO 1

Is a fiscal year always the same as a calendar year? Explain how a natural business year is related to a fiscal year.

_____

_____

_____

_____

AS-3 LO 1

Why must adjustments be made at the end of the accounting period?

_____

_____

_____

AS-4 LO 1

What does accrual-based accounting state regarding revenue and expenses?

_____

_____

_____

AS-5 `LO 1`

What are the five broad categories of adjusting entries?

_____

_____

AS-6 `LO 2`

Define accrued revenue.

_____

_____

AS-7 `LO 2`

When making an adjustment to record accrued revenue, which accounts are used and how are they affected?

_____

_____

AS-8 `LO 3`

Define accrued expenses.

_____

_____

AS-9 `LO 3`

When making an adjustment to record accrued interest on a bank loan, which accounts are used and how are they affected?

_____

_____

AS-10 `LO 4`

When making an adjustment to record unearned revenue that is now earned, which accounts are used and how are they affected?

_____

_____

AS-11 `LO 5`

When making an adjustment to record the used portion of prepaid insurance, which accounts are used and how are they affected?

_____

_____

AS-12 `LO 6`

When making an adjustment to record depreciation on equipment, which accounts are used and how are they affected?

_____

_____

AS-13 LO 6

What is the purpose of a contra account?

_____

_____

_____

AS-14 LO 6

True or False: All assets that are part of property, plant and equipment depreciate.

_____

_____

AS-15 LO 6

How does accumulated depreciation affect the value of property, plant and equipment?

_____

_____

_____

AS-16 LO 7

What is an adjusted trial balance?

_____

_____

_____

AS-17 LO 7

What is the purpose of a spreadsheet?

_____

_____

_____

AS-18 LO 8

Provide an example of an internal control procedure that can ensure that all necessary adjustments are accounted for.

_____

_____

_____

_____

_____

_____

Application Questions Group A

AP-1A LO 2

Metropolitan Tailors finished tailoring clothes for a client on December 31, 2018. The client picked up the clothes and paid the invoice of $180 on January 3, 2019. Record any necessary adjusting entries for Metropolitan Tailors in 2018 and the cash receipt transaction in 2019. Metropolitan Tailors has a December 31 year end.

Date	Account Title and Explanation	PR	Debit	Credit

AP-2A LO 3

Lexcon Farm employs one worker. The employee works Monday to Friday and is paid a weekly salary of $560 every Friday. As of July 31, 2018, all of July's weekly salaries have been paid except the amounts for Monday, July 30 and Tuesday, July 31. The last two days of July's salary are paid on Friday, August 3 along with the first three days of August's salary. Lexcon Farm records all adjusting entries on a monthly basis.

Required

a) Prepare an adjusting entry on July 31, 2018 to accrue the employee's salary for Monday, July 30 and Tuesday, July 31.

Date	Account Title and Explanation	PR	Debit	Credit

b) Record the payment of salary on August 3, 2018.

Date	Account Title and Explanation	PR	Debit	Credit

AP-3A LO 4

On December 15, 2018, Peaceful Living Inc. received $200 cash from a customer in advance for two rounds of bug spraying services, which took place on December 31, 2018 and January 31, 2019.

Required

a) Record the cash receipt transaction on December 15, 2018.

Date	Account Title and Explanation	PR	Debit	Credit

b) Record any necessary adjusting entries on December 31, 2018.

Date	Account Title and Explanation	PR	Debit	Credit

AP-4A LO 5

At the beginning of the fiscal year 2018, Samat Company did not have any office supplies. On January 2, 2018, it used $800 cash to purchase some office supplies. On December 31, 2018, the company's year end, a physical count showed that $210 worth of office supplies remained. Prepare journal entries related to office supplies for Samat Company for the fiscal year 2018.

Date	Account Title and Explanation	PR	Debit	Credit

AP-5A LO 4 5 6 7

Swordfish Programming is owned by Mark Kulak and provides computer solutions to the security industry. At the end of April 2018, Swordfish had the following adjustments.

Apr 30   A count of office supplies showed that there was $550 worth of supplies remaining in the office
Apr 30   The balance of prepaid insurance is for a 12-month policy; one month of insurance has been used
Apr 30   During April, Swordfish Programming earned $900 of unearned revenue
Apr 30   The computers were purchased on April 1, 2018 and have an expected useful life of five years, after which they will have no residual value; record the depreciation for April

Using the following trial balance, complete the adjustments and the adjusted trial balance in the spreadsheet.

Swordfish Programming Spreadsheet April 30, 2018						
	Unadjusted Trial Balance		Adjustments		Adjusted Trial Balance	
Account Title	**DR**	**CR**	**DR**	**CR**	**DR**	**CR**
Cash	$4,200					
Accounts Receivable	2,300					
Prepaid Insurance	1,800					
Office Supplies	800					
Computers	9,600					
Accumulated Depreciation—Computers		$0				
Accounts Payable		1,640				
Unearned Revenue		1,950				
Notes Payable		3,200				
Kulak, Capital		10,235				
Kulak, Withdrawals	1,500					
Service Revenue		4,750				
Depreciation Expense	0					
Insurance Expense	0					
Office Supplies Expense	0					
Rent Expense	1,300					
Telephone Expense	275					
Total	**$21,775**	**$21,775**				

AP-6A LO 3 4 5 6 7

Chirp Hearing is owned by Christina Howell and provides hearing aids and other auditory services. At the end of November 2018, the company had the following adjustments.

Nov 30   Interest on the bank loan is set at 10%; one month of interest has accrued

Nov 30   The balance of the prepaid insurance is for the remaining 10 months of the insurance policy; one month of insurance has been used

Nov 30   The equipment was purchased on September 1, 2018 and will have a useful life of seven years, after which it will have no residual value; depreciation is recorded every month; record depreciation for November

Nov 30   Chirp Hearing completed $650 of work that was previously unearned

Nov 30   Office supplies used during the month totaled $400

Using the following trial balance, complete the adjustments and the adjusted trial balance in the spreadsheet.

	Chirp Hearing Spreadsheet November 30, 2018					
	Unadjusted Trial Balance		Adjustments		Adjusted Trial Balance	
Account Title	**DR**	**CR**	**DR**	**CR**	**DR**	**CR**
Cash	$6,250					
Accounts Receivable	3,440					
Prepaid Insurance	2,200					
Office Supplies	1,140					
Equipment	15,120					
Accumulated Depreciation—Equipment		$360				
Accounts Payable		2,260				
Interest Payable		0				
Unearned Revenue		1,240				
Notes Payable		4,800				
Howell, Capital		12,640				
Howell, Withdrawals	2,100					
Service Revenue		12,500				
Depreciation Expense	0					
Insurance Expense	0					
Interest Expense	0					
Office Supplies Expense	0					
Rent Expense	1,650					
Salaries Expense	1,900					
Total	**$33,800**	**$33,800**				

AP-7A LO 2 3 5 6

Allan Poe operates an advertising business called A-Plus Advertising. The company had the following adjustments for the month of December 2018.

Dec 31   Recognized $1,250 rent expense used for the month

Dec 31   A monthly magazine subscription was prepaid for one year on December 1, 2018 for $600; by December 31, one issue had been received

Dec 31   Computers' depreciation for the month is $400

Dec 31   Salaries for employees accrued by $1,300 by the end of the month

Dec 31   A 30-day contract was started on December 16; the customer will pay $5,000 at the end of the contract in January; accrue the revenue earned by the end of December

Prepare the journal entries for the adjustments.

Date	Account Title and Explanation	PR	Debit	Credit

AP-8A LO 3 4 5 6

MJ Sandblasting is in its second year of operations. At the end of April 2018, it had the following adjustments.

Apr 30   Recognized $300 of prepaid insurance expense for the month

Apr 30   Depreciation on equipment for the month was $200

Apr 30   A count of office supplies showed that $650 worth of supplies had been used

Apr 30   Accrued interest on a bank loan was $30

Apr 30   Outstanding work for a client worth $800 was completed during the month; the client had paid for the work in March

Prepare the journal entries for the adjustments.

Date	Account Title and Explanation	PR	Debit	Credit

AP-9A LO 4 5 6 7

Sigmund Services has completed all its journal entries for the month of April 2018 and posted them to the general ledger. Based on the ledger balances, an unadjusted trial balance has been prepared.

Sigmund Services Unadjusted Trial Balance April 30, 2018		
Account Title	**DR**	**CR**
Cash	$32,050	
Accounts Receivable	9,000	
Prepaid Insurance	1,200	
Equipment	15,000	
Accounts Payable		$25,550
Unearned Revenue		4,500
Notes Payable		1,500
Sigmund, Capital		18,000
Service Revenue		25,000
Interest Expense	50	
Rent Expense	1,000	
Salaries Expense	8,000	
Telephone Expense	250	
Travel Expense	8,000	
Total	**$74,550**	**$74,550**

The following adjustments must be made at the end of April.

Apr 30	The balance of prepaid insurance represents a 12-month policy; one month has been used
Apr 30	Depreciation of equipment for the month is $120
Apr 30	Sigmund Services has earned $1,300 that was previously unearned

Required

a) Fill in the unadjusted trial balance on the spreadsheet and complete the rest of the spreadsheet.

	Unadjusted Trial Balance		Adjustments		Adjusted Trial Balance	
Account Title	**DR**	**CR**	**DR**	**CR**	**DR**	**CR**

b) Create the journal entries for the adjustments from the spreadsheet.

Date	Account Title and Explanation	PR	Debit	Credit

AP-10A LO 3 4 5 6 7

High Flying Biplane has completed all its journal entries for the month of June 2018 and posted them to the general ledger. Based on the ledger balances, an unadjusted trial balance has been prepared.

High Flying Biplane Unadjusted Trial Balance June 30, 2018		
Account Title	**DR**	**CR**
Cash	$8,800	
Accounts Receivable	6,800	
Prepaid Insurance	1,200	
Equipment	64,000	
Accounts Payable		$7,700
Unearned Revenue		4,700
Notes Payable		19,000
High, Capital		48,800
High, Withdrawals	1,200	
Service Revenue		2,400
Advertising Expense	400	
Telephone Expense	200	
Total	$82,600	$82,600

The following adjustments must be made at the end of June.

Jun 30   One month of insurance worth $100 has been used

Jun 30   Depreciation on the equipment was $450 this month

Jun 30   Of the unearned revenue amount, $4,080 still remains unearned

Jun 30   Interest accrued on the bank loan was $75

Required

a) Fill in the unadjusted trial balance on the spreadsheet and complete the rest of the spreadsheet.

Account Title	Unadjusted Trial Balance		Adjustments		Adjusted Trial Balance	
	DR	CR	DR	CR	DR	CR

b) Create the journal entries for the adjustments from the worksheet.

Date	Account Title and Explanation	PR	Debit	Credit

AP-11A LO 4 5 6 7

Limbo Lower has completed all its journal entries for the month of September 2018 and posted them to the general ledger. Based on the ledger balances, an unadjusted trial balance has been prepared.

Limbo Lower Unadjusted Trial Balance September 30, 2018		
Account Title	DR	CR
Cash	$5,800	
Accounts Receivable	1,450	
Prepaid Insurance	1,800	
Office Supplies	1,100	
Equipment	9,300	
Accounts Payable		$3,050
Unearned Revenue		1,400
Notes Payable		4,640
Roberts, Capital		11,450
Roberts, Withdrawals	1,600	
Service Revenue		1,900
Interest Expense	40	
Rent Expense	1,350	
Total	$22,440	$22,440

The following adjustments must be made at the end of September.

Sep 30	The amount of prepaid insurance is for 12 months; one month has been used
Sep 30	Depreciation for the month on equipment was $120
Sep 30	Unearned revenue of $360 has now been earned
Sep 30	A count of office supplies shows that $650 worth of supplies remains

Required

a) Fill in the unadjusted trial balance on the spreadsheet and complete the rest of the spreadsheet.

	Unadjusted Trial Balance		Adjustments		Adjusted Trial Balance	
Account Title	DR	CR	DR	CR	DR	CR

b)   Create the journal entries for the adjustments from the worksheet.

Date	Account Title and Explanation	PR	Debit	Credit

AP-12A LO 3 4 5 6 7

Zig Zag Robotics has the following adjustments to make at the end of September 2018, the end of its fiscal year.

Sep 30   Unearned revenue of $850 has now been earned

Sep 30   A count of the office supplies shows that $430 worth of supplies still remains on hand

Sep 30   Salaries accrued but not yet paid amount to $2,430

Sep 30   Monthly depreciation on equipment was $600

The chart of accounts is shown below.

Account Description	Account #
ASSETS	
Cash	101
Accounts Receivable	105
Office Supplies	110
Equipment	120
Accumulated Depreciation—Equipment	130

Account Description	Account #
OWNER'S EQUITY	
Rizzo, Capital	300
Rizzo, Withdrawals	310

Account Description	Account #
REVENUE	
Service Revenue	400

Account Description	Account #
LIABILITIES	
Accounts Payable	200
Unearned Revenue	210
Salaries Payable	220

Account Description	Account #
EXPENSES	
Salaries Expense	530
Depreciation Expense	535
Supplies Expense	540

Required

a) Complete the six-column spreadsheet.

Zig Zag Robotics Spreadsheet September 30, 2018						
	Unadjusted Trial Balance		Adjustments		Adjusted Trial Balance	
Account Title	DR	CR	DR	CR	DR	CR
Cash	$3,000					
Accounts Receivable	950					
Office Supplies	830					
Equipment	5,500					
Accumulated Depreciation—Equipment		$1,800				
Accounts Payable		1,250				
Unearned Revenue		1,700				
Rizzo, Capital		4,030				
Rizzo, Withdrawals	500					
Service Revenue		4,200				
Salaries Expense	2,200					
Total	$12,980	$12,980				

b) Journalize the adjustments.

Date	Account Title and Explanation	PR	Debit	Credit

c)   Post the transactions to the general ledger accounts provided.

Account: Office Supplies — **GL No:** 110

Date:	Description	PR	DR	CR	Balance
	Opening Balance				

Account: Accumulated Depreciation—Equipment — **GL No:** 130

Date:	Description	PR	DR	CR	Balance
	Opening Balance				

Account: Unearned Revenue — **GL No:** 210

Date:	Description	PR	DR	CR	Balance
	Opening Balance				

Account: Salaries Payable — **GL No:** 220

Date:	Description	PR	DR	CR	Balance
	Opening Balance				

Account: Service Revenue — **GL No:** 400

Date:	Description	PR	DR	CR	Balance
	Opening Balance				

Account: Salaries Expense — **GL No:** 530

Date	Description	PR	DR	CR	Balance
	Opening Balance				

Account: Depreciation Expense — **GL No:** 535

Date	Description	PR	DR	CR	Balance
	Opening Balance				

Account: Supplies Expense — **GL No:** 540

Date	Description	PR	DR	CR	Balance
	Opening Balance				

Analysis

What is the purpose of preparing a spreadsheet before journalizing and posting adjusting entries, and before preparing financial statements?

_____

_____

_____

AP-13A LO 6

On January 1, 2018, Precision Machinery purchased a new piece of equipment for $100,000. The equipment is expected to last five years and will have no residual value. Precision Machinery has a December 31 year end. Prepare the table below showing the yearly depreciation, accumulated depreciation and net book value of the equipment.

Year	Original Cost of Equipment	Depreciation Expense	Accumulated Depreciation	Net Book Value
2018				
2019				
2020				
2021				
2022				
Total				

AP-14A LO 6

On March 1, 2018, Jefferson Consulting purchased new computers for $19,000. The computers are expected to last three years and have an estimated residual value of $1,000. Jefferson has a December 31 year end. Prepare the table below showing the yearly depreciation, accumulated depreciation and net book value of the computers.

Year	Original Cost of Computers	Depreciation Expense	Accumulated Depreciation	Net Book Value
2018				
2019				
2020				
2021				
Total				

AP-15A LO 8

Gwen Feng works as an accountant for Yellow Dragon Chinese Cuisine, which is owned by Lian Huang. In an effort to increase sales, Lian advertised his restaurant on a radio station in December 2018. The total cost of running the advertisement was $2,000, and the restaurant paid the full amount in cash on December 20, 2018. Gwen recorded the $2,000 advertising cost on December 20 by debiting advertising expense and crediting cash. However, Lian argued that half of the amount should be recorded as an asset. Due to the catchy song used in the advertisement, Lian guessed that the radio audience would remember the advertisement in January 2019 even after it stopped airing at the end of December 2018. Believing that the advertising campaign would contribute to an increase in both December 2018 and January 2019 sales, Lian asked Gwen to prepare an adjusting entry at the end of December to reverse half of the advertising cost from advertising expense to prepaid advertising by debiting prepaid advertising and crediting advertising expense for $1,000. Lian argued that doing so would not only improve the matching of revenue and expense timing, but also increase the 2018 net income figure, making it easier to convince the bank to lend some money to the restaurant. Which course of action would be most ethical for Gwen? Explain.

Application Questions Group B

AP-1B LO 2 4

Enlightenment Tutoring provides in-home tutoring services to elementary school students. In December 2018, it provided four tutoring sessions to a client, who agreed to pay $400 after every 10 sessions. The company has a December 31 year end.

Required

a) Assume that Enlightenment Tutoring Services will provide six more sessions to the client in January 2019, when the client will pay $400. Record any adjusting entries required on December 31, 2018.

Date	Account Title and Explanation	PR	Debit	Credit

b) Assume instead that the client paid $400 in advance on December 1, 2018 for the ten sessions. Record the cash receipt transaction on December 1 and any adjusting entries required on December 31, 2018.

Date	Account Title and Explanation	PR	Debit	Credit

AP-2B LO 3

Sugoi Manufacturing borrowed $75,000 from the bank on November 1, 2018 and must repay the loan principal and interest on February 1, 2019. The bank charges an annual interest rate of 6% on the loan.

Required

a) Prepare the adjusting entry to accrue the interest on December 31, which is Sugoi Manufacturing's year end. Sugoi Manufacturing has not accrued any interest before December 31, 2018.

Date	Account Title and Explanation	PR	Debit	Credit

b) Record the payment of loan principal and interest on February 1, 2019.

Date	Account Title and Explanation	PR	Debit	Credit

AP-3B LO 4

Meyers Office owns a number of offices for rent. The following information pertains to Meyers Office from October to December of 2018.

Oct 30   Collected $24,000 cash from Kawalin Inc. for 12 months of rent in advance; Kawalin Inc. moved in on November 1

Dec 1   Collected $9,000 cash from Zand Company for three months of rent in advance; Zand Company occupied the office immediately on December 1

Journalize the above transactions and any necessary adjusting entries for Meyers Office's year end on December 31, 2018.

Date	Account Title and Explanation	PR	Debit	Credit

AP-4B LO 2 3 4 5

Yeesom Properties rented out a retail space to Ziphant Gift Shop for $3,300 per month. Ziphant Gift Shop prepaid $3,300 on September 15, 2018 for October's rent and started its occupancy on October 1, 2018. Unfortunately, Ziphant Gift Shop experienced short-term cash flow problems and could not afford to pay November's rent on time. Yeesom Properties agreed to let Ziphant Gift Shop pay for both November and December rent on December 31. Ziphant Gift Shop paid $6,600 cash to Yeesom Properties on December 31. Both Yeesom Properties and Ziphant Gift Shop record adjusting entries at the end of every month.

Required

a) Record all necessary journal entries for Yeesom Properties from September 15 to December 31, 2018.

Date	Account Title and Explanation	PR	Debit	Credit

b) Record all necessary journal entries for Ziphant Gift Shop from September 15 to December 31, 2018.

Date	Account Title and Explanation	PR	Debit	Credit

AP-5B LO 4 5 6 7

Decodely Programming provides custom computer programming and web design. At the end of December 2018, it had four adjustments.

Dec 31   During December, Decodely Programming earned $830 of unearned revenue

Dec 31 $1,250 worth of office supplies was used during the month

Dec 31   The balance of prepaid insurance represents 11 months remaining on the policy; one month of insurance has been used

Dec 31   Equipment depreciated $110 during December

Using the following trial balance, complete the adjustments and the adjusted trial balance in the spreadsheet.

	Decodely Programming Spreadsheet December 31, 2018					
	Unadjusted Trial Balance		Adjustments		Adjusted Trial Balance	
Account Title	**DR**	**CR**	**DR**	**CR**	**DR**	**CR**
Cash	$4,000					
Accounts Receivable	2,620					
Prepaid Insurance	2,750					
Office Supplies	1,790					
Equipment	9,400					
Accumulated Depreciation—Equipment		$400				
Accounts Payable		1,900				
Unearned Revenue		4,500				
Notes Payable		3,410				
Singh, Capital		9,930				
Singh, Withdrawals	1,560					
Service Revenue		4,090				
Depreciation Expense	0					
Insurance Expense	0					
Office Supplies Expense	0					
Rent Expense	1,970					
Utilities Expense	140					
Total	**$24,230**	**$24,230**				

AP-6B LO 3 5 6 7

Counterpoint Studios has completed all the entries for the month of November 2018, except the monthly adjusting entries. The following information is available to make the adjustments.

Nov 30   Annual depreciation on equipment totals $9,000
Nov 30   Interest accrued on the bank loan is $500
Nov 30   Office supplies on hand are valued at $2,300
Nov 30   The annual insurance policy was purchased on December 1, 2017 for $21,900

Complete the six-column spreadsheet for Counterpoint Studios.

Counterpoint Studios Spreadsheet November 30, 2018						
	Unadjusted Trial Balance		**Adjustments**		**Adjusted Trial Balance**	
Account Title	**DR**	**CR**	**DR**	**CR**	**DR**	**CR**
Cash	$52,250					
Accounts Receivable	24,800					
Office Supplies	10,400					
Prepaid Insurance	1,825					
Equipment	295,400					
Accumulated Depreciation—Equipment		$107,250				
Accounts Payable		31,500				
Notes Payable		140,000				
Jones, Capital		96,750				
Jones, Withdrawals	60,000					
Service Revenue		382,500				
Advertising Expense	100,000					
Salaries Expense	185,000					
Insurance Expense	20,075					
Depreciation Expense	8,250					
Total	$758,000	$758,000				

AP-7B LO 3 4 5 6

Spring Gardening Service provides seasonal gardening services. At the end of August 2018, the company must make the following adjustments.

Aug 31   Depreciation for equipment is $120

Aug 31   Interest due on a bank loan is $50; it will be paid next month

Aug 31   Accrued salary expense for an employee at the end of the month; the company owes the employee $450

Aug 31   One month of prepaid insurance at $70 per month has been used

Aug 31   A physical count of office supplies shows that $300 worth of supplies was used during August

Aug 31   Spring Gardening earned $670 that was previously unearned

Prepare the adjusting journal entries.

Date	Account Title and Explanation	PR	Debit	Credit

AP-8B LO 3 4 5 6

Speak Up sells voice recognition software. At the end of March 2018, it had the following account balances.

Speak Up Trial Balance March 31, 2018		
Account Title	**DR**	**CR**
Cash	$6,380	
Accounts Receivable	3,590	
Prepaid Insurance	999	
Office Supplies	1,120	
Equipment	15,170	
Accumulated Depreciation—Equipment		$400
Accounts Payable		2,120
Unearned Revenue		1,570
Notes Payable		4,930
Jones, Capital		12,659
Jones, Withdrawals	2,930	
Service Revenue		12,570
Rent Expense	1,920	
Salaries Expense	2,140	
Total	**$34,249**	**$34,249**

The following adjustments have to be made at the end of March.

Mar 31   Accrued $43 interest on the bank loan
Mar 31   The balance of the prepaid insurance is for the remaining nine months of the insurance policy; the insurance coverage for March has not been recorded
Mar 31   Speak Up completed $942 of work that was previously unearned
Mar 31   One month of depreciation is $250
Mar 31   Office supplies used during the month totaled $448

Complete the adjusting entries.

Date	Account Title and Explanation	PR	Debit	Credit

AP-9B LO 4 5 6 7

Thomas Topology has completed journal entries for the month of October and posted them to the general ledger. Based on the ledger balances, an unadjusted trial balance has been prepared.

The following adjustments must be made at the end of October.

Oct 31   One month of prepaid rent worth $720 has been used

Oct 31   Depreciation on equipment for the month was $340

Oct 31   Unearned revenue worth $1,330 has now been earned

Required

a) Fill in the unadjusted trial balance on the spreadsheet and complete the rest of the spreadsheet.

	Thomas Topology Spreadsheet October 31, 2018					
	Unadjusted Trial Balance		Adjustments		Adjusted Trial Balance	
Account Title	DR	CR	DR	CR	DR	CR
Cash	$32,000					
Accounts Receivable	9,500					
Prepaid Rent	5,760					
Equipment	15,000					
Accumulated Depreciation—Equipment		$950				
Accounts Payable		27,800				
Unearned Revenue		5,800				
Notes Payable		1,960				
Thomas, Capital		9,330				
Service Revenue		30,000				
Depreciation Expense						
Insurance Expense	570					
Interest Expense	150					
Rent Expense	0					
Salaries Expense	6,400					
Supplies Expense	360					
Utilities Expense	6,100					
Total	$75,840	$75,840				

b) Create the journal entries for the adjustments from the worksheet.

Date	Account Title and Explanation	PR	Debit	Credit

AP-10B LO 3 4 5 6 7

Floating Speed Boat has completed its journal entries for the month of September and posted them to the general ledger. Based on the ledger balances, an unadjusted trial balance has been prepared.

The following adjustments must be made at the end of September.

Sep 30   Depreciation on equipment for the month is $390

Sep 30   Prepaid insurance of $250 has been used up this month

Sep 30   Interest of $150 has accrued on the bank loan

Sep 30   Unearned revenue of $570 has now been earned

Required

a)   Complete the spreadsheet.

Floating Speed Boat Spreadsheet September 30, 2018						
	Unadjusted Trial Balance		Adjustments		Adjusted Trial Balance	
Account Title	**DR**	**CR**	**DR**	**CR**	**DR**	**CR**
Cash	$8,800					
Accounts Receivable	7,900					
Prepaid Insurance	1,500					
Equipment	64,000					
Accumulated Depreciation—Equipment		$870				
Accounts Payable		9,900				
Interest Payable		0				
Unearned Revenue		6,500				
Notes Payable		15,500				
Fathom, Capital		49,000				
Fathom, Withdrawals	1,200					
Service Revenue		3,400				
Advertising Expense	430					
Depreciation Expense	0					
Insurance Expense	0					
Interest Expense	0					
Rent Expense	1,340					
Total	**$85,170**	**$85,170**				

b) Create the journal entries for the adjustments from the spreadsheet.

Date	Account Title and Explanation	PR	Debit	Credit

AP-11B LO 3 4 5 6 7

Space Jam Storage offers storage space and transportation services for customers. Space Jam Storage has already completed the transactions for the month and posted them to the general ledger. The following adjustments for December 2018 have not yet been prepared.

Dec 31   Provided services worth $1,500 to a customer who had paid in advance

Dec 31   One month of insurance of $1,000 was used

Dec 31   Depreciation for the month was $500

Dec 31   Salaries accrued at the end of December amounted to $3,370

Required

a) Prepare the six-column spreadsheet.

	Unadjusted Trial Balance		Adjustments		Adjusted Trial Balance	
Account Title	**DR**	**CR**	**DR**	**CR**	**DR**	**CR**
Cash	$3,250					
Accounts Receivable	2,750					
Prepaid Insurance	13,000					
Equipment	285,000					
Accumulated Depreciation—Equipment		$45,000				
Accounts Payable		5,500				
Salaries Payable		0				
Unearned Revenue		3,600				
Notes Payable		191,680				
Jordan, Capital		46,200				
Jordan, Withdrawals	13,500					
Service Revenue		78,000				
Maintenance Expense	5,200					
Depreciation Expense	4,000					
Interest Expense	1,280					
Insurance Expense	11,000					
Salaries Expense	31,000					
Total	**$369,980**	**$369,980**				

Space Jam Storage — Spreadsheet — December 31, 2018

b) Record the journal entries for the adjusting entries.

Date	Account Title and Explanation	PR	Debit	Credit

AP-12B LO 3 4 5 6 7

Presto Chango has the following adjustments to make at the end of December 2018, the end of its fiscal year.

Dec 31   Salaries accrued but not yet paid amount to $750

Dec 31   Unearned revenue of $620 has now been earned

Dec 31   A count of the office supplies shows that $320 worth still remains on hand

Dec 31   Interest accrued on the bank loan but not yet paid amounts to $70

Dec 31   Monthly depreciation on equipment was $400

Presto Chango Chart of Accounts (GL No.)

Account Description	Account #	Account Description	Account #
ASSETS		**OWNER'S EQUITY**	
Cash	101	Presto, Capital	300
Accounts Receivable	105	Presto, Withdrawals	310
Office Supplies	110		
Equipment	120	**REVENUE**	
Accumulated Depreciation—Equipment	130	Service Revenue	400
LIABILITIES		**EXPENSES**	
Accounts Payable	200	Salaries Expense	520
Unearned Revenue	205	Depreciation Expense	525
Interest Payable	210	Interest Expense	530
Salaries Payable	220	Supplies Expense	535
Notes Payable	225		

Required

a) Complete the six-column spreadsheet.

Presto Chango Spreadsheet December 31, 2018						
	Unadjusted Trial Balance		**Adjustments**		**Adjusted Trial Balance**	
Account Title	**DR**	**CR**	**DR**	**CR**	**DR**	**CR**
Cash	$4,200					
Accounts Receivable	1,350					
Office Supplies	680					
Equipment	14,500					
Accumulated Depreciation—Equipment		$800				
Accounts Payable		1,300				
Unearned Revenue		1,250				
Notes Payable		6,000				
Presto, Capital		4,880				
Presto, Withdrawals	800					
Service Revenue		8,700				
Salaries Expense	1,400					
Total						

b)   Journalize the adjustments.

Date	Account Title and Explanation	PR	Debit	Credit

c)   Post the transactions to the general ledger accounts.

Account:					GL No:	
Date	Description	PR	DR	CR	Balance	
	Opening Balance					

Account:					GL No:	
Date	Description	PR	DR	CR	Balance	
	Opening Balance					

Account:					GL No:	
Date	Description	PR	DR	CR	Balance	
	Opening Balance					

Account:					GL No:	
Date	Description	PR	DR	CR	Balance	
	Opening Balance					

Account:					GL No:
Date	Description	PR	DR	CR	Balance
	Opening Balance				

Account:					GL No:
Date	Description	PR	DR	CR	Balance
	Opening Balance				

Account:					GL No:
Date	Description	PR	DR	CR	Balance
	Opening Balance				

Account:					GL No:
Date	Description	PR	DR	CR	Balance
	Opening Balance				

Account:					GL No:
Date	Description	PR	DR	CR	Balance
	Opening Balance				

Account:					GL No:
Date	Description	PR	DR	CR	Balance
	Opening Balance				

AP-13B LO 6

On January 1, 2018, Hackerton purchased a new machine for $60,000. The machine is expected to last six years and will have no residual value. Hackerton has a December 31 year end. Prepare the table below showing the yearly depreciation, accumulated depreciation and net book value of the machine.

Year	Original Cost of Machine	Depreciation Expense	Accumulated Depreciation	Net Book Value
2018				
2019				
2020				
2021				
2022				
2023				
Total				

AP-14B LO 6

On November 1, 2018, Gregory Accounting refurnished the entire office for $25,000. The furniture is expected to last four years and has an estimated residual value of $1,000. Gregory Accounting has a December 31 year end. Prepare the table below showing the yearly depreciation, accumulated depreciation and net book value of the furniture.

Year	Original Cost of Furniture	Depreciation Expense	Accumulated Depreciation	Net Book Value
2018				
2019				
2020				
2021				
2022				
Total				

AP-15B LO 8

Enza Martinez is the owner of Menza Consulting, which operates as a sole proprietorship. On December 27, 2018, Rose Hill Inc. signed a $12,000 contract to hire Menza Consulting for a project, starting in January 2019 and ending in March 2019. Rose Hill Inc. paid a $2,000 deposit on December 27, 2018 and agreed to pay the remaining amount to Menza Consulting at the end of the project on March 31, 2019. To avoid reporting a net loss for the fiscal year 2018, Enza decided to record the transaction related to Rose Hill Inc.'s contract as follows.

Date	Account Title and Explanation	PR	Debit	Credit
2018				
Dec 27	Cash		2,000	
	Service Revenue			2,000
	Received deposit from Rose Hill Inc.			
Dec 31	Accounts Receivable		10,000	
	Service Revenue			10,000
	Accrued revenue from Rose Hill Inc.			

Was it ethical for Enza to record the above journal entries? Why or why not? If you believe that Enza's action is unethical, describe how the transaction related to Rose Hill Inc.'s contract should be recorded in the fiscal year 2018.

Case Study

CS-1 LO 2 3 4 5 6 8

One Stop Consulting is preparing year-end financial statements dated December 31, 2018 and has to make several adjustments before the financial statements can be prepared. The owner has approached the accountant with the following information.

1. A large contract worth a lot of money was started in November of this year that will be completed in early January. The customer will not pay until the contract is completed in January. The owner does not want to include any work already completed in revenue and would rather record the entire amount earned in January when the contract is complete.

2. Interest, utilities and salaries expense will be accrued on December 31, 2018. Utility bills are usually received on the 15th of the month and are usually the same amount each month. The owner wants to accrue the full amount of the utilities on December 31, 2018 instead of just half that would normally be accrued.

3. An insurance policy was purchased in September covering one year. The owner wants to include the entire amount of the policy as an expense for the 2018 year end.

4. A customer paid a deposit in October for work to be completed in December and January. The initial receipt of cash was recorded in unearned revenue. The majority of the work was completed by December 31, 2018. The owner wants to wait until the work is 100% complete in January before recording any of it as revenue.

5. Equipment and furniture are depreciated using the straight-line method over five years. The owner wants to change the estimate from five years to three years for the depreciation calculation on December 31, 2018.

Required

a) For each action the owner wants, identify if there is any violation of GAAP principles or constraints.

_____

_____

_____

_____

_____

_____

_____

b) For each action the owner wants, identify how it affects the financial statements.

_____

_____

_____

_____

_____

_____

_____

_____

c) What are some possible reasons the owner would want to make these changes to the adjustment process?

_____

_____

_____

_____

Chapter 6

THE ACCOUNTING CYCLE: STATEMENTS AND CLOSING ENTRIES

LEARNING OBJECTIVES

LO 1   Prepare financial statements using the adjusted trial balance

LO 2   Prepare closing journal entries and post them to the general ledger

LO 3   Prepare the post-closing trial balance to complete the accounting cycle

LO 4   Prepare the classified balance sheet

LO 5   Analyze the financial statements using liquidity measures

LO 6   Describe the benefits of a computerized accounting system over a manual system

Appendix

LO 7   Prepare a 10-column spreadsheet

AMEENGAGE *Access **ameengage.com** for integrated resources including tutorials, practice exercises, the digital textbook and more.*

Assessment Questions

AS-1   LO 1

What does the income statement report?

AS-2   LO 1

Which statement is prepared after the income statement but before the balance sheet?

AS-3   LO 1

What does the statement of owner's equity report?

AS-4   LO 1

What two items cause owner's equity to increase and what two items cause owner's equity to decrease?

AS-5   LO 1

Which categories of accounts are reported on the balance sheet?

AS-6 LO 1

How does accumulated depreciation affect the value of property, plant and equipment?

_____

_____

AS-7 LO 2

What does it mean to close the books?

_____

_____

_____

AS-8 LO 2

What are the three steps to close directly to owner's capital?

_____

_____

_____

AS-9 LO 2

What are the four steps to close the accounts using the income summary?

_____

_____

_____

_____

AS-10 LO 2

If a company has a net income for the period and closes its books using the income summary account, will the income summary account have a debit or credit balance before it is closed to the capital account?

_____

_____

AS-11 LO 3

Which categories of accounts appear on the post-closing trial balance?

_____

_____

AS-12 LO 4

Define operating cycle.

_____

_____

_____

AS-13 LO 4

Define current assets.

_____

_____

_____

_____

AS-14 LO 4

Define noncurrent assets.

_____

_____

_____

_____

_____

AS-15 LO 4

What are current liabilities? Provide two examples of current liabilities.

_____

_____

_____

_____

AS-16 LO 4

What are long-term liabilities? Provide two examples of long-term liabilities.

_____

_____

_____

AS-17 LO 4

What is one difference between a non-classified balance sheet and a classified balance sheet?

_____

_____

_____

_____

AS-18 LO 5

How do you calculate the working capital? What does negative working capital mean?

_____

_____

_____

_____

AS-19 `LO 5`

How do you calculate the current ratio and what does it measure?

_____

_____

_____

_____

_____

AS-20 `LO 5`

How do you calculate the quick ratio and what does it measure?

_____

_____

_____

_____

_____

AS-21 `LO 6`

Identify two benefits of a computerized accounting system.

_____

_____

_____

_____

_____

Application Questions Group A

AP-1A LO 1

Floating Speed Boat has completed all its journal entries and adjusting entries for the month of September 2018. The adjusted trial balance is shown below.

Note: During the month of September, the owner of Floating Speed Boat invested $6,900 into the business.

Floating Speed Boat Adjusted Trial Balance September 30, 2018		
Account Title	DR	CR
Cash	$8,800	
Accounts Receivable	7,900	
Prepaid Insurance	1,150	
Equipment	64,000	
Accumulated Depreciation—Equipment		$1,260
Accounts Payable		9,900
Interest Payable		150
Unearned Revenue		5,930
Notes Payable		15,400
Murray, Capital		49,000
Murray, Withdrawals	1,200	
Service Revenue		3,970
Advertising Expense	430	
Depreciation Expense	390	
Insurance Expense	250	
Interest Expense	150	
Rent Expense	1,340	
Total	**$85,610**	**$85,610**

Required

a) Prepare the income statement from the adjusted trial balance.

b) Prepare the statement of owner's equity from the adjusted trial balance.

c) Prepare the balance sheet from the adjusted trial balance.

AP-2A LO 1 2 3

Regina Consulting has completed all its journal entries and adjusting entries for the month of October 2018. The adjusted trial balance is shown below.

Regina Consulting Adjusted Trial Balance October 31, 2018		
Account Title	DR	CR
Cash	$32,000	
Accounts Receivable	9,500	
Prepaid Rent	4,680	
Equipment	15,000	
Accumulated Depreciation—Equipment		$1,290
Accounts Payable		27,800
Unearned Revenue		4,470
Notes Payable		1,600
Regina, Capital		9,330
Service Revenue		31,330
Depreciation Expense	340	
Insurance Expense	570	
Interest Expense	150	
Rent Expense	720	
Salaries Expense	6,400	
Supplies Expense	360	
Utilities Expense	6,100	
Total	$75,820	$75,820

Required

a) Prepare the income statement from the adjusted trial balance.

b) Prepare the statement from the adjusted trial balance.

c)   Prepare the balance sheet from the adjusted trial balance.

d)   Prepare the closing entries using the income summary account.

Date	Account Title and Explanation	PR	Debit	Credit

e)   Prepare the post-closing trial balance.

AP-3A LO 2 3

Keynote Consulting has journalized its adjusting entries and prepared its adjusted trial balance.

Keynote Consulting Adjusted Trial Balance August 31, 2018		
Account Title	**DR**	**CR**
Cash	$6,200	
Accounts Receivable	1,750	
Prepaid Insurance	1,650	
Office Supplies	1,150	
Equipment	10,650	
Accumulated Depreciation—Equipment		$320
Accounts Payable		1,640
Interest Payable		50
Unearned Revenue		1,420
Notes Payable		3,000
Nichols, Capital		14,290
Nichols, Withdrawals	2,000	
Service Revenue		4,100
Depreciation Expense	150	
Insurance Expense	170	
Interest Expense	50	
Rent Expense	800	
Telephone Expense	250	
Total	**$24,820**	**$24,820**

Required

a) Prepare the closing entries using the income summary account for August.

Date	Account Title and Explanation	PR	Debit	Credit

b) Prepare the post-closing trial balance.

AP-4A LO 2 3

Frank's Custom Framing has journalized its adjusting entries and prepared its adjusted trial balance.

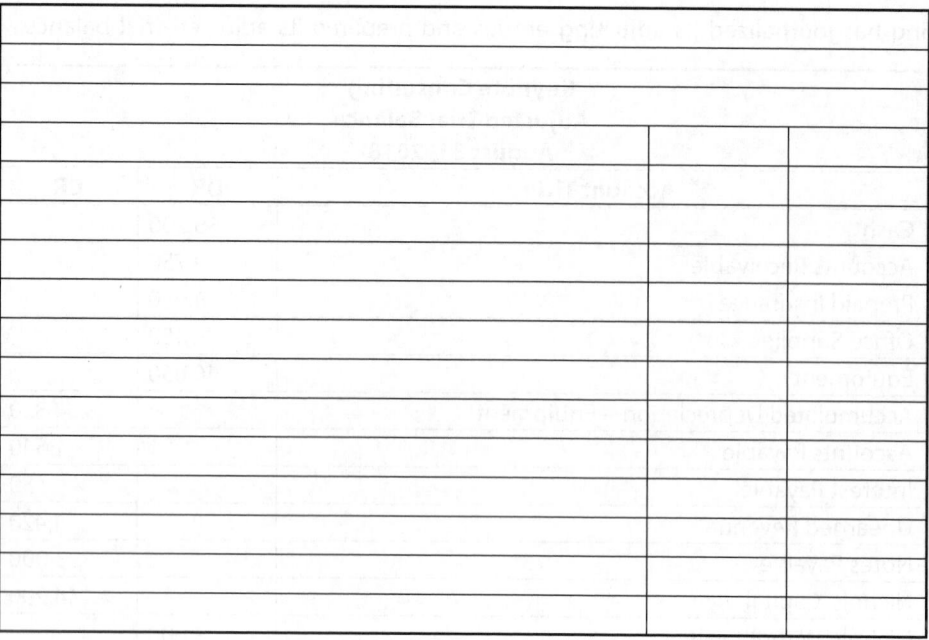

Frank's Custom Framing Adjusted Trial Balance October 31, 2018		
Account Title	**DR**	**CR**
Cash	$8,620	
Accounts Receivable	2,340	
Prepaid Insurance	2,650	
Office Supplies	1,840	
Equipment	23,400	
Accumulated Depreciation—Equipment		$1,640
Accounts Payable		3,540
Interest Payable		120
Unearned Revenue		2,110
Notes Payable		5,500
Frank, Capital		24,080
Frank, Withdrawals	3,200	
Service Revenue		8,750
Depreciation Expense	260	
Insurance Expense	185	
Interest Expense	120	
Rent Expense	1,200	
Telephone Expense	275	
Salaries Expense	1,650	
Total	**$45,740**	**$45,740**

Required

a) Prepare the closing entries using the income summary account for October.

Date	Account Title and Explanation	PR	Debit	Credit

b) Prepare the post-closing trial balance.

AP-5A LO 2 3

Home Protector has journalized its adjusting entries and prepared its adjusted trial balance.

Home Protector Adjusted Trial Balance December 31, 2018		
Account Title	**DR**	**CR**
Cash	$12,650	
Accounts Receivable	5,420	
Prepaid Insurance	2,820	
Office Supplies	2,240	
Equipment	25,600	
Accumulated Depreciation—Equipment		$2,340
Accounts Payable		6,250
Salaries Payable		650
Unearned Revenue		4,250
Notes Payable		7,500
Holmes, Capital		21,645
Holmes, Withdrawals	4,300	
Service Revenue		16,875
Depreciation Expense	320	
Insurance Expense	220	
Interest Expense	160	
Rent Expense	1,890	
Telephone Expense	350	
Salaries Expense	3,540	
Total	**$59,510**	**$59,510**

Required

a) Prepare the closing entries directly to owner's capital for the month of December.

Date	Account Title and Explanation	PR	Debit	Credit

b)   Prepare the post-closing trial balance.

AP-6A LO 2 3

Luminary Electric has journalized its adjusting entries and prepared its adjusted trial balance.

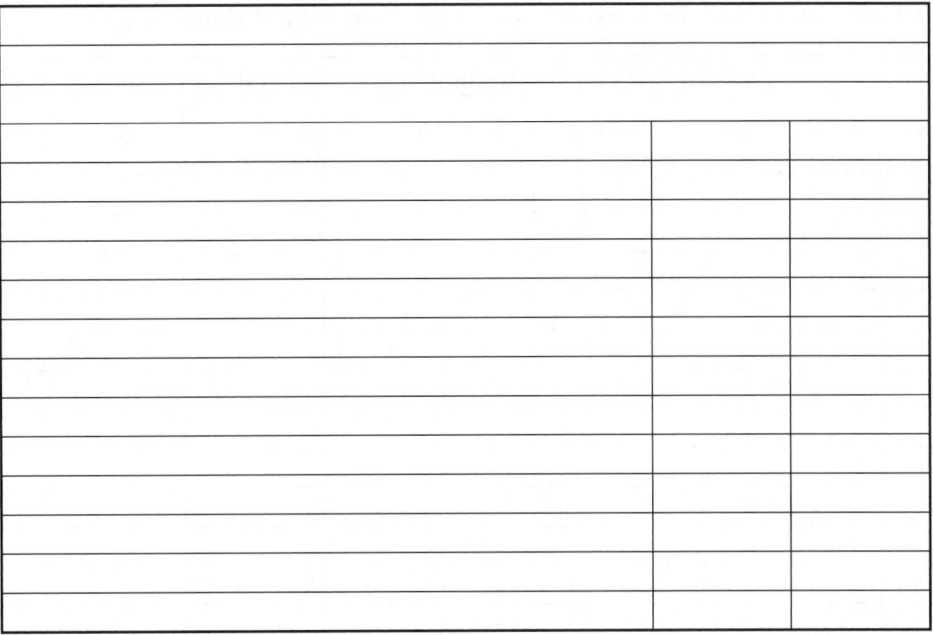

Luminary Electric Adjusted Trial Balance March 31, 2018		
Account Title	**DR**	**CR**
Cash	$10,420	
Accounts Receivable	6,350	
Prepaid Insurance	2,350	
Office Supplies	1,860	
Equipment	32,500	
Accumulated Depreciation—Equipment		$5,480
Accounts Payable		4,870
Salaries Payable		840
Unearned Revenue		5,340
Notes Payable		9,000
Watts, Capital		23,745
Watts, Withdrawals	5,200	
Service Revenue		17,850
Depreciation Expense	410	
Insurance Expense	195	
Interest Expense	210	
Office Supplies Expense	670	
Rent Expense	2,150	
Telephone Expense	450	
Salaries Expense	4,360	
Total	**$67,125**	**$67,125**

Required

a)   Prepare the closing entries directly to owner's capital for the month of March.

Date	Account Title and Explanation	PR	Debit	Credit

b)   Prepare the post-closing trial balance.

AP-7A LO 1 2 3

Thomas Topology has completed all its journal entries and adjusting entries for the month of April 2018. The chart of accounts and adjusted trial balance are shown below.

Account Description	Account #
ASSETS	
Cash	101
Accounts Receivable	105
Prepaid Insurance	110
Equipment	120
Accumulated Depreciation—Equipment	125
LIABILITIES	
Accounts Payable	200
Unearned Revenue	210
Notes Payable	215
OWNER'S EQUITY	
Thompson, Capital	300
Thompson, Withdrawals	310
Income Summary	315

Account Description	Account #
REVENUE	
Service Revenue	400
EXPENSES	
Depreciation Expense	510
Insurance Expense	515
Interest Expense	520
Rent Expense	540
Salaries Expense	545
Telephone Expense	550
Travel Expense	555

Thomas Topology
Adjusted Trial Balance
April 30, 2018

Account Title	DR	CR
Cash	$32,050	
Accounts Receivable	9,000	
Prepaid Insurance	1,100	
Equipment	15,000	
Accumulated Depreciation—Equipment		$120
Accounts Payable		25,550
Unearned Revenue		3,200
Notes Payable		1,500
Thompson, Capital		18,000
Service Revenue		26,300
Depreciation Expense	120	
Insurance Expense	100	
Interest Expense	50	
Rent Expense	1,000	
Salaries Expense	8,000	
Telephone Expense	250	
Travel Expense	8,000	
Total	**$74,670**	**$74,670**

Required

a) Prepare the income statement for Thomas Topology.

b) Prepare the statement of owner's equity for Thomas Topology.

c) Prepare the balance sheet for Thomas Topology.

d) Create the closing entries using the income summary account and post the closing entries to the ledger accounts on the next page.

Date	Account Title and Explanation	PR	Debit	Credit

e) Prepare the post-closing trial balance. Note: The daily transactions and adjustments for the month of April have already been posted in the general ledger. You are only responsible for posting the closing entries.

GENERAL LEDGER

Account: Cash					GL No: 101	
Date	Description	PR	DR	CR	Balance	
2018						
Apr 1	Opening Balance				22,000	DR
Apr 2		J1	25,000		47,000	DR
Apr 3		J1		1,000	46,000	DR
Apr 4		J1		1,200	44,800	DR
Apr 10		J1		200	44,600	DR
Apr 14		J1		8,000	36,600	DR
Apr 20		J1		50	36,550	DR
Apr 30		J1		4,500	32,050	DR

Account: Accounts Receivable — GL No: 105

Date	Description	PR	DR	CR	Balance	
2018						
Apr 1	Opening Balance				9,000	DR

Account: Prepaid Insurance — GL No: 110

Date	Description	PR	DR	CR	Balance	
2018						
Apr 1	Opening Balance				0	DR
Apr 4		J1	1,200		1,200	DR
Apr 30	Adjustment	J2		100	1,100	DR

Account: Equipment — GL No: 120

Date	Description	PR	DR	CR	Balance	
2018						
Apr 1	Opening Balance				8,000	DR
Apr 1		J1	7,000		15,000	DR

Account: Accumulated Depreciation—Equipment — GL No: 125

Date	Description	PR	DR	CR	Balance	
2018						
Apr 30	Adjustment	J2		120	120	CR

Account: Accounts Payable — GL No: 200

Date	Description	PR	DR	CR	Balance	
2018						
Apr 1	Opening Balance				10,500	CR
Apr 1		J1		7,000	17,500	CR
Apr 10		J1	200		17,300	CR
Apr 22		J1		250	17,550	CR
Apr 24		J1		8,000	25,550	CR

Account: Unearned Revenue — GL No: 210

Date	Description	PR	DR	CR	Balance	
2018						
Apr 1	Opening Balance				4,500	CR
Apr 30	Adjustment	J2	1,300		3,200	CR

Account: Notes Payable — GL No: 215

Date	Description	PR	DR	CR	Balance	
2018						
Apr 1	Opening Balance				6,000	CR
Apr 30		J1	4,500		1,500	CR

Account: Thompson, Capital — GL No: 300

Date	Description	PR	DR	CR	Balance	
2018						
Apr 1	Opening Balance				18,000	CR

Account: Thompson, Withdrawals — GL No: 310

Date	Description	PR	DR	CR	Balance	

Account: Income Summary					GL No: 315	
Date	Description	PR	DR	CR	Balance	

Account: Service Revenue					GL No: 400	
Date	Description	PR	DR	CR	Balance	
2018						
Apr 2		J1		25,000	25,000	CR
Apr 30	Adjustment	J2		1,300	26,300	CR

Account: Depreciation Expense					GL No: 510	
Date	Description	PR	DR	CR	Balance	
2018						
Apr 30	Adjustment	J2	120		120	DR

Account: Insurance Expense					GL No: 515	
Date	Description	PR	DR	CR	Balance	
2018						
Apr 30	Adjustment	J2	100		100	DR

Account: Interest Expense					GL No: 520	
Date	Description	PR	DR	CR	Balance	
2018						
Apr 20		J1	50		50	DR

Account: Rent Expense					GL No: 540	
Date	Description	PR	DR	CR	Balance	
2018						
Apr 3		J1	1,000		1,000	DR

Account: Salaries Expense					GL No: 545	
Date	Description	PR	DR	CR	Balance	
2018						
Apr 14		J1	8,000		8,000	DR

Account: Telephone Expense					GL No: 550	
Date	Description	PR	DR	CR	Balance	
2018						
Apr 22		J1	250		250	DR

Account: Travel Expense					GL No: 555	
Date	Description	PR	DR	CR	Balance	
2018						
Apr 24		J1	8,000		8,000	DR

AP-8A LO 1 2 3

Space Jam Storage offers storage space and delivery services for customers. Space Jam Storage has already completed most of the transactions for the month and posted them to the general ledger. The following transactions during December 2018 have not yet been prepared.

Dec 2	Prepaid $12,000 for one year of insurance in advance
Dec 5	Paid $1,400 cash for regular maintenance on delivery vehicles
Dec 12	The owner, Stephen Bugs, withdrew $3,500 cash from the business for personal use
Dec 18	Received $2,200 cash payment from a customer for future storage services
Dec 23	Paid $1,000 to reduce the bank loan, of which $870 was principal and the rest was interest
Dec 28	Received $450 cash from a customer who owed money for previous services

Required

a) Prepare the journal entries for the transactions for the month of December. The chart of accounts is on the next page.

Date	Account Title and Explanation	PR	Debit	Credit

b) Post the journal entries from part a) to the general ledger. The chart of accounts is shown below for your reference.

Account Description	Account #
ASSETS	
Cash	101
Accounts Receivable	105
Prepaid Insurance	110
Equipment	120
Accumulated Depreciation—Equipment	125

Account Description	Account #
OWNER'S EQUITY	
Bugs, Capital	300
Bugs, Withdrawals	310
Income Summary	315

Account Description	Account #
LIABILITIES	
Accounts Payable	200
Salaries Payable	210
Unearned Revenue	220
Notes Payable	250

Account Description	Account #
REVENUE	
Service Revenue	400

Account Description	Account #
EXPENSES	
Maintenance Expense	500
Depreciation Expense	520
Interest Expense	540
Insurance Expense	560
Salaries Expense	570

GENERAL LEDGER

Account: Cash — **GL No: 101**

Date	Description	PR	DR	CR	Balance	
2018	Opening Balance				18,500	DR

Account: Accounts Receivable — **GL No: 105**

Date	Description	PR	DR	CR	Balance	
2018	Opening Balance				3,200	DR

Account: Prepaid Insurance — **GL No: 110**

Date	Description	PR	DR	CR	Balance	
2018	Opening Balance				1,000	DR

Account: Equipment — **GL No: 120**

Date	Description	PR	DR	CR	Balance	
2018	Opening Balance				285,000	DR

Account: Accumulated Depreciation—Equipment — **GL No: 125**

Date	Description	PR	DR	CR	Balance	
2018	Opening Balance				45,000	CR

Account: Accounts Payable — **GL No: 200**

Date	Description	PR	DR	CR	Balance	
2018	Opening Balance				5,500	CR

Account: Salaries Payable					GL No: 210	
Date	Description	PR	DR	CR	Balance	
2018	Opening Balance				0	CR

Account: Unearned Revenue					GL No: 220	
Date	Description	PR	DR	CR	Balance	
2018	Opening Balance				1,400	CR

Account: Notes Payable					GL No: 250	
Date	Description	PR	DR	CR	Balance	
2018	Opening Balance				192,550	CR

Account: Bugs, Capital					GL No: 300	
Date	Description	PR	DR	CR	Balance	
2018	Opening Balance				46,200	CR

Account: Bugs, Withdrawals					GL No: 310	
Date	Description	PR	DR	CR	Balance	
2018	Opening Balance				10,000	DR

Account: Income Summary					GL No: 315	
Date	Description	PR	DR	CR	Balance	
2018	Opening Balance				0	CR

Account: Service Revenue					GL No: 400	
Date	Description	PR	DR	CR	Balance	
2018	Opening Balance				78,000	CR

Account: Maintenance Expense					GL No: 500	
Date	Description	PR	DR	CR	Balance	
2018	Opening Balance				3,800	DR

Account: Depreciation Expense					GL No: 520	
Date	Description	PR	DR	CR	Balance	
2018	Opening Balance				4,000	DR

Account: Interest Expense					GL No: 540	
Date	Description	PR	DR	CR	Balance	
2018	Opening Balance				1,150	DR

Account: Insurance Expense					GL No: 560	
Date	Description	PR	DR	CR	Balance	
2018	Opening Balance				11,000	DR

Account: Salaries Expense					GL No: 570	
Date	Description	PR	DR	CR	Balance	
2018	Opening Balance				31,000	DR

c) Prepare a six-column spreadsheet, starting with the account balances from the general ledger in part b). Space Jam Storage had the following year-end adjustments.

Dec 31   Provided $1,500 worth of services to customer who paid in advance

Dec 31   One month of insurance worth $1,000 has been used

Dec 31   One month of depreciation is $500

Dec 31   Accrued salaries owed to employees worth $3,370

	Unadjusted Trial Balance		Adjustments		Adjusted Trial Balance	
Account Title	DR	CR	DR	CR	DR	CR

d) Prepare the income statement for Space Jam Storage.

e) Prepare the statement of owner's equity for Space Jam Storage.

f) Prepare the balance sheet for Space Jam Storage.

g) Record the journal entries for the adjusting and closing transactions. Use the income summary method. Post these entries in the general ledger above from part b).

Date	Account Title and Explanation	PR	Debit	Credit

h) Prepare the post-closing trial balance for Space Jam Storage.

Analysis

The accountant for Space Jam Storage found that a journal entry back in November had been entered incorrectly. The account that should have been debited was credited and vice versa. Why wasn't this error detected during the preparation of trial balances and financial statements?

_____

_____

_____

_____

_____

AP-9A LO 4

The following information is taken from the records of Ginger Consulting.

Accounts Payable	$19,000
Short-Term Investment	12,000
Land	52,000
Cash	23,000
Factory Equipment	29,000
Notes Payable	30,000
Office Furniture	18,000
Prepaid Expense	9,000
Unearned Revenue	6,000

Required

a) Calculate total current assets.

_____

_____

_____

_____

b) Calculate total noncurrent assets.

_____

_____

_____

_____

c) Calculate total assets.

_____

_____

_____

_____

AP-10A LO 4

Suppose a business has a $400,000 long-term bank loan on December 31, 2018. The borrowing arrangement requires the business to pay $100,000 of this debt by September 2019. Show how the business will report both current and long-term liabilities on its December 31, 2018 balance sheet.

_____

_____

_____

_____

AP-11A LO 4

Pelican Accounting borrowed a $1,000,000 interest-free bank loan on January 1, 2018. Payment will be made in four years in four equal annual installments. Calculate the current and long-term liabilities as at December 31 for the following years.

	As at December 31			
	2018	**2019**	**2020**	**2021**
Notes Payable, Current Portion				
Notes Payable, Long-Term Portion				

AP-12A LO 4

Renegade Landscaping's general ledger includes the following account balances on December 31, 2018.

Accounts Payable	$12,000
Interest Payable	3,000
Salaries Payable	2,000
Notes Payable	
Current Portion	10,000
Long-Term Portion	20,000

Required

a) Calculate current liabilities.

_____

_____

_____

_____

_____

b) Calculate long-term liabilities.

_____

_____

_____

AP-13A LO 4

For the following independent transactions, determine the amount of current and long-term liabilities.

Transaction	Current Liability	Long-Term Liability
1. On December 31, 2018, Frankie Flowershop borrowed $300,000 from the bank. The entire amount is due on December 30, 2019.		
2. KLM Company purchased a small building at a cost of $190,000. The down payment is $100,000. The remaining balance is payable in three years with an annual payment of $30,000, starting next year.		
3. During June 2018, a business owner obtained an interest-free loan from a financing company. The loan amount was $60,000. The agreed terms of payment is four annual installments of $15,000.		
4. A business owner borrowed $20,000 from his close friend for a business expansion. They both signed an agreement that the full payment will be made after two years.		

AP-14A LO 4 5

Empowered Solutions has the following balances as at May 31, 2018.

Cash	$22,000
Accounts Receivable	15,000
Merchandise Inventory	12,000
Equipment	73,000
Accounts Payable	13,000
Unearned Revenue	8,000
Notes Payable, Current Portion	10,000
Notes Payable, Long-Term Portion	20,000
Powers, Capital	71,000

Required

a) Prepare a classified balance sheet using the balances listed.

b) Calculate the working capital for Empowered Solutions.

c) Calculate the current ratio for Empowered Solutions.

d) Calculate the quick ratio for Empowered Solutions.

AP-15A LO 4 5

Preston Services' financial accounting information for the year ending September 30, 2018 is presented on the next page. Assume all accounts have a normal balance.

Cash	$7,500
Accounts Receivable	2,400
Merchandise Inventory	6,000
Prepaid Insurance	1,800
Equipment	35,000
Accumulated Depreciation—Equipment	800
Accounts Payable	5,100
Unearned Revenue	1,100
Notes Payable	18,000
Presto, Capital	27,700

The notes payable is payable over three years and $6,000 will be paid by September 30, 2019.

Required

a) Prepare a classified balance sheet.

b) Calculate the working capital for Preston Services.

_____

c) Calculate the current ratio for Preston Services.

_____

d) Calculate the quick ratio for Preston Services.

_____

AP-16A LO 7

Below is Coleson Services' unadjusted trial balance at the end of December 2018. Adjusting entries have not yet been made. Use the trial balance and the information below to complete the spreadsheet.

Dec 31   A physical count showed that $320 of supplies is still on hand.

Dec 31   The equipment was purchased at the beginning of the year and is expected to last four years with no residual value.

Dec 31   Of the balance of unearned revenue, $600 has been earned.

Dec 31   The amount in prepaid insurance is for an annual policy that was paid on September 1, 2018.

		Coleson Services Spreadsheet December 31, 2018								
	Unadjusted Trial Balance		Adjustments		Adjusted Trial Balance		Income Statement		Balance Sheet	
Account Title	DR	CR	DR	CR	DR	CR	DR	CR	DR	CR
Cash	$1,500									
Accounts Receivable	3,000									
Prepaid Insurance	1,800									
Office Supplies	800									
Equipment	6,000									
Accumulated Depreciation—Equipment		$0								
Accounts Payable		4,000								
Unearned Revenue		1,000								
Notes Payable		2,500								
Coleson, Capital		2,850								
Coleson, Withdrawals	1,200									
Service Revenue		8,000								
Depreciation Expense	0									
Insurance Expense	0									
Interest Expense	0									
Maintenance Expense	900									
Supplies Expense	0									
Rent Expense	1,900									
Salaries Expense	150									
Telephone Expense	700									
Travel Expense	400									
Total	$18,350	$18,350								
Net Income										
Total										

Application Questions Group B

AP-1B LO 1

Below is Caprio Services' adjusted trial balance for the year ending December 31, 2018. Note that during the year, the owner contributed $20,000 to the business. This is already included in Caprio, Capital.

Caprio Services Adjusted Trial Balance December 31, 2018		
Account Title	**DR**	**CR**
Cash	$90,200	
Accounts Receivable	47,800	
Prepaid Insurance	32,000	
Equipment	415,000	
Accumulated Depreciation—Equipment		$145,000
Accounts Payable		26,000
Unearned Revenue		15,800
Notes Payable		260,000
Caprio, Capital		108,200
Caprio, Withdrawals	40,000	
Service Revenue		545,000
Advertising Expense	100,000	
Insurance Expense	40,000	
Maintenance Expense	5,900	
Rent Expense	78,000	
Salaries Expense	228,500	
Telephone Expense	3,200	
Travel Expense	19,400	
Total	**$1,100,000**	**$1,100,000**

a) Using the information provided, prepare the income statement for the end of December 31, 2018.

b) Prepare the statement of owner's equity for the end of December 31, 2018.

c)   Prepare the balance sheet as at December 31, 2018.

Analysis

In the accounting cycle, why is the income statement prepared first, then the statement of owner's equity, and finally the balance sheet?

_____

_____

_____

_____

AP-2B LO 1

Counterpoint Studios has completed all the entries for the fiscal year ending November 30, 2018, except the month of November's adjusting entries. The following information is available to make the adjustments.

- Annual depreciation on equipment totals $9,000

- Interest accrued on the notes payable is $500

- Office supplies on hand are valued at $2,300

- The annual insurance policy was purchased December 1, 2017 for $21,900

- The balance of owner's equity at the beginning of the year was $86,750

Required

a) Complete the six-column spreadsheet for Counterpoint Studios.

Counterpoint Studios Spreadsheet November 30, 2018						
	Unadjusted Trial Balance		Adjustments		Adjusted Trial Balance	
Account Title	DR	CR	DR	CR	DR	CR
Cash	$52,250					
Accounts Receivable	24,800					
Office Supplies	10,400					
Prepaid Insurance	1,825					
Equipment	295,400					
Accumulated Depreciation—Equipment		$107,250				
Accounts Payable		31,500				
Notes Payable		140,000				
Wu, Capital		96,750				
Wu, Withdrawals	60,000					
Service Revenue		382,500				
Advertising Expense	100,000					
Salaries Expense	185,000					
Insurance Expense	20,075					
Depreciation Expense	8,250					
Total	$758,000	$758,000				

b) Prepare the income statement for the year ended November 30, 2018.

c) Prepare the statement of owner's equity for the year ended November 30, 2018.

d) Prepare the balance sheet for the year ended November 30, 2018.

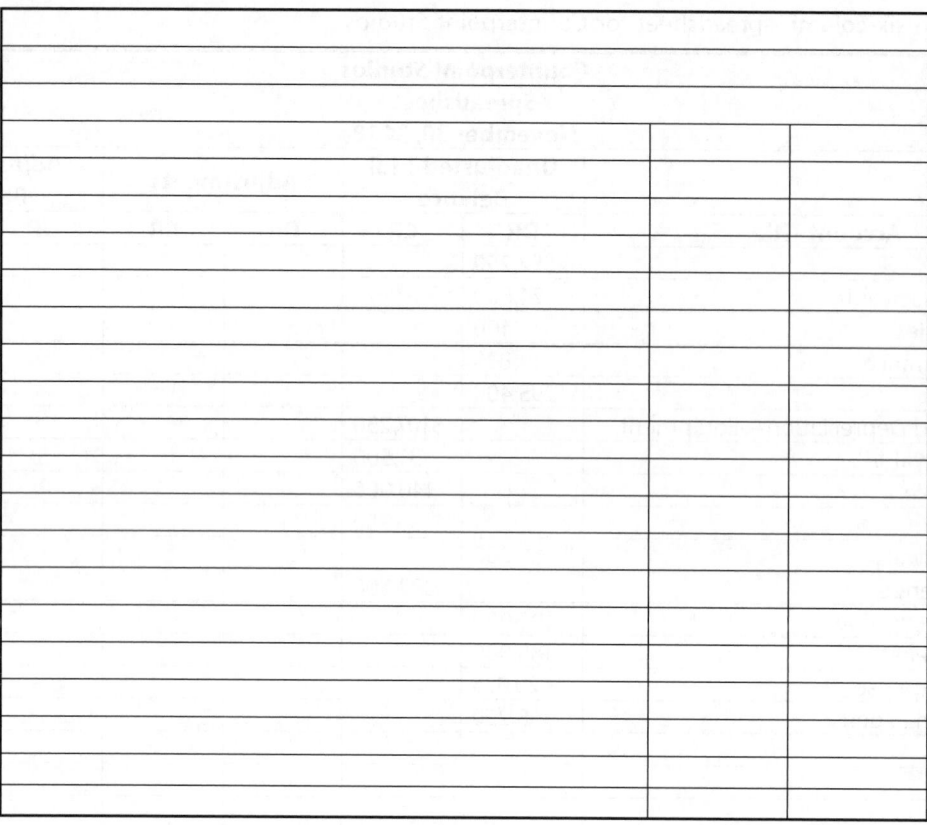

AP-3B LO 2 3

Jim's Custom Painting has journalized its adjusting entries and prepared its adjusted trial balance.

Jim's Custom Painting Adjusted Trial Balance August 31, 2018		
Account Title	**DR**	**CR**
Cash	$8,400	
Accounts Receivable	2,900	
Prepaid Rent	2,100	
Office Supplies	2,400	
Equipment	20,700	
Accumulated Depreciation—Equipment		$2,700
Accounts Payable		3,200
Interest Payable		300
Unearned Revenue		2,900
Mortgage Payable		5,400
Gordon, Capital		22,360
Gordon, Withdrawals	4,000	
Service Revenue		7,600
Depreciation Expense	150	
Insurance Expense	240	
Interest Expense	300	
Rent Expense	1,420	
Supplies Expense	350	
Travel Expense	1,500	
Total	**$44,460**	**$44,460**

Required

a) Prepare the closing entries using the income summary account for August.

Date	Account Title and Explanation	PR	Debit	Credit

b) Prepare the post-closing trial balance.

AP-4B LO 2

Portal Delivery Services has prepared its income statement and statement of owner's equity.

Portal Delivery Services		
Income Statement		
For the Year Ended October 31, 2018		
Service Revenue		$500,000
Expenses		
Transportation Expense	$95,000	
Salaries Expense	240,000	
Maintenance Expense	70,000	
Depreciation Expense	45,000	
Total Expenses		450,000
Net Income (Loss)		$50,000

Portal Delivery Services
Statement of Owner's Equity
For the Year Ended October 31, 2018

Jones, Capital at November 1, 2017		$120,000
Add:		
Additional Investments	$30,000	
Net Income (Loss)	50,000	80,000
Subtotal		200,000
Less:		
Jones, Withdrawals		100,000
Jones, Capital at October 31, 2018		$100,000

Prepare the closing entries using the income summary method for Portal Delivery Services.

Date	Account Title and Explanation	PR	Debit	Credit

Analysis

What is the purpose of preparing closing entries at the end of each period? Explain.

_____

_____

_____

_____

_____

AP-5B LO 2 3

Home Protector has journalized its adjusting entries and prepared its adjusted trial balance.

Home Protector Adjusted Trial Balance January 31, 2018		
Account Title	DR	CR
Cash	$14,200	
Accounts Receivable	6,900	
Prepaid Services	4,000	
Office Supplies	2,000	
Equipment	37,700	
Accumulated Depreciation—Equipment		$5,700
Accounts Payable		4,800
Salaries Payable		950
Unearned Revenue		4,800
Mortgage Payable		8,800
Sherlock, Capital		32,750
Sherlock, Withdrawals	4,900	
Service Revenue		18,200
Depreciation Expense	350	
Insurance Expense	290	
Maintenance Expense	470	
Rent Expense	1,500	
Telephone Expense	490	
Utilities Expense	3,200	
Total	$76,000	$76,000

Required

a) Prepare the closing entries directly to owner's capital for the month of January.

Date	Account Title and Explanation	PR	Debit	Credit

b) Prepare the post-closing trial balance.

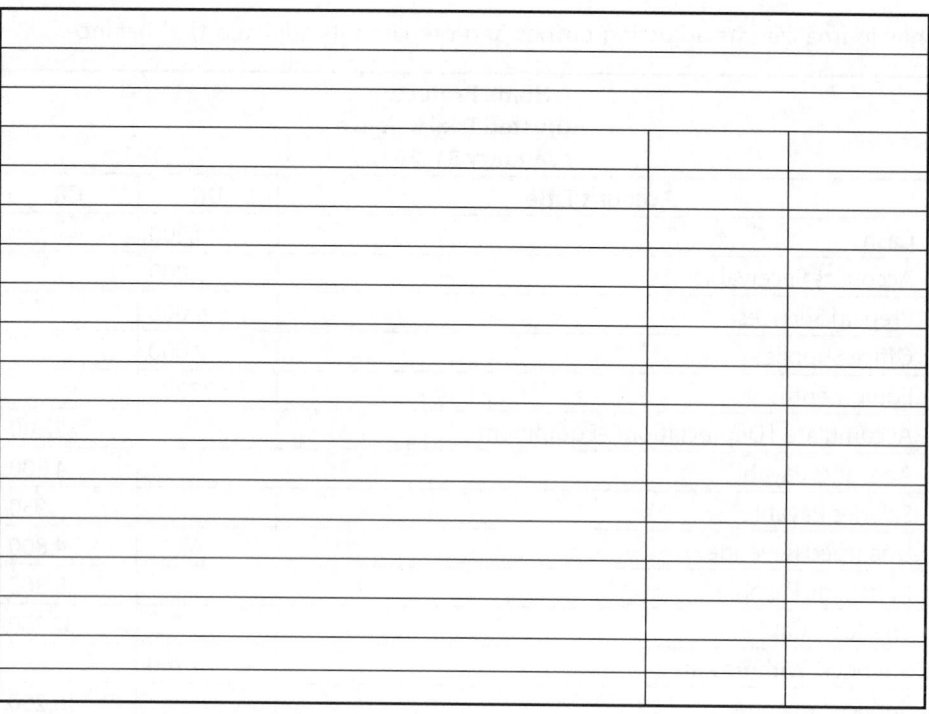

AP-6B LO 2 3

Health Foods has journalized its adjusting entries and prepared its adjusted trial balance.

Health Foods Adjusted Trial Balance May 31, 2018		
Account Title	**DR**	**CR**
Cash	$14,800	
Accounts Receivable	7,600	
Prepaid Rent	3,300	
Office Supplies	2,300	
Equipment	39,300	
Accumulated Depreciation—Equipment		$5,200
Accounts Payable		4,200
Salaries Payable		980
Unearned Revenue		4,800
Mortgage Payable		11,000
Schmitt, Capital		34,820
Schmitt, Withdrawals	4,400	
Service Revenue		17,000
Depreciation Expense	140	
Insurance Expense	140	
Maintenance Expense	160	
Office Supplies Expense	880	
Rent Expense	1,400	
Telephone Expense	280	
Utilities Expense	3,300	
Total	**$78,000**	**$78,000**

Required

a)   Prepare the closing entries directly to owner's capital for the month of May.

Date	Account Title and Explanation	PR	Debit	Credit

b)   Prepare the post-closing trial balance

High Flying Biplane has completed all its journal entries and adjusting entries for the month of June 2018. The chart of accounts and adjusted trial balance are shown below.

Account Description	Account #
ASSETS	
Cash	101
Accounts Receivable	105
Prepaid Insurance	110
Equipment	120
Accumulated Depreciation—Equipment	125
LIABILITIES	
Accounts Payable	200
Interest Payable	205
Unearned Revenue	210
Notes Payable	215
OWNER'S EQUITY	
Singh, Capital	300
Singh, Withdrawals	310
Income Summary	315

Account Description	Account #
REVENUE	
Service Revenue	400
EXPENSES	
Advertising Expense	500
Depreciation Expense	510
Insurance Expense	515
Interest Expense	520
Telephone Expense	550

High Flying Biplane Adjusted Trial Balance June 30, 2018		
Account Title	**DR**	**CR**
Cash	$8,800	
Accounts Receivable	6,800	
Prepaid Insurance	1,100	
Equipment	64,000	
Accumulated Depreciation—Equipment		$450
Accounts Payable		7,700
Interest Payable		75
Unearned Revenue		4,080
Notes Payable		19,000
Singh, Capital		48,800
Singh, Withdrawals	1,200	
Service Revenue		3,020
Advertising Expense	400	
Depreciation Expense	450	
Insurance Expense	100	
Interest Expense	75	
Telephone Expense	200	
Total	**$83,125**	**$83,125**

Note: The daily transactions and adjustments for the month of June have already been posted in the general ledger. You are only responsible for posting the closing entries. Recall that the owner invested $5,000 into the business during the month.

Required

a) Prepare the income statement.

b) Prepare the statement of owner's equity.

c) Prepare the balance sheet.

d) Create the closing entries using the income summary account and post the closing entries to the ledger
    accounts on the next page.

Date	Account Title and Explanation	PR	Debit	Credit

e) Prepare the post-closing trial balance.

GENERAL LEDGER

Account: Cash					GL No: 101	
Date	Description	PR	DR	CR	Balance	
2018						
Jun 1	Opening Balance				8,000	DR
Jun 1		J1	5,000		13,000	DR
Jun 2		J1	1,500		14,500	DR
Jun 4		J1		200	14,300	DR
Jun 14		J1		4,000	10,300	DR
Jun 20		J1	1,600		11,900	DR
Jun 22		J1		900	11,000	DR
Jun 24		J1		1,000	10,000	DR
Jun 30		J1		1,200	8,800	DR

Account: Accounts Receivable					GL No: 105	
Date	Description	PR	DR	CR	Balance	
2018						
Jun 1	Opening Balance				6,000	DR
Jun 10		J1	2,400		8,400	DR
Jun 20		J1		1,600	6,800	DR

Account: Prepaid Insurance					GL No: 110	
Date	Description	PR	DR	CR	Balance	
2018						
Jun 1	Opening Balance				1,200	DR
Jun 30	Adjustment	J2		100	1,100	DR

Account: Equipment					GL No: 120	
Date	Description	PR	DR	CR	Balance	
2018						
Jun 1	Opening Balance				60,000	DR
Jun 14		J1	4,000		64,000	DR

Account: Accumulated Depreciation—Equipment					GL No: 125	
Date	Description	PR	DR	CR	Balance	
2018						
Jun 30	Adjustment	J2		450	450	CR

Account: Accounts Payable					GL No: 200	
Date	Description	PR	DR	CR	Balance	
2018						
Jun 1	Opening Balance				8,200	CR
Jun 3		J1		400	8,600	CR
Jun 22		J1	900		7,700	CR

Account: Interest Payable   **GL No: 205**

Date	Description	PR	DR	CR	Balance	
2018						
Jun 30	Adjustment	J2		75	75	CR

Account: Unearned Revenue   **GL No: 210**

Date	Description	PR	DR	CR	Balance	
2018						
Jun 1	Opening Balance				3,200	CR
Jun 2		J1		1,500	4,700	CR
Jun 30	Adjustment	J2	620		4,080	CR

Account: Notes Payable   **GL No: 215**

Date	Description	PR	DR	CR	Balance	
2018						
Jun 1	Opening Balance				20,000	CR
Jun 24		J1	1,000		19,000	CR

Account: Singh, Capital   **GL No: 300**

Date	Description	PR	DR	CR	Balance	
2018						
Jun 1	Opening Balance				43,800	CR
Jun 1		J1		5,000	48,800	CR

Account: Singh, Withdrawals   **GL No: 310**

Date	Description	PR	DR	CR	Balance	
2018						
Jun 30		J1	1,200		1,200	DR

Account: Income Summary   **GL No: 315**

Date	Description	PR	DR	CR	Balance	

Account: Service Revenue   **GL No: 400**

Date	Description	PR	DR	CR	Balance	
2018						
Jun 10		J1		2,400	2,400	CR
Jun 30	Adjustment	J2		620	3,020	CR

Account: Advertising Expense					GL No: 500	
Date	**Description**	**PR**	**DR**	**CR**	**Balance**	
2018						
Jun 3		J1	400		400	DR

Account: Depreciation Expense					GL No: 510	
Date	**Description**	**PR**	**DR**	**CR**	**Balance**	
2018						
Jun 30	Adjustment	J2	450		450	DR

Account: Insurance Expense					GL No: 515	
Date	**Description**	**PR**	**DR**	**CR**	**Balance**	
2018						
Jun 30	Adjustment	J2	100		100	DR

Account: Interest Expense					GL No: 520	
Date	**Description**	**PR**	**DR**	**CR**	**Balance**	
2018						
Jun 30	Adjustment	J2	75		75	DR

Account: Telephone Expense					GL No: 550	
Date	**Description**	**PR**	**DR**	**CR**	**Balance**	
2018						
Jun 4		J1	200		200	DR

AP-8B LO 1 2 3

Limbo Lower has completed all its journal entries and adjusting entries for the month of September 2018. The chart of accounts and adjusted trial balance are shown below.

Account Description	Account #
ASSETS	
Cash	101
Accounts Receivable	105
Prepaid Insurance	110
Office Supplies	115
Equipment	120
Accumulated Depreciation—Equipment	125
LIABILITIES	
Accounts Payable	200
Unearned Revenue	210
Notes Payable	215
OWNER'S EQUITY	
Patel, Capital	300
Patel, Withdrawals	310
Income Summary	315

Account Description	Account #
REVENUE	
Service Revenue	400
EXPENSES	
Depreciation Expense	510
Insurance Expense	515
Interest Expense	520
Office Supplies Expense	530
Rent Expense	540

Limbo Lower Adjusted Trial Balance September 30, 2018		
Account Title	DR	CR
Cash	$5,800	
Accounts Receivable	1,450	
Prepaid Insurance	1,650	
Office Supplies	650	
Equipment	9,300	
Accumulated Depreciation—Equipment		$120
Accounts Payable		3,050
Unearned Revenue		1,040
Notes Payable		4,640
Patel, Capital		11,450
Patel, Withdrawals	1,600	
Service Revenue		2,260
Depreciation Expense	120	
Insurance Expense	150	
Interest Expense	40	
Office Supplies Expense	450	
Rent Expense	1,350	
Total	$22,560	$22,560

Note: The daily transactions and adjustments for the month of September have already been posted in the general ledger. You are only responsible for posting the closing entries.

Required

a) Prepare the income statement.

b) Prepare the statement of owner's equity.

c) Prepare the balance sheet.

d) Create the closing entries using the income summary account and post the closing entries to the ledger accounts on the next page.

Date	Account Title and Explanation	PR	Debit	Credit

e) Prepare the post-closing trial balance.

GENERAL LEDGER

Account: Cash | | | | | GL No: 101

Date	Description	PR	DR	CR	Balance	
2018						
Sep 1	Opening Balance				7,200	DR
Sep 1		J1		1,800	5,400	DR
Sep 2		J1	1,900		7,300	DR
Sep 3		J1		1,350	5,950	DR
Sep 10		J1		40	5,910	DR
Sep 10		J1		960	4,950	DR
Sep 20		J1	2,200		7,150	DR
Sep 22		J1	850		8,000	DR
Sep 24		J1		600	7,400	DR
Sep 30		J1		1,600	5,800	DR

Account: Accounts Receivable | | | | | GL No: 105

Date	Description	PR	DR	CR	Balance	
2018						
Sep 1	Opening Balance				2,300	DR
Sep 22		J1		850	1,450	DR

Account: Prepaid Insurance | | | | | GL No: 110

Date	Description	PR	DR	CR	Balance	
2018						
Sep 1	Opening Balance				0	DR
Sep 1		J1	1,800		1,800	DR
Sep 30	Adjustment	J2		150	1,650	DR

Account: Office Supplies | | | | | GL No: 115

Date	Description	PR	DR	CR	Balance	
2018						
Sep 1	Opening Balance				850	DR
Sep 4		J1	250		1,100	DR
Sep 30	Adjustment	J2		450	650	DR

Account: Equipment | | | | | GL No: 120

Date	Description	PR	DR	CR	Balance	
2018						
Sep 1	Opening Balance				11,500	DR
Sep 20		J1		2,200	9,300	DR

Account: Accumulated Depreciation—Equipment | | | | | GL No: 125

Date	Description	PR	DR	CR	Balance	
2018						
Sep 30	Adjustment	J2		120	120	CR

Account: Accounts Payable | | | | | GL No: 200

Date	Description	PR	DR	CR	Balance	
2018						
Sep 1	Opening Balance				3,400	CR
Sep 4		J1		250	3,650	CR
Sep 24		J1	600		3,050	CR

Account: Unearned Revenue   **GL No: 210**

Date	Description	PR	DR	CR	Balance	
2018						
Sep 1	Opening Balance				1,400	CR
Sep 30	Adjustment	J2	360		1,040	CR

Account: Notes Payable   **GL No: 215**

Date	Description	PR	DR	CR	Balance	
2018						
Sep 1	Opening Balance				5,600	CR
Sep 10		J1	960		4,640	CR

Account: Patel, Capital   **GL No: 300**

Date	Description	PR	DR	CR	Balance	
2018						
Sep 1	Opening Balance				11,450	CR

Account: Patel, Withdrawals   **GL No: 310**

Date	Description	PR	DR	CR	Balance	
2018						
Sep 30		J1	1,600		1,600	DR

Account: Income Summary   **GL No: 315**

Date	Description	PR	DR	CR	Balance	

Account: Service Revenue   **GL No: 400**

Date	Description	PR	DR	CR	Balance	
2018						
Sep 2		J1		1,900	1,900	CR
Sep 30	Adjustment	J2		360	2,260	CR

Account: Depreciation Expense   **GL No: 510**

Date	Description	PR	DR	CR	Balance	
2018						
Sep 30	Adjustment	J2	120		120	DR

Account: Insurance Expense   **GL No: 515**

Date	Description	PR	DR	CR	Balance	
2018						
Sep 30	Adjustment	J2	150		150	DR

Account: Interest Expense   **GL No: 520**

Date	Description	PR	DR	CR	Balance	
2018						
Sep 10		J1	40		40	DR

Account: Office Supplies Expense   **GL No: 530**

Date	Description	PR	DR	CR	Balance	
2018						
Sep 30	Adjustment	J2	450		450	DR

Account: Rent Expense   **GL No: 540**

Date	Description	PR	DR	CR	Balance	
2018						
Sep 3		J1	1,350		1,350	DR

AP-9B `LO` `4`

The following information is taken from the records of Basil Cleaning.

Accounts Payable	$18,000
Merchandise Inventory	14,000
Land	55,000
Cash	31,000
Factory Equipment	20,000
Notes Payable, Current Portion	21,000
Office Furniture	18,000
Prepaid Insurance	13,000
Unearned Revenue	8,000

Required

a) Calculate total current assets.

b) Calculate total noncurrent assets.

c) Calculate total assets.

AP-10B LO 4

Manuel Consulting borrowed a $1,180,000 interest-free bank loan on January 1, 2018. Payment will be made in four years in four equal annual installments (paid on each subsequent January 1). Calculate the current and long-term liabilities as at December 31 before the annual installments are made for the following years.

	December 31			
	2018	**2019**	**2020**	**2021**
Notes Payable, Current Portion				
Notes Payable, Long-Term Portion				

AP-11B LO 4

On July 1, 2018, Bryte Services took out a $200,000 bank loan. The loan will be repaid in equal annual installments over the next 10 years. Show how the bank loan will appear on Bryte Services' classified balance sheet on June 30, 2024.

Analysis

Show the journal entries required to record the receipt of the loan and the first principal payment.

Date	Account Title and Explanation	PR	Debit	Credit

AP-12B LO 4

On January 1, 2018, Detmore Consulting took out a $100,000 bank loan. The loan will be repaid in two equal payments; one on December 31, 2019, and the other on December 31, 2021. Complete the table below with the correct balances for the accounts at the dates listed.

	Notes Payable	
	Current	**Long-Term**
Dec 31, 2018		
Dec 31, 2019		
Dec 31, 2020		
Dec 31, 2021		

Analysis

Why is it helpful to split some liabilities into current and long-term portions for reporting purposes?

_____

_____

_____

_____

AP-13B LO 4

Identify the following accounts as either current or long-term, and as either assets or liabilities.

Account Name	Current or Long-Term	Asset or Liability
Accounts Receivable		
Salaries Payable		
Equipment		
Cash		
Notes Payable due in six months		
Office Furniture		
Accounts Payable		
Prepaid Rent		
Notes Payable due in two years		
Merchandise Inventory		

AP-14B LO 4 5 6

Below is Bravolo's adjusted trial balance for the year ending September 30, 2018. Assume all accounts have a normal balance. The notes payable is payable over three years and $6,000 will be paid by September 30, 2019.

Cash	$17,400
Accounts Receivable	5,800
Prepaid Insurance	1,800
Equipment	23,000
Accumulated Depreciation—Equipment	1,100
Accounts Payable	7,600
Unearned Revenue	1,500
Notes Payable	18,000
Bravolo, Capital	19,800

Required

a) Prepare a classified balance sheet.

b) Calculate the working capital for Bravolo.

_____

_____

c) Calculate the current ratio for Bravolo.

_____

_____

d) Calculate the quick ratio for Bravolo.

_____

_____

AP-15B LO 4 5

Below is Canduro's financial information for the year ending June 30, 2018. Assume all accounts have a normal balance.

Accounts Payable	$8,900
Accounts Receivable	6,100
Accumulated Depreciation—Equipment	1,200
Notes Payable	21,000
Cash	19,000
Prepaid Insurance	3,250
Equipment	25,000
Canduro, Capital	20,550
Unearned Revenue	1,700

The notes payable is payable over five years and $4,200 will be paid by June 30, 2019.

Required

a) Prepare a classified balance sheet.

b) Calculate the working capital for Canduro.

_____

c) Calculate the current ratio for Canduro.

_____

d) Calculate the quick ratio for Canduro.

_____

AP-16B LO 7

Charles Ly is the owner of Gamma Services. He has hired you to prepare the financial statements for his company on April 30, 2018. As part of the process, you need to create the spreadsheet. Use the unadjusted trial balance and the adjustments to complete the spreadsheet.

Apr 30   Recognized prepaid insurance worth $100 for this month

Apr 30   Recorded $400 depreciation on equipment

Apr 30   Recognized $1,800 of unearned revenue that is now earned

	Gamma Services Spreadsheet April 30, 2018									
	Unadjusted Trial Balance		Adjustments		Adjusted Trial Balance		Income Statement		Balance Sheet	
Account Title	DR	CR	DR	CR	DR	CR	DR	CR	DR	CR
Cash	$21,750									
Accounts Receivable	13,000									
Prepaid Insurance	1,200									
Equipment	17,500									
Accumulated Depreciation—Equipment		$2,000								
Accounts Payable		10,300								
Unearned Revenue		4,500								
Notes Payable		18,000								
Ly, Capital		14,000								
Service Revenue		9,000								
Insurance Expense	0									
Salaries Expense	4,000									
Telephone Expense	200									
Depreciation Expense	0									
Interest Expense	150									
Total	$57,800	$57,800								
Net Profit (Loss)										
Total										

Case Study

CS-1 LO 1 2 3 4

Grindstone Paving provides residential and commercial paving services. Its balance sheet at the end of June 2018 is shown below, along with its chart of accounts.

Grindstone Paving Balance Sheet As at June 30, 2018			
Assets		**Liabilities**	
Cash	$7,580	Accounts Payable	$15,800
Accounts Receivable	6,000	Unearned Revenue	6,200
Prepaid Insurance	1,800	Notes Payable	22,000
Equipment	55,000	**Total Liabilities**	44,000
		Owner's Equity	
		Stone, Capital	26,380
Total Assets	$70,380	**Total Liabilities and Owner's Equity**	$70,380

Account Description	Account #
ASSETS	
Cash	101
Accounts Receivable	105
Prepaid Insurance	110
Equipment	120
Accumulated Depreciation—Equipment	125
LIABILITIES	
Accounts Payable	200
Interest Payable	205
Salary Payable	210
Unearned Revenue	215
Notes Payable	220
OWNER'S EQUITY	
Stone, Capital	300
Stone, Withdrawals	310
Income Summary	315

Account Description	Account #
REVENUE	
Service Revenue	400
EXPENSES	
Advertising Expense	500
Depreciation Expense	510
Insurance Expense	515
Interest Expense	520
Salaries Expense	545
Telephone Expense	550

For the month of July 2018, Grindstone Paving had the following transactions.

Jul 1   The owner invested $8,000 cash into the business

Jul 2   Received $2,530 cash for work that will be provided in August

Jul 5   Received an advertising bill for $600, which will be paid next month

Jul 8   Paid the $350 telephone bill with cash

Jul 10 Provided $4,680 worth of services to customers who will pay later

Jul 14 Purchased equipment with $8,200 cash

Jul 20 Received $2,350 in payment from customers paying their accounts

Jul 22 Paid $1,970 toward accounts payable

Jul 24 Paid $1,300 toward principal of the note payable

Jul 28 Paid salary of $2,400 to an employee

Jul 30 The owner withdrew $2,200 cash for personal use

At the end of July, the following adjustments had to be journalized to properly report the balances of the company's accounts.

Jul 31   One month of prepaid insurance worth $100 has been used
Jul 31   Monthly depreciation on the equipment was $450
Jul 31   Unearned revenue worth $620 has now been earned
Jul 31   Interest of $75 has accrued on the of the note payable
Jul 31   Accrued salary expense of $500 for an employee

Note: Of the remaining balance of the note payable, $5,000 will be paid within the next year.

Required

a) Enter the opening balances from the June 2018 balance sheet into the general ledger accounts (the ledger accounts are presented at the end of this question).

b) Prepare the journal entries for the month of July and post them to the appropriate general ledger accounts.

Date	Account Title and Explanation	PR	Debit	Credit

c)   Create the trial balance in the spreadsheet and then complete the remaining section of the spreadsheet.

	Unadjusted Trial Balance		Adjustments		Adjusted Trial Balance	
Account Title	**DR**	**CR**	**DR**	**CR**	**DR**	**CR**

d)   Prepare the income statement.

e)   Prepare the statement of owner's equity.

f) Prepare the classified balance sheet.

g) Prepare the journal entries for the adjustments and post them to the appropriate general ledger accounts.

Date	Account Title and Explanation	PR	Debit	Credit

h) Prepare the journal entries to close the books for the month of July 2018 (use the income summary account), and post the journal entries to the appropriate general ledger accounts, which start on the next page.

JOURNAL				Page 3
Date	**Account Title and Explanation**	**PR**	**Debit**	**Credit**

i) Create the post-closing trial balance.

GENERAL LEDGER

Account:						GL No:	
Date	Description	PR	DR	CR	Balance		

Account:						GL No:	
Date	Description	PR	DR	CR	Balance		

Account:						GL No:	
Date	Description	PR	DR	CR	Balance		

Account:						GL No:	
Date	Description	PR	DR	CR	Balance		

Account:						GL No:	
Date	Description	PR	DR	CR	Balance		

Account:						GL No:	
Date	Description	PR	DR	CR	Balance		

Account:					GL No:	
Date	Description	PR	DR	CR	Balance	

Account:					GL No:	
Date	Description	PR	DR	CR	Balance	

Account:					GL No:	
Date	Description	PR	DR	CR	Balance	

Account:					GL No:	
Date	Description	PR	DR	CR	Balance	

Account:					GL No:	
Date	Description	PR	DR	CR	Balance	

Account:					GL No:	
Date	Description	PR	DR	CR	Balance	

Account:					GL No:	
Date	Description	PR	DR	CR	Balance	

Account:					GL No:	
Date	**Description**	**PR**	**DR**	**CR**	**Balance**	

Account:					GL No:	
Date	**Description**	**PR**	**DR**	**CR**	**Balance**	

Account:					GL No:	
Date	**Description**	**PR**	**DR**	**CR**	**Balance**	

Account:					GL No:	
Date	**Description**	**PR**	**DR**	**CR**	**Balance**	

Account:					GL No:	
Date	**Description**	**PR**	**DR**	**CR**	**Balance**	

Account:					GL No:	
Date	**Description**	**PR**	**DR**	**CR**	**Balance**	

Account:					GL No:	
Date	**Description**	**PR**	**DR**	**CR**	**Balance**	

Chapter 7

INVENTORY: MERCHANDISING TRANSACTIONS

LEARNING OBJECTIVES

LO 1 Define a merchandising business

LO 2 Differentiate between the perpetual and the periodic inventory systems

LO 3 Record journal entries under the perpetual inventory system

LO 4 Calculate gross profit and gross profit margin percentages

LO 5 Prepare the income statement under the perpetual inventory system

LO 6 Prepare closing entries for a merchandising business under the perpetual inventory system

LO 7 Identify inventory controls

Appendix

LO 8 Record journal entries under the periodic inventory system

LO 9 Calculate cost of goods sold under the periodic inventory system

LO 10 Prepare a multiple-step income statement under the periodic inventory system

LO 11 Prepare closing entries for a merchandising business under the periodic inventory system

AMEENGAGE™ Access **ameengage.com** for integrated resources including tutorials, practice exercises, the digital textbook and more.

———— Assessment Questions ————

AS-1 LO 1

What is a merchandiser?

_____

_____

AS-2 LO 1

Mulo Pet Food manufactures pet food and sells its products only to Krong Company. Krong Company resells the pet food to Chai Canine Care, among others. Chai Canine Care in turn resells the pet food to pet owners. Explain which company (Mulo Pet Food, Krong Company, and Chai Canine Care), acts as a wholesaler and which company acts as a retailer.

_____

_____

_____

AS-3 LO 1

What is merchandise inventory?

_____

_____

AS-4 LO 1

What does a merchandiser's operating cycle usually involve?

_____

_____

AS-5 LO 1

What is COGS and what type of account is it?

_____

_____

AS-6 LO 1

How is gross profit calculated?

_____

_____

AS-7 LO 2

In a perpetual inventory system, how often are inventory levels updated?

_____

_____

AS-8 LO 2

In a periodic inventory system, how often are inventory levels updated?

_____

_____

AS-9 LO 5

Define operating expenses.

_____

_____

AS-10 LO 3

What are some reasons purchase returns occur?

_____

_____

_____

AS-11 LO 3

When does a purchase allowance occur?

_____

_____

AS-12 `LO 3`

Indicate a possible incentive for a seller to give a sales discount.

_____

_____

AS-13 `LO 3`

What is a trade discount?

_____

_____

_____

AS-14 `LO 3`

If a cash discount term is written as 3/10, n/30, what does this mean?

_____

_____

AS-15 `LO 3`

Explain the difference between a sales allowance and a sales discount.

_____

_____

_____

_____

AS-16 `LO 9`

Explain how cost of goods available for sale is calculated in a periodic inventory system.

_____

_____

_____

AS-17 `LO 3`

What are the two possible Freight on Board (FOB) points?

_____

_____

AS-18 `LO 3`

What does FOB shipping point indicate?

_____

_____

AS-19 LO 3

What does FOB destination indicate?

_____

_____

AS-20 LO 3

What type of account is sales returns and allowances and what is it used for?

_____

_____

AS-21 LO 4

What is the formula for gross profit margin?

_____

_____

AS-22 LO 3

In a perpetual inventory system, describe the transaction(s) required to record the sale of merchandise inventory.

_____

_____

AS-23 LO 8

In a periodic inventory system, describe the transaction(s) required to record the sale of merchandise inventory.

_____

_____

AS-24 LO 5

What is one difference between a single-step income statement and a multiple-step income statement?

_____

_____

_____

AS-25 LO 5

What are selling expenses? What are some examples of selling expenses?

_____

_____

AS-26 LO 5

What are administrative expenses? What are some examples of administrative expenses?

_____

_____

_____

AS-27 LO 5

In a typical multiple-step income statement, which category do items such as interest revenue and loss from a lawsuit fall under?

_____

_____

AS-28 LO 6

What is inventory shrinkage? How is it journalized under the perpetual inventory system?

_____

_____

_____

AS-29 LO 7

Provide an example of how an accountant can manage inventory to ensure the economical and efficient use of resources.

_____

_____

_____

AS-30 LO 10

What is the difference between the income statement under a periodic inventory system and the income statement under a perpetual inventory system?

_____

_____

_____

AS-31 LO 2

What is the benefit to a company of using a perpetual inventory system?

_____

_____

_____

_____

_____

AS-32 LO 7

List two safety measures that can be taken to avoid inventory losses through theft.

_____

_____

_____

_____

Application Questions Group A

AP-1A LO 3

Super Shirt Wholesalers spent $10,000 to purchase 1,000 shirts from a shirt manufacturer as inventory. Hip Top Retailers paid $15,000 for the 1,000 shirts from Super Shirt Wholesalers on March 15, 2018. Payment is due on April 15. Both companies use the perpetual inventory system.

Required

a) Prepare the journal entry for Hip Top Shirt Retailers on March 15.

Date	Account Title and Explanation	Debit	Credit

b) Prepare the journal entries for Super Shirt Wholesalers on March 15.

Date	Account Title and Explanation	Debit	Credit

AP-2A LO 3

JB Supermarkets bought $3,000 worth of groceries on account from a produce supplier on May 10, 2018. On May 11, JB's bookkeeper was informed that $200 worth of tomatoes was substandard and returned to the supplier. Prepare the journal entry to record the purchase return using the perpetual inventory system.

Date	Account Title and Explanation	Debit	Credit

AP-3A LO 8

Refer to AP-2A and record the purchase return assuming JB Supermarkets uses a periodic inventory system.

Date	Account Title and Explanation	Debit	Credit

AP-4A LO 3

On January 12, 2018, Corner-Mart received a shipment of T-shirts from Promo Novelties for an event. The invoice amounted to $5,000 and was recorded in the accounting system. Soon after the delivery was made, the marketing manager discovered that the logo was printed incorrectly. The goods were returned to Promo Novelties on January 31. Prepare the journal entry for Corner-Mart to record the return using the perpetual inventory system.

Date	Account Title and Explanation	Debit	Credit

AP-5A LO 8

Refer to AP-4A. Record the purchase return assuming Corner-Mart uses a periodic inventory system.

Date	Account Title and Explanation	Debit	Credit

AP-6A LO 3

a) Beds Unlimited received a shipment of bed sheets on April 3, 2018. The value of the bed sheets was $8,000, and the sheets were shipped FOB shipping point. Freight charges came to $100. Prepare the journal entry to record the receipt of goods by Beds Unlimited, assuming payment will be made in May, using the perpetual inventory system.

Date	Account Title and Explanation	Debit	Credit

b) The bed sheets delivered to Beds Unlimited were the wrong material. After some negotiation, the manager agreed to keep the products with a 10% allowance. Prepare the entry on April 10, 2018 to record the purchase allowance. (Assume all bed sheets were still in inventory.) Allowances are not granted on freight charges.

Date	Account Title and Explanation	Debit	Credit

c) Journalize the transaction for Beds Unlimited when the payment is made on May 3, 2018.

Date	Account Title and Explanation	Debit	Credit

AP-7A LO 3

The following is written on an invoice relating to goods that were purchased: 5/10, n/30. What does it mean?

_____

_____

AP-8A LO 4

If a computer company bought computers for $10,000 and sold them for $14,000, how much would the gross profit be on the entire shipment if the business took advantage of the early cash payment terms of 2/15, n/30 from its supplier?

_____

_____

_____

_____

AP-9A LO 3

Shoe Retailers uses the perpetual inventory system. It purchased $10,000 worth of shoes from Runner Wear Supplies on March 1, 2018. Runner Wear's invoice shows terms of 2/10, n/30.

Required

a) What is the latest date Shoe Retailers can pay the bill and apply the discount?

_____

_____

b) As bookkeeper for Shoe Retailers, prepare the journal entry to record the March 1 purchase.

Date	Account Title and Explanation	Debit	Credit

c) Journalize the transaction for payment of the invoice, assuming the payment was made on March 5.

Date	Account Title and Explanation	Debit	Credit

d) Journalize the transaction for payment of the invoice, assuming the payment was made on April 3.

Date	Account Title and Explanation	Debit	Credit

AP-10A LO 3

On May 1, 2018, Food Wholesalers purchased $3,000 worth of dried fruit inventory and paid $100 for freight charges on account. On May 15, Food Wholesalers sold all of the dried fruit inventory to Retail Grocers for $4,000 on account. As the bookkeeper for Food Wholesalers, journalize the transactions using the perpetual inventory system.

Date	Account Title and Explanation	Debit	Credit

AP-11A LO 3

Johnson is a maker of cotton garments that are sold to various retailers. On September 1, 2018, Craig's Retailers sent back a shipment of goods that were unsatisfactory. The goods had a cost of $4,620 and were sold on account for $7,700. Johnson returned the goods to inventory. Johnson uses a perpetual inventory system.

Required

a) As Johnson's bookkeeper, prepare the journal entries to reflect the return.

Date	Account Title and Explanation	Debit	Credit

b) Journalize the entry if Craig's only returned half of the shipment.

Date	Account Title and Explanation	Debit	Credit

AP-12A LO 3 4

Assume you are the bookkeeper for Moira's Wholesalers, a distributor of kitchen furniture. Your sales manager informed you that Ted's Retailers is unhappy with the quality of some tables delivered on August 12, 2018, and will be shipping back all the goods. The original invoice amounted to $1,500 and the goods cost Moira's $1,000. Using a perpetual inventory system, complete the journal entries for Moira's Wholesalers for each of the following independent scenarios.

Required

a) Rather than taking back the tables, your sales manager allows Ted's Retailers a 10% discount if it agrees to keep the goods. Record Ted's payment in settlement of the invoice on September 12 assuming the allowance is not recorded until the settlement date.

Date	Account Title and Explanation	Debit	Credit

b) Suppose that Ted's shipped back all the goods on August 15 and the inventory was put back on the sales floor. Journalize the transactions.

Date	Account Title and Explanation	Debit	Credit

c) Suppose that Ted's shipped back half the goods on August 15 and kept the other half with a 10% allowance. Journalize the transactions that took place on August 15.

Date	Account Title and Explanation	Debit	Credit

d) Continue from part b). Since all the goods were sold and returned in the same period, what happened to Moira's gross profit? (Disregard the additional shipping and administration costs.) Explain your answer.

_____

_____

AP-13A LO 3 4

The following information pertains to Wicked Kitchen Supplies for March 2018.

Mar 1	Purchased merchandise for $16,000 on credit from Hotel Supplies, terms 1/20, n/30
Mar 1	Wicked paid $35 cash to have the merchandise from Hotel Supplies delivered (FOB shipping point)
Mar 5	Sold merchandise on credit to Four Boars Restaurant for $8,000, terms 2/10, n/30; cost of goods was $5,500
Mar 5	Paid $25 cash to ship the goods to Four Boars Restaurant (FOB destination)
Mar 8	Four Boars returned $1,900 (sales price) worth of merchandise purchased on March 5, cost of goods was $800; there was nothing wrong with the merchandise and it will be resold
Mar 12	Returned $500 of the merchandise purchased on March 1 as it was the wrong design
Mar 15	Received payment from Four Boars Restaurant for the March 5 sale
Mar 15	Paid for merchandise purchased from Hotel Supplies on March 1
Mar 23	Sold merchandise on credit to Black Kettle Kitchen for $4,000, terms 2/10, n/30; cost of goods was $2,000
Mar 26	Black Kettle Kitchen returned $200 (sales price) worth of merchandise purchased on March 23; cost of goods was $50; merchandise was returned to inventory
Mar 31	Received payment from Black Kettle Kitchen for the March 23 sale

Journalize the above transactions assuming that Wicked Kitchen Supplies uses a perpetual inventory system. Round all calculations to the nearest whole dollar.

Date	Account Title and Explanation	Debit	Credit

Date	Account Title and Explanation	Debit	Credit

Analysis

Calculate Wicked Kitchen Supplies' gross profit for the month.

AP-14A LO 3

The following information was presented by the bookkeeper for Switch Company for the month of January 2018.

Jan 5   Purchased merchandise for $12,000 on credit from Outdoor Pursuits, terms 1/10, n/30

Jan 5   Switch Company paid $25 to have the merchandise delivered (FOB shipping point)

Jan 12   Purchased merchandise for $7,000 on credit from Cambleback, terms 2/10, n/30

Jan 14   Returned $300 of the merchandise purchased on January 5 from Outdoor Pursuits as it was defective

Jan 15   Paid for merchandise purchased from Outdoor Pursuits on January 5

Jan 26   Paid for merchandise purchased from Cambleback on January 12

Journalize the above transactions assuming that Switch Company uses a perpetual inventory system. Round all calculations to the nearest whole dollar.

Date	Account Title and Explanation	Debit	Credit

AP-15A LO 2 3 8

For each business transaction in the table below, identify which accounts are debited and credited. Do this for both the perpetual and periodic inventory systems.

Transaction	Perpetual Inventory System		Periodic Inventory System	
	DR	CR	DR	CR
1. Purchased inventory on account				
2. Returned a portion of the inventory purchased in transaction 1				
3. Paid for remaining invoice balance after taking advantage of the early payment discount				
4. Sold inventory on account				
5. Customer found that a portion of goods sold in transaction 4 were of lower quality; however, she agreed to keep them at a 10% discount				
6. Customer paid the remaining invoice balance after taking advantage of an early payment discount				

AP-16A LO 4

If net sales is $300,000 and cost of goods sold is $180,000, what is the gross profit and gross margin percentage?

_____

_____

_____

_____

_____

_____

_____

_____

_____

AP-17A LO 3

The following transactions took place at Science Supplies during May 2018.

May 14   Sold merchandise on credit to Elements for $10,000, terms 2/10, n/30; cost of goods was $8,500

May 14   Science Supplies paid $50 to ship the goods to Elements (FOB destination)

May 16   Elements returned $500 (sales price) worth of merchandise purchased on May 14, cost of goods was $375; goods were returned to inventory

May 17   Received payment from Elements for the May 14 sale

May 18   Sold merchandise on credit to Litmus for $6,000, terms 2/10, n/30; cost of goods was $3,600

May 26   Litmus kept the merchandise purchased on May 18; however, some of it was defective so Science Supplies agreed to a 50% allowance on the total sale

May 31   Received payment from Litmus for the May 18 sale

Journalize the above transactions assuming that Science Supplies uses a perpetual inventory system. Round all calculations to the nearest dollar.

Date	Account Title and Explanation	Debit	Credit

AP-18A LO 2

Suppose that on March 15, 2018, both Company A and Company B sold inventory with a cost of $40,000. The updated balance of merchandise inventory as at March 1 for both companies was $90,000. Company A uses the perpetual inventory system. Company B uses the periodic inventory system and performs an inventory count at the end of each month. What is the value of merchandise inventory on record as at March 15 for each of Company A and Company B?

AP-19A LO 8 9 10 11

Crystal Crockery, owned by Crystal Kleer, has provided you with the following information about the transactions occurring in March 2018.

Mar 2   Crystal Crockery received a shipment of gift mugs for resale from Cup Makers. The amount on the invoice is $7,000 and the stated terms are 2/15, n/45.

Mar 2   Crystal Crockery paid $400 cash for shipping charges.

Mar 5   The manager of Crystal Crockery checked the shipped cups and found that goods worth $700 were defective. The defective goods were returned to the supplier.

Mar 13   Crystal Crockery paid the remaining invoice balance and, in doing so, took advantage of the early payment discount.

Mar 20   Crystal Crockery sold the goods costing $6,174 to EatFresh Supermarket for $9,500.

Mar 22   EatFresh Supermarket found 10% worth of items to be defective and returned these to Crystal Crockery. The goods cannot be resold.

Mar 28   The invoice showed terms 2/10, n/60. EatFresh Supermarket paid the remaining invoice balance after taking advantage of the early settlement discount

The opening inventory balance was $500 and the closing inventory balance was $847.

Required

Assume Crystal Crockery uses the periodic inventory system.

a)   Prepare the journal entries to record the purchase and sales transactions.

Date	Account Title and Explanation	Debit	Credit

b) Prepare the journal entries to record the closing entries for the month using the income summary method. Assume that the accounting period for Crystal Crockery is one month.

Date	Account Title and Explanation	Debit	Credit

c) Prepare the cost of goods sold section of the income statement.

d) Prepare the net purchases section of the income statement.

AP-20A  LO 6

The following is Glueman Industries' adjusted trial balance **in account order** for the year ended September 30, 2018.

Glueman Industries Adjusted Trial Balance September 30, 2018		
Account Title	**DR**	**CR**
Cash	$3,800	
Accounts Receivable	2,800	
Prepaid Insurance	4,500	
Prepaid Rent	8,100	
Equipment	43,800	
Accumulated Depreciation—Equipment		$1,000
Accounts Payable		2,330
Unearned Revenue		2,000
Wages Payable		2,820
Kiefer, Capital		48,800
Sales Revenue		79,000
Sales Discounts	1,750	
Sales Returns & Allowances	430	
Cost of Goods Sold	36,780	
Rent Expense	9,300	
Utilities Expense	8,240	
Wages Expense	15,800	
Depreciation Expense	650	
Total	**$135,950**	**$135,950**

Required

a) Prepare the journal entries to close the appropriate accounts using the income summary.

Date	Account Title and Explanation	Debit	Credit

b) Prepare journal entries to close appropriate accounts directly to the capital account.

Date	Account Title and Explanation	Debit	Credit

AP-21A LO 5

Glent Company prepared the following trial balance at its year end of September 30, 2018. The company is owned by Wayne Glent.

Glent Company		
Trial Balance		
September 30, 2018		
Account Title	DR	CR
Cash	$14,600	
Accounts Receivable	6,000	
Merchandise Inventory	6,600	
Prepaid Expenses	2,000	
Store Equipment	40,000	
Accumulated Depreciation—Store Equipment		$2,500
Accounts Payable		8,000
Unearned Revenue		6,000
Notes Payable		9,000
Glent, Capital		38,750
Glent, Withdrawals	1,000	
Sales Revenue		61,750
Gain on Sale of Equipment		4,000
Cost of Goods Sold	30,000	
Depreciation Expense—Store Equipment	500	
Interest Expense	600	
Advertising Expense	1,200	
Rent Expense—Retail Space	10,000	
Rent Expense—Office Space	5,000	
Sales Salaries Expense	8,000	
Office Salaries Expense	4,500	
Total	$130,000	$130,000

Notes:
1. Assume the balance of owner's equity is the opening balance.
2. The note payable is payable over the next nine years in equal annual installments.

Required

a) Prepare a multiple-step income statement using the trial balances.

b) Prepare a statement of owner's equity using the trial balances.

c) Prepare a classified balance sheet using the trial balances.

AP-22A LO 5

A Bit of Fit operates several retail stores that specialize in products for a healthy lifestyle. Some of its financial information is shown below for its fiscal year ended December 31, 2018.

Cost of Goods Sold	$60,000
Depreciation Expense—Store Equipment	10,000
Gain on Sale of Equipment	3,000
Interest Expense	500
Insurance Expense	7,000
Office Salaries Expense	10,000
Sales Discounts	2,500
Sales Returns & Allowances	6,500
Sales Revenue	154,000
Sales Salaries Expense	40,000
Office Supplies Expense	2,000
Utilities Expense—Retail Space	6,750
Utilities Expense—Office Space	2,250

Required

a) Create a single-step income statement for A Bit of Fit.

b) Create a multiple-step income statement for A Bit of Fit.

Analysis

Give a reason why income and expenses are categorized into "operating" and "other" on the multiple-step income statement.

_____

_____

_____

_____

_____

_____

AP-23A LO 9 11

The following information was taken from the financial records of Redmond Distribution, owned by Marcus Redmond, at its year end of December 31, 2018. The company uses the periodic inventory system.

Freight-In	$1,400
Interest Expense	3,200
Merchandise Inventory, January 1, 2018	150,000
Merchandise Inventory, December 31, 2018	120,000
Purchase Returns & Allowances	13,800
Purchases	100,000
Rent Expense	30,000
Salaries Expense	44,000
Sales Discounts	9,200
Sales Revenue	250,000

Required

a) Calculate the cost of goods sold for Redmond Distribution for 2018.

b) Prepare the closing entries for Redmond Distribution for 2018 using the income summary method.

Date	Account Title and Explanation	Debit	Credit

AP-24A LO 3

Shirley's Wraps operates as a sandwich and wrap shop. Its customers can pay by cash, debit or credit card. For each debit transaction, Shirley pays $0.20. For credit cards, she pays 2% of the total of credit card transactions. On May 13, 2018, Shirley compiled the following summary for the work day.

Transaction Type	Total	Number of Transactions
Cash	$425	52
Debit Card	327	43
Credit Card	0	0

Required

a) Calculate the total debit/credit card expense for May 13.

b) Record the journal entry for the day's sales. (Ignore COGS.)

Date	Account Title and Explanation	Debit	Credit

AP-25A LO 3

Tom's Bistro operates as a restaurant. Its customers can pay by cash, debit or credit card. For each debit transaction, Tom pays $0.15. For credit cards, he pays 3% of the total of credit card transactions. On March 22, 2018, Tom compiled the following summary for the work day.

Transaction Type	Total	Number of Transactions
Cash	$2,203	49
Debit Card	0	0
Credit Card	3,731	83

Required

a) Calculate the total debit/credit card expense for March 22.

b) Record the journal entry for the day's sales. (Ignore COGS.)

Date	Account Title and Explanation	Debit	Credit

AP-26A LO 3

Leslie and Ben run a dry cleaners together, called Pawny Cleaners. Their customers can pay by cash, debit or credit card. For each debit transaction, they pay $0.35. For credit cards, they pay 1.5% of the total of credit card transactions. On August 20, 2018, Ben compiled the following summary for the work day.

Transaction Type	Total	Number of Transactions
Cash	$741	35
Debit Card	4,376	120
Credit Card	2,883	68

Required

a) Calculate the total debit/credit card expense for August 20.

_____

_____

_____

b) Record the journal entry for the day's sales. (Ignore COGS.)

Date	Account Title and Explanation	Debit	Credit

Application Questions Group B

AP-1B LO 3

On September 1, 2018, Fruit Wholesalers purchased $3,700 worth of dried fruit inventory and paid $120 for freight charges on account. On September 16, Fruit Wholesalers sold all of the dried fruit inventory to Retail Grocers for $5,920 on account. As the bookkeeper for Fruit Wholesalers, journalize the transactions under the perpetual inventory system.

Date	Account Title and Explanation	Debit	Credit

AP-2B LO 3

JB Supermarkets bought $2,140 worth of groceries on account from a produce supplier on December 8, 2018. On December 9, JB's bookkeeper was informed that 15% of the produce was substandard and returned to the supplier. Prepare the journal entry to record the purchase return using the perpetual inventory system.

Date	Account Title and Explanation	Debit	Credit

AP-3B LO 3

Top Mop Retailers bought $12,900 worth of mops from Super Mop Wholesalers Ltd. on March 15, 2018. Payment is due in April.

Required

a) Prepare the journal entry for Top Mop Retailers using the perpetual inventory system.

Date	Account Title and Explanation	Debit	Credit

b) Prepare the journal entry for Top Mop Retailers for the payment of $12,900 made to Super Mop Wholesalers Ltd. on April 15.

Date	Account Title and Explanation	Debit	Credit

AP-4B LO 3

a) Signs Unlimited received a shipment of plastic sheets on February 15, 2018. The sheets were shipped FOB shipping point. The value of the plastic was $9,000, and the shipping charges totaled $110. Prepare the journal entry to record the receipt of goods by Signs Unlimited, assuming the payments for the inventory and freight will be made in March, using the perpetual inventory system.

Date	Account Title and Explanation	Debit	Credit

b) The plastic sheets delivered to Signs Unlimited were the wrong color. After some negotiation, the manager agreed to keep the products with a 6% allowance on the value of the inventory. Prepare the entry on February 22 to record the purchase allowance. (Assume all items were still in inventory.) Allowances are not granted on freight charges.

Date	Account Title and Explanation	Debit	Credit

c) Journalize the transaction for Signs Unlimited when the payment is made on March 15.

Date	Account Title and Explanation	Debit	Credit

AP-5B LO 3

a) Sandal Retailers purchased $8,100 worth of sandals from Comfy Wear Supplies on April 10, 2018. Comfy Wear's invoice shows terms of 2/15, n/30. What is the latest date Sandal Retailers can pay the bill to take advantage of the discount?

b) As the bookkeeper for Sandal Retailers, prepare the journal entry to record the purchase on April 10, using a perpetual inventory system.

Date	Account Title and Explanation	Debit	Credit

c) Journalize the transaction for payment of the invoice, assuming the payment was made on April 18.

Date	Account Title and Explanation	Debit	Credit

d) Journalize the transaction for payment of the invoice, assuming the payment was made on April 26.

Date	Account Title and Explanation	Debit	Credit

AP-6B LO 8

a) Boards Unlimited received a shipment of skateboards on April 3, 2018. The value of the skateboards was $8,000, and they were shipped FOB shipping point. Freight charges came to $100. Prepare the journal entry to record the receipt of goods by Boards Unlimited, assuming payment will be made in May, using the periodic inventory system.

Date	Account Title and Explanation	Debit	Credit

b) The skateboards delivered to Boards Unlimited were the wrong color. After some negotiation, the manager agreed to keep the products with a 10% discount. Prepare the entry on April 10 to record the purchase allowance. (Assume all skateboards were still in inventory.)

Date	Account Title and Explanation	Debit	Credit

c) Journalize the transaction for Boards Unlimited when the payment is made on May 3.

Date	Account Title and Explanation	Debit	Credit

AP-7B LO 3

Rock Retailers purchased $11,200 worth of shoes from Runner Wear Supplies on April 4, 2018. Runner Wear's invoice shows terms of 2/10, n/30. What is the latest date that Rock Retailers can pay the bill to take advantage of the discount? How much cash is exchanged if the full discount is taken advantage of?

_____

_____

AP-8B LO 4

If a cell phone retail business bought cell phones for $10,800 and sold them for $14,500, how much would the gross profit be on the entire shipment, assuming the business took advantage of the early cash payment terms of 3/10, n/30 from its supplier?

_____

_____

_____

_____

_____

_____

AP-9B LO 8

Footloose Retailers uses the periodic inventory system. It purchased $10,000 worth of shoes from Jogger Wear Supplies on March 1, 2018. Jogger Wear's invoice terms are 2/15, n/30.

Required

a) What is the latest date Footloose Retailers can pay the bill to apply the discount?

_____

_____

b) As Footloose Retailers' bookkeeper, prepare the journal entry to record the March 1 purchase.

Date	Account Title and Explanation	Debit	Credit

c)   Journalize the transaction for payment of the invoice on March 5.

Date	Account Title and Explanation	Debit	Credit

d)   Journalize the transaction for payment of the invoice on April 3.

Date	Account Title and Explanation	Debit	Credit

AP-10B LO 3

On March 20, 2018, Cup-A-Java received a shipment of gift mugs for resale from Cup Makers in the amount of $5,000. The terms stated on the invoice from Cup Makers were 3/15, n/60. Under a perpetual inventory system, journalize the following scenarios for Cup-A-Java.

Required

a)   As the bookkeeper for Cup-A-Java, record the purchase of inventory.

Date	Account Title and Explanation	Debit	Credit

b)   If Cup-A-Java decides to take advantage of the early payment cash discount, by when should the payment be made to qualify for the discount?

_____

_____

c)   The payment by Cup-A-Java to Cup Makers was made on March 31. Prepare the journal entry for the payment of goods.

Date	Account Title and Explanation	Debit	Credit

d) Journalize the entry if payment had instead been made on May 20.

Date	Account Title and Explanation	Debit	Credit

e) On March 25, 20% of the shipment was returned because the mugs were the wrong size. The invoice has not yet been paid. Prepare the journal entry for this transaction.

Date	Account Title and Explanation	Debit	Credit

f) Continue from e). Journalize the entry if Cup-A-Java took advantage of the early payment cash discount when paying for the balance of the mugs on March 31.

Date	Account Title and Explanation	Debit	Credit

AP-11B LO 3

Macks makes garments that are sold to retailers. On June 1, 2018, Cory's Retailers sent back a shipment of goods. The goods sold on account for $6,000 and cost Macks $4,000 to make. Macks put the returned goods back into inventory for resale. Macks uses a perpetual inventory system.

Required

a) As Macks' bookkeeper, prepare the journal entries to reflect the return.

Date	Account Title and Explanation	Debit	Credit

b) Journalize the entry if Cory's only returned half of the shipment.

Date	Account Title and Explanation	Debit	Credit

c) What happened to the value of Macks' owner's equity when Cory's returned the merchandise? Did it increase, decrease or stay the same? Explain your answer.

_____

_____

_____

d) Explain the logic behind debiting the sales returns and allowances as a contra account instead of debiting the revenue account directly.

_____

_____

AP-12B LO 3

Pete's Wholesalers imports and distributes towels. It sells its products to various retailers throughout the country and offers payment terms of 2/10, n/30. On October 1, 2018, Pete's made a large sale to Ernie's Bathroom Retailers in the amount of $15,000, which cost Pete's $9,000. Pete's uses a perpetual inventory system. Complete the following.

Required

a) Journalize the sale that was made on account for Pete's Wholesalers.

Date	Account Title and Explanation	Debit	Credit

b) By what date must Ernie's pay the invoice to qualify for the early cash payment discount?

_____

_____

299

c)   Assume Ernie's paid the bill on October 5. Record the journal entry for Pete's Wholesalers.

Date	Account Title and Explanation	Debit	Credit

d)   If Ernie's had returned half the shipment and paid for the balance owing on October 5, how would the transactions be journalized by Pete's Wholesaler's? Assume the inventory was restocked by Pete's Wholesalers.

Date	Account Title and Explanation	Debit	Credit

e)   Suppose instead that Ernie's found the goods unsatisfactory and agreed to keep the goods with a 10% allowance. Prepare the journal entries for Pete's Wholesalers to record the sales allowance and Ernie's payment on October 20.

Date	Account Title and Explanation	Debit	Credit

AP-13B LO 3 4

Wilde Wilderness Supplies had the following transactions during January 2018.

Jan 1   Sold merchandise on credit to Merril for $15,000, terms 2/10, n/30; cost of goods was $8,500

Jan 1   Wilde paid $50 to ship the goods to Merril

Jan 5   Purchased inventory for $12,000 on credit from Outdoor Experts, terms 1/10, n/30

Jan 5   Wilde paid $25 to have the merchandise from Outdoor Experts delivered

Jan 8   Merril returned $1,200 (sales price) of merchandise purchased on January 1; the cost of goods sold was $800. The inventory will be resold.

Jan 12   Some of the merchandise purchased on January 5 was the wrong size. Wilde decided to keep the merchandise in exchange for a 25% allowance on the purchase. Allowances are not granted on shipping charges.

Jan 15   Received payment from Merril for the January 1 sale

Jan 18   Sold merchandise on credit to Forest Outfitters for $5,000, terms 2/15, n/30; cost of goods was $2,600

Jan 23   Paid for merchandise purchased from Outdoor Experts on January 5

Jan 26   Wilde granted Forest Outfitters a 20% allowance on the January 18 sale due to defective products

Jan 31   Received payment from Forest Outfitters for the January 18 sale

Journalize the above transactions assuming that Wilde Wilderness Supplies uses a perpetual inventory system. Round all calculations to the nearest whole dollar.

Date	Account Title and Explanation	Debit	Credit

Date	Account Title and Explanation	Debit	Credit

Analysis

Calculate Wilde Wilderness Supplies' gross profit margin for the month.

_____

_____

_____

_____

_____

_____

_____

_____

_____

_____

_____

_____

AP-14B LO 3 6

AB Retailers had the following business transactions during the month of April 2018.

Apr 10	AB Retailers bought $3,500 worth of T-shirts from Unique Designers. The invoice showed payment terms of 2/10, n/30.
Apr 10	Soon after AB Retailers received the products, it was discovered that $500 worth of T-shirts did not meet quality standards. These goods were returned to the supplier.
Apr 20	AB Retailers paid the remaining invoice balance.
Apr 22	AB Retailers sold *all* the goods for $4,500 to SK Stores on terms 3/10, n/45.
Apr 28	SK Stores paid for the goods purchased.

Required

a) Prepare the journal entries to record the above transactions. Assume AB Retailers uses the perpetual inventory system.

Date	Account Title and Explanation	Debit	Credit

b) Calculate April's ending inventory based on the above transactions. Assume that merchandise inventory at the beginning of April amounted to $1,500.

_____

_____

_____

c) At the end of April, an inventory count was performed. The balance of inventory according to the count was $1,300. Management deemed that the difference between the ledger account and physical inventory account is due to theft (shrinkage). Prepare the journal entry to adjust the merchandise inventory balance on April 30.

Date	Account Title and Explanation	Debit	Credit

AP-15B LO 2 3 8

On January 1, 2018, a company purchases 1,000 units of inventory at $12 per unit on account. On January 5, the company sells 25 units for $50 per unit on account.

Required

a) Write the journal entries to record the transactions under the perpetual inventory system.

Date	Account Title and Explanation	Debit	Credit

b) Write the journal entries to record the transactions under the periodic inventory system.

Date	Account Title and Explanation	Debit	Credit

AP-16B LO 4

If sales are $290,000 and cost of goods sold is $130,000, what is the gross profit and gross margin percentage?

AP-17B LO 5

Let's Talk Shop is a store that sells cell phone accessories. The following information is available for the year ending June 30, 2018.

Cost of Goods Sold	$11,200
Interest Expense	1,000
Advertising Expense	800
Office Salaries Expense	12,000
Sales Revenue	49,000
Sales Salaries Expense	26,000
Rent Expense—Retail Space	2,000
Rent Expense—Office Space	1,000

Prepare the multiple-step income statement for June 2018.

Analysis

Let's Talk Shop sold 3,500 phone cases at an average price of $14 each during the year. The company buys phone case inventory at an average price of $3.20 each. If Let's Talk Shop had sold 4,000 phone cases instead, would it have a positive net income? Assume operating expenses would remain the same. Show your work.

AP-18B LO 1 3

Suppose that SCOOP Pet Supplies' gross profit margin is 40% and that all sales are cash sales. Prepare any journal entries required to record sales for the year ended December 31, 2018, assuming that the company had $846,500 in sales revenue for the year and uses a perpetual inventory system.

Date	Account Title and Explanation	Debit	Credit

AP-19B LO 6

The following are the T-accounts for Direct Sales for the year ended September 30, 2018.

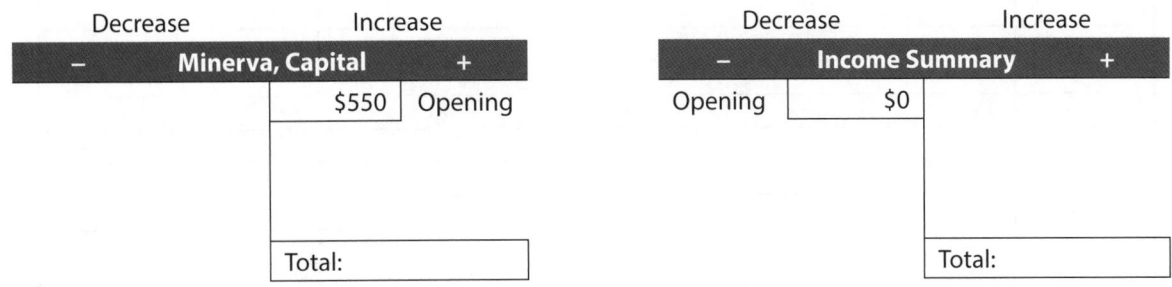

BALANCE SHEET

Decrease		Increase
−	Minerva, Capital	+
	$550	Opening
	Total:	

Decrease		Increase
−	Income Summary	+
Opening	$0	
	Total:	

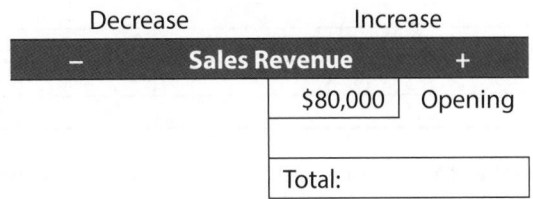

INCOME STATEMENT

Decrease		Increase
−	Sales Revenue	+
	$80,000	Opening
	Total:	

MINUS
EXPENSES

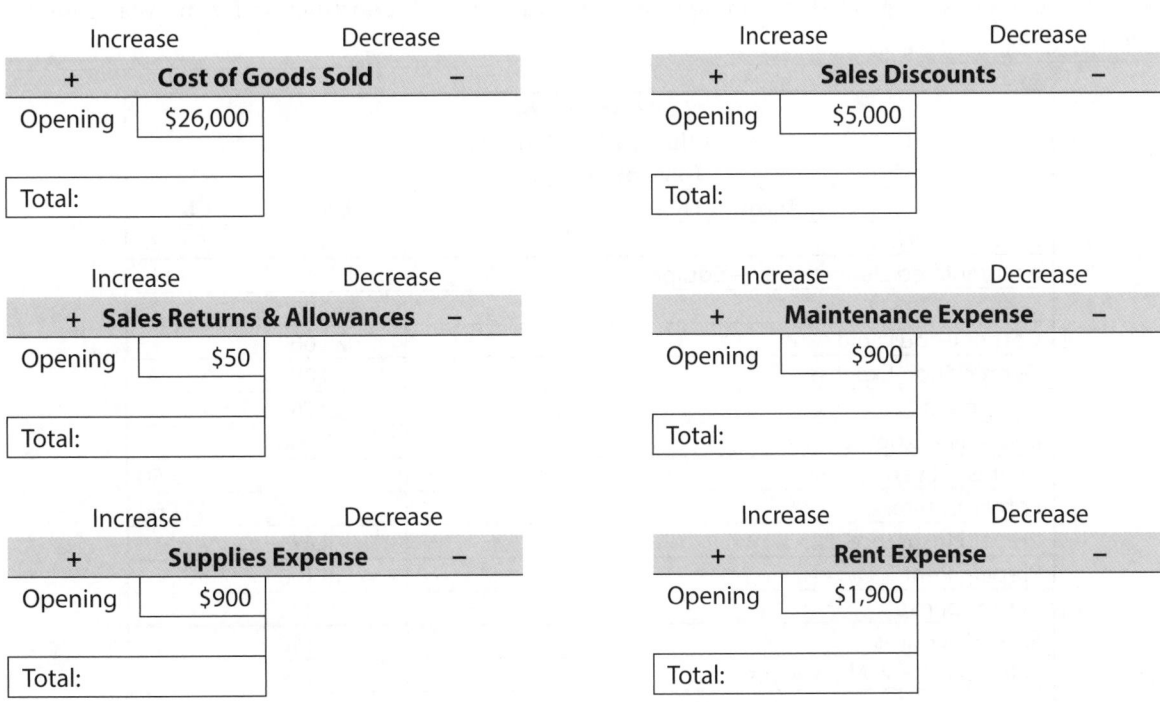

Increase		Decrease
+	Cost of Goods Sold	−
Opening	$26,000	
Total:		

Increase		Decrease
+	Sales Discounts	−
Opening	$5,000	
Total:		

Increase		Decrease
+ Sales Returns & Allowances		−
Opening	$50	
Total:		

Increase		Decrease
+	Maintenance Expense	−
Opening	$900	
Total:		

Increase		Decrease
+	Supplies Expense	−
Opening	$900	
Total:		

Increase		Decrease
+	Rent Expense	−
Opening	$1,900	
Total:		

Required

a) Prepare the journal entries to close the appropriate accounts using the income summary.

Date	Account Title and Explanation	Debit	Credit

b) Post the journal entries from part a) to the appropriate T-accounts on the previous page, and calculate the totals.

AP-20B LO 6

The following is the adjusted trial balance **in alphabetical order** for LCP Construction for the year ended December 31, 2018.

LCP Construction Adjusted Trial Balance December 31, 2018		
Account Title	**DR**	**CR**
Accounts Payable		$2,330
Accumulated Depreciation—Equipment		1,140
Cash	$10,800	
Cost of Goods Sold	28,660	
Depreciation Expense	9,080	
Equipment	27,766	
Insurance Expense	5,260	
Interest Revenue		7,650
Pohler, Capital		48,060
Prepaid Insurance	4,675	
Prepaid Rent	18,100	
Rent Expense	9,300	
Sales Discounts	440	
Sales Returns & Allowances	1,749	
Sales Revenue		60,945
Unearned Revenue		1,000
Utilities Expense	2,240	
Wages Expense	5,800	
Wages Payable		2,745
Total	**$123,870**	**$123,870**

Prepare the journal entries to close the appropriate accounts using the income summary.

Date	Account Title and Explanation	Debit	Credit

AP-21B LO 5

Bugle News operates by selling newspaper and magazines to consumers. Peter has prepared the income statement and balance sheet for Bugle News as shown below.

The note payable is due in annual payments of $50,000.

Bugle News Income Statement For the Year Ended December 31, 2018		
Revenues		
Sales Revenue	$975,000	
Interest Revenue	25,000	
Total Revenues		$1,000,000
Expenses		
Cost of Goods Sold	150,000	
Advertising Expense	50,200	
Rent Expense—Newsstand	50,000	
Rent Expense—Office Space	5,800	
Office Salaries Expense	125,000	
Sales Salaries Expense	160,000	
Loss on Property Damage	59,000	
Total Expenses		600,000
Net Income		$400,000

Bugle News Balance Sheet As at December 31, 2018		
Assets		
Cash	$121,000	
Accounts Receivable	5,000	
Prepaid Insurance	514,000	
Merchandise Inventory	310,000	
Equipment	800,000	
Accumulated Depreciation	(250,000)	
Total Assets		$1,500,000
Liabilities		
Accounts Payable	$15,000	
Unearned Revenue	530,000	
Notes Payable	300,000	
Total Liabilities		$845,000
Owner's Equity		
Parker, Capital		655,000
Total Owner's Equity		655,000
Total Liabilities and Owner's Equity		$1,500,000

Required

a) Prepare the multiple-step income statement for Bugle News.

b)   Prepare the classified balance sheet for Bugle News.

Analysis

Calculate and interpret the current ratio for Bugle News.

AP-22B [LO 5]

Rita Retail is a merchandising business. The store's building contains a large selling area with merchandise displays and shelves, and a smaller back office area where administrative tasks are performed, such as payroll, marketing and HR. The following information is available.

- Salaries are for the salespeople, as well as the office staff. Office staff salaries totaled $80,000 for the year.
- The office area is allocated 20% of the utility costs.
- Depreciation is charged on the merchandise displays only.

Rita Retail		
Income Statement		
For the Year Ended December 31, 2018		
Sales Revenue		$1,400,000
Expenses		
Cost of Goods Sold	$890,000	
Salaries Expense	210,000	
Office Supplies Expense	12,000	
Insurance Expense	42,000	
Utilities Expense	7,000	
Depreciation Expense	5,000	
Total Expenses		1,166,000
Net Income		$234,000

Prepare a multiple-step income statement for Rita Retail.

Analysis

Give a reason why it is useful to separate expenses into selling and administrative categories on the income statement.

_____

_____

_____

AP-23B LO 10 11

Tommy Greggson, owner of Greggson Retail, prepared the following adjusted trial balance at its year end of October 31, 2018.

Greggson Retail		
Trial Balance		
October 31, 2018		
Account Title	**DR**	**CR**
Cash	$78,000	
Accounts Receivable	30,000	
Merchandise Inventory	165,000	
Prepaid Expenses	6,000	
Store Equipment	250,000	
Accumulated Depreciation—Store Equipment		$80,000
Accounts Payable		126,000
Unearned Revenue		8,000
Notes Payable		50,000
Greggson, Capital		300,000
Greggson, Withdrawals	20,000	
Sales Revenue		360,000
Purchase Returns & Allowances		12,000
Purchase Discounts		5,000
Sales Returns & Allowances	30,000	
Sales Discounts	3,000	
Purchases	235,000	
Freight-In	7,000	
Depreciation Expense—Store Equipment	4,000	
Interest Expense	1,000	
Sales Salaries Expense	62,000	
Office Salaries Expense	50,000	
Total	**$941,000**	**$941,000**

A year-end inventory count revealed that $210,000 of inventory is on hand.

Required

a) Prepare a multiple-step income statement for Greggson Retail.

b) Prepare the closing entries for Greggson Retail using the income summary method.

Date	Account Title and Explanation	Debit	Credit

AP-24B LO 3

Brad Chang runs his own restaurant. Customers can pay by cash, debit or credit card. For each debit transaction, Brad pays $0.25. For credit cards, he pays 2% of the total of credit card transactions. On May 9, 2018, Brad compiled the following summary for the work day.

Transaction Type	Total	Number of Transactions
Cash	$1,459	23
Debit Card	4,632	72
Credit Card	0	0

Required

a) Calculate the total debit/credit card expense for May 9.

_____

_____

b) Record the journal entry for the day's sales. (Ignore COGS.)

Date	Account Title and Explanation	Debit	Credit

AP-25B LO 3

Burt Mecklin operates a large pet store. Customers can pay by cash, debit or credit card. For each debit transaction, Burt pays $0.15. For credit cards, he pays 2% of the total of credit card transactions. On November 15, 2018, Burt compiled the following summary for the work day.

Transaction Type	Total	Number of Transactions
Cash	$2,640	33
Debit Card	0	0
Credit Card	5,440	68

Required

a) Calculate the total debit/credit card expense for November 15.

b) Record the journal entry for the day's sales. (Ignore COGS.)

Date	Account Title and Explanation	Debit	Credit

AP-26B LO 3

Ron runs his own butcher shop. His customers can pay by cash, debit or credit card. For each debit transaction, Ron pays $0.25. For credit cards, Ron pays 3% of the total of credit card transactions. On April 3, 2018, Ron compiled the following summary for the work day.

Transaction Type	Total	Number of Transactions
Cash	$836	27
Debit Card	1,298	40
Credit Card	1,366	32

Required

a) Calculate the total debit/credit card expense for April 3.

b) Record the journal entry for the day's sales. (Ignore COGS.)

Date	Account Title and Explanation	Debit	Credit

Case Study

CS-1 LO 3 4 5

George K. Connor is a company that sells goods using a perpetual inventory system. During its first month of operations, February 2018, the following transactions occurred.

Feb 1   Purchased inventory on account for $20,000, terms of 2/10, n/30

Feb 1   Received a deposit of $10,000 from a customer for products to be delivered later

Feb 1   Returned damaged inventory from the February 1 purchase worth $3,500

Feb 5   Sold products for cash of $13,000, the cost of goods was $6,000

Feb 10   Paid the balance owing to the supplier of inventory from Febuary 1

Feb 16   Received an advertising bill for $3,000, which will be paid next month

Feb 21   Sold products on account for $31,000, the cost of goods was $10,000

Feb 22   Paid wages and benefits with $6,000 cash; this amount includes sales salaries of $4,000 and office salaries of $2,000

Feb 25   Purchased new computers on account for $4,000

Feb 26   A customer agreed to keep a defective product for a 30% allowance, the customer originally paid $1,000 on account for the product

Feb 27   A customer returned an incorrect product for cash; this product had a sales price of $500 and a cost of $300; the item was returned to the sales floor for resale

Feb 28   Incurred maintenance expense at the head office of $2,000 on account

The company uses the following chart of accounts to implement its accounting system.

Account Description	Account #
ASSETS	
Cash	101
Accounts Receivable	105
Merchandise Inventory	115
Computers	120
LIABILITIES	
Accounts Payable	200
Unearned Revenue	215
OWNER'S EQUITY	
Connor, Capital	300
Connor, Withdrawals	310

Account Description	Account #
REVENUE	
Sales Revenue	400
Sales Returns & Allowances	455
EXPENSES	
Cost of Goods Sold	500
Advertising Expense	505
Maintenance Expense	520
Salaries Expense	545

Required

a) Prepare the journal entries for the period.

Date	Account Title and Explanation	PR	Debit	Credit

Date	Account Title and Explanation	PR	Debit	Credit

b) Post the entries to the general ledger.

Account: | | | | | | **GL No:**
Date	Description	PR	DR	CR	Balance	

Account: | | | | | | **GL No:**
Date	Description	PR	DR	CR	Balance	

Account: | | | | | | **GL No:**
Date	Description	PR	DR	CR	Balance	

Account:			GL No:			
Date	Description	PR	DR	CR	Balance	

Account:			GL No:			
Date	Description	PR	DR	CR	Balance	

Account:			GL No:			
Date	Description	PR	DR	CR	Balance	

Account:			GL No:			
Date	Description	PR	DR	CR	Balance	

Account:			GL No:			
Date	Description	PR	DR	CR	Balance	

Account:			GL No:			
Date	Description	PR	DR	CR	Balance	

Account:			GL No:			
Date	Description	PR	DR	CR	Balance	

Account:					GL No:	
Date	**Description**	**PR**	**DR**	**CR**	**Balance**	

Account:					GL No:	
Date	**Description**	**PR**	**DR**	**CR**	**Balance**	

Account:					GL No:	
Date	**Description**	**PR**	**DR**	**CR**	**Balance**	

Account:					GL No:	
Date	**Description**	**PR**	**DR**	**CR**	**Balance**	

c) Prepare a trial balance.

d) Prepare a multiple-step income statement for the period.

e) Prepare a statement of owner's equity for the period.

f) Prepare a classified balance sheet for the period.

g) Calculate the gross profit margin on product sales.

h) Calculate the current ratio at the end of the period.

CS-2 LO 3 4 5 6

Freestyle Fashion is an urban clothing retailer using the perpetual inventory system. Its balance sheet as at January 1, 2018 is presented below.

Freestyle Fashion Balance Sheet As at January 1, 2018		
Current Assets		
Cash	$28,400	
Merchandise Inventory	50,000	
Prepaid Rent	12,000	
Total Current Assets		$90,400
Property, Plant & Equipment		
Equipment	32,000	
Total Property, Plant & Equipment		32,000
Total Assets		$122,400
Current Liabilities		
Accounts Payable	$20,500	
Unearned Revenue	12,000	
Total Current Liabilities		$32,500
Long-Term Liabilities		
Notes Payable	60,000	
Total Long-Term Liabilities		60,000
Total Liabilities		92,500
Owner's Equity		
Styles, Capital		29,900
Total Liabilities and Owner's Equity		$122,400

During January 2018, Freestyle Fashion had the following transactions.

Jan 2 Purchased 490 jackets at $50 each on account (with terms 2/10, n/30)

Jan 5 Sold $50,000 worth of inventory on account; this inventory cost $39,000

Jan 9 Purchased 100 pairs of jeans at $20 each on account (with terms 4/15, n/30)

Jan 11 Paid the balance owed to the supplier for all the jackets purchased on January 2

Jan 16 Paid wages of $2,000

Jan 18 A customer returned products for cash to the store due to a defect; these products were originally sold for $200 and cost $75

Jan 21 Paid the balance owed to the supplier for jeans purchased on January 9

Jan 24 Received $25,000 cash from sales previously made on account

Jan 26 Incurred $2,500 in utilities expenses, to be paid next month

Jan 30 Sold $20,000 worth of inventory for cash; this inventory cost $15,000

The company uses the following chart of accounts to implement its accounting system.

Account Description	Account #		Account Description	Account #
ASSETS			**REVENUE**	
Cash	101		Sales Revenue	400
Accounts Receivable	105		Sales Returns & Allowances	405
Prepaid Rent	110		Sales Discounts	410
Merchandise Inventory	115			
Equipment	120		**EXPENSES**	
Accumulated Depreciation—Equipment	125		Cost of Goods Sold	500
			Advertising Expense	505
LIABILITIES			Depreciation Expense	510
Accounts Payable	200		Insurance Expense	515
Interest Payable	205		Interest Expense	520
Salary Payable	210		Maintenance Expense	525
Unearned Revenue	215		Office Supplies Expense	530
Notes Payable	220		Professional Fees Expense	535
			Rent Expense	540
OWNER'S EQUITY			Salaries Expense	545
Styles, Capital	300		Utilities Expense	550
Styles, Withdrawals	310		Travel Expense	555
Income Summary	315			

Required

a) Journalize the transactions for January 2018.

Date	Account Title and Explanation	PR	Debit	Credit

Date	Account Title and Explanation	PR	Debit	Credit

b) Journalize the following adjustments (to be recorded on January 31, 2018).

Jan 31   Prepaid rent represents one year of retail space rent; one month of prepaid rent has been used

Jan 31   Depreciation of store equipment for the month is $2,000

Jan 31 $1,000 of unearned revenue has now been earned

Jan 31 $100 of interest is accrued and owed on the notes payable

Date	Account Title and Explanation	PR	Debit	Credit

c) Prepare the month-end closing journal entries. Use the income summary account.

Date	Account Title and Explanation	PR	Debit	Credit

d) Post the transactions to the general ledger.

General Ledger

Account:					GL No:	
Date	Description	PR	DR	CR	Balance	

Account:					GL No:	
Date	Description	PR	DR	CR	Balance	

Account:					GL No:	
Date	Description	PR	DR	CR	Balance	

Account:					GL No:	
Date	Description	PR	DR	CR	Balance	

Account:					GL No:	
Date	Description	PR	DR	CR	Balance	

Account:					GL No:	
Date	Description	PR	DR	CR	Balance	

Account:					GL No:	
Date	Description	PR	DR	CR	Balance	

Account:					GL No:	
Date	Description	PR	DR	CR	Balance	

Account:					GL No:	
Date	Description	PR	DR	CR	Balance	

Account:					GL No:	
Date	Description	PR	DR	CR	Balance	

Account:					GL No:	
Date	Description	PR	DR	CR	Balance	

Account:					GL No:	
Date	Description	PR	DR	CR	Balance	

Account:					GL No:	
Date	Description	PR	DR	CR	Balance	

Account: GL No:

Date	Description	PR	DR	CR	Balance	

Account: GL No:

Date	Description	PR	DR	CR	Balance	

Account: GL No:

Date	Description	PR	DR	CR	Balance	

Account: GL No:

Date	Description	PR	DR	CR	Balance	

Account: GL No:

Date	Description	PR	DR	CR	Balance	

Account:						GL No:	
Date	**Description**	**PR**	**DR**	**CR**	**Balance**	

Account:						GL No:	
Date	**Description**	**PR**	**DR**	**CR**	**Balance**	

e) Prepare a multiple-step income statement for January 2018. Assume that $2,000 of the utilities expense is for retail space and $500 is for head office. Assume that $1,200 of the salaries expense is for sales and $800 is for office staff.

f)   Prepare a statement of owner's equity for January 2018.

g)   Prepare a balance sheet for January 2018.

Chapter 8

INVENTORY VALUATION

LEARNING OBJECTIVES

LO 1   Determine the value of merchandise inventory under the perpetual inventory system

LO 2   Explain the impact of inventory errors

LO 3   Apply the lower of cost and net realizable value (LCNRV) rule to value merchandise inventory

LO 4   Measure a company's management of inventory using inventory ratios

LO 5   Describe ethics relating to inventory

Appendix

LO 6   Determine the value of merchandise inventory under the periodic inventory system

LO 7   Estimate the value of merchandise inventory under the periodic inventory system

AMEENGAGE   *Access **ameengage.com** for integrated resources including tutorials, practice exercises, the digital textbook and more.*

——— Assessment Questions ———

AS-1   LO 1

List the four different inventory valuation methods allowed under GAAP.

_____

_____

AS-2   LO 1

In times of rising prices, which inventory valuation method results in the lowest closing inventory? Explain your answer.

_____

_____

AS-3   LO 1

Different inventory valuation methods result in different inventory values. What factors may cause a company to select FIFO, LIFO, weighted-average cost or specific identification?

_____

_____

_____

_____

_____

_____

_____

_____

AS-4 `LO 1`

Is a physical inventory count necessary for a company that uses the periodic inventory system? Why or why not?

_____

_____

_____

_____

AS-5 `LO 1`

Is a physical inventory count necessary for a company that uses the perpetual inventory system? Why or why not?

_____

_____

_____

_____

AS-6 `LO 2`

What is consigned inventory? Should it be recorded on the consignor's or the consignee's books?

_____

_____

_____

_____

_____

AS-7 `LO 3`

What is net realizable value?

_____

_____

_____

AS-8 `LO 3`

Which accounting constraint is the use of lower of cost and net realizable value based on?

_____

_____

_____

AS-9 `LO 7`

Name two methods that can be used to estimate inventory for interim statement purposes under the periodic inventory system.

_____

_____

AS-10 LO 1

How does the actual flow of inventory affect the choice of inventory valuation method? How often can the inventory valuation method be changed?

_____

_____

AS-11 LO 2

What does it mean for inventory errors to be self-correcting?

_____

_____

AS-12 LO 1

Which of the inventory valuation methods show more ending inventory and less COGS in the case of rising prices?

_____

_____

_____

AS-13 LO 2

Describe the impact of inventory errors on financial statement users.

_____

_____

_____

_____

_____

_____

_____

_____

_____

AS-14 LO 5

How can a company monitor and prevent inventory shrinkage?

_____

_____

_____

_____

_____

AS-15 LO 2 5

What is the impact on financial statements of inflating inventory? What is the ethical responsibility of management in this regard?

_____

_____

_____

_____

_____

_____

AS-16 LO 6

Describe the differences between the specific identification method under the perpetual and the periodic inventory systems.

_____

_____

_____

_____

AS-17 LO 4

How do you calculate the inventory turnover ratio and what does it measure?

_____

_____

_____

_____

AS-18 LO 4

How do you calculate days' sales in inventory and what does it measure?

_____

_____

_____

_____

_____

_____

_____

_____

_____

Application Questions Group A

AP-1A LO 1

The following purchases and sales took place at ZZZ Co. during the month of May 2018. The company had no inventory on hand on May 1. ZZZ Co. uses the perpetual inventory system.

May 5 Purchased 200 units from AAA Co. for $10 per unit
May 7 Sold 100 units to SSS Co.
May 13 Sold 50 units to TTT Co.
May 15 Purchased 70 units from BBB Co. for $13 per unit
May 24 Sold 20 units to UUU Co.

Required

a) Fill in the inventory schedule using the weighted-average cost inventory valuation method.

Date	Purchases			Sales			Balance		
	Quantity	Unit Cost	Value	Quantity	Unit Cost	Value	Quantity	Unit Cost	Value
May 1									
May 5									
May 7									
May 13									
May 15									
May 24									
Ending Inventory									

b) Fill in the inventory schedule using the LIFO method.

Date	Purchases			Sales			Balance		
	Quantity	Unit Cost	Value	Quantity	Unit Cost	Value	Quantity	Unit Cost	Value
May 1							0	$0	$0
May 5									
May 7									
May 13									
May 15									
May 24									
Ending Inventory									

c) If the FIFO method had instead been used, what would the value of COGS have been for the sale to UUU Co.? Explain.

_____

_____

d) If the specific identification method had been used, what would the value of COGS have been for the sale to UUU Co.? Assume that 10 of the units sold to UUU Co. were purchased from AAA Co. and the other 10 units were purchased from BBB Co.

_____

_____

e) Complete the following table to compare the COGS figures for the different inventory valuation methods on the sale to UUU Co.

	Specific Identification	Weighted-Average Cost	FIFO	LIFO
COGS on sale to UUU				

AP-2A LO 1

Simplex Company has a fiscal year end on December 31. The company has only one product in inventory, and all units of that product are identical (homogenous). Complete the following schedule to calculate the value of ending inventory using the weighted-average cost method under the perpetual inventory system. Then calculate the cost of goods sold for the year 2018. Calculate unit cost to two decimal places. Round all value amounts to the nearest dollar.

Date	Purchases Quantity	Purchases Unit Cost	Purchases Value	Sales Quantity	Sales Unit Cost	Sales Value	Balance Quantity	Balance Unit Cost	Balance Value
Jan 1							15	$10.00	$150
Feb 13	25	$12							
Mar 26	16	$13							
Apr 17				40					
Jul 25	34	$14							
Sep 28				14					
Nov 3				11					
Ending Inventory									

Cost of goods sold:

AP-3A LO 1

An inventory record card for item A–903 shows the following details in 2018.

Mar 1   60 units in opening inventory at a cost of $70 per unit
Mar 9   120 units purchased at a cost of $64 per unit
Mar 18   70 units sold
Mar 24   44 units purchased at a cost of $80 per unit
Mar 29   100 units sold

Required

The company uses the perpetual inventory method. Calculate the value of inventory at each of the above dates and determine the ending inventory at the end of March using the following methods.

a) FIFO

Date	Purchases Quantity	Purchases Unit Cost	Purchases Value	Sales Quantity	Sales Unit Cost	Sales Value	Balance Quantity	Balance Unit Cost	Balance Value
Mar 1									
Mar 9									
Mar 18									
Mar 24									
Mar 29									
Ending Inventory									

b)   LIFO

Date	Purchases			Sales			Balance		
	Quantity	Unit Cost	Value	Quantity	Unit Cost	Value	Quantity	Unit Cost	Value
Mar 1									
Mar 9									
Mar 18									
Mar 24									
Mar 29									
Ending Inventory									

c)   Weighted-average cost

Date	Purchases			Sales			Balance		
	Quantity	Unit Cost	Value	Quantity	Unit Cost	Value	Quantity	Unit Cost	Value
Mar 1									
Mar 9									
Mar 18									
Mar 24									
Mar 29									
Ending Inventory									

AP-4A LO 1

GB, a bookseller, had the following transactions during the month of August 2018 and uses the perpetual inventory system.

Aug 1	Bought 10 novels at $30 each
Aug 2	Bought 10 bags at $45 each
Aug 5	Sold 5 novels
Aug 10	Bought 15 pencil cases at $5 each
Aug 21	Sold 3 bags

Required

a)   Calculate the value of inventory at each date using the specific identification method. Show the ending inventory for August 2018.

Date	Purchases			Sales			Balance		
	Quantity	Unit Cost	Value	Quantity	Unit Cost	Value	Quantity	Unit Cost	Value
Aug 1							0	$0	$0
Aug 1									
Aug 2									
Aug 5									
Aug 10									
Aug 21									
Ending Inventory									

b)   Calculate the COGS for August.

AP-5A LO 1

Poppy Company uses a perpetual inventory system. It reported the following data related to beginning inventory and inventory purchases and sales for the month of July 2018.

Jul 1   Beginning inventory consisted of 300 units at $13 per unit
Jul 9   Sold 200 units at $20 per unit
Jul 16   Purchased 120 units at $12 per unit
Jul18   Purchased 300 units at $10 per unit
Jul 30   Sold 150 units at $20 per unit

Required

a)   Fill in the inventory schedule and calculate the values of ending inventory, COGS and gross profit using the specific identification method. Assume that the 150 units sold on July 30 consist of 15 units from the beginning inventory, 35 units from the July 16 purchase and 100 units from the July 18 purchase.

Date	Purchases			Sales			Balance		
	Quantity	Unit Cost	Value	Quantity	Unit Cost	Value	Quantity	Unit Cost	Value
Jul 1									
Jul 9									
Jul 16									
Jul 18									
Jul 30									
Ending Inventory									

Cost of Goods Sold:

Gross Profit:

b)   Fill in the inventory schedule and calculate the values of ending inventory, COGS and gross profit using the FIFO method.

Date	Purchases			Sales			Balance		
	Quantity	Unit Cost	Value	Quantity	Unit Cost	Value	Quantity	Unit Cost	Value
Jul 1									
Jul 9									
Jul 16									
Jul 18									
Jul 30									
Ending Inventory									

Cost of Goods Sold:

c) Fill in the inventory schedule and calculate the values of ending inventory, COGS and gross profit using the LIFO method.

Date	Purchases			Sales			Balance		
	Quantity	Unit Cost	Value	Quantity	Unit Cost	Value	Quantity	Unit Cost	Value
Jul 1									
Jul 9									
Jul 16									
Jul 18									
Jul 30									
Ending Inventory									

Cost of Goods Sold:

Gross Profit:

d) Fill in the inventory schedule and calculate the values of ending inventory, COGS and gross profit using the weighted-average cost method.

Date	Purchases			Sales			Balance		
	Quantity	Unit Cost	Value	Quantity	Unit Cost	Value	Quantity	Unit Cost	Value
Jul 1									
Jul 9									
Jul 16									
Jul 18									
Jul 30									
Ending Inventory									

Cost of Goods Sold:

Gross Profit:

AP-6A LO 3

A company has three types of products: gadgets, widgets and gizmos. The cost and market price of each type is listed below. Complete the table by applying the lower of cost and net realizable value. The shaded areas do not require any entries.

Description	Category	Cost	NRV	LCNRV Applied to		
				Individual	Category	Total
Gadget Type 1	Gadgets	$1,000	$900			
Gadget Type 2	Gadgets	5,000	5,200			
Total Gadgets						
Widget A	Widgets	100	100			
Widget B	Widgets	20	200			
Total Widgets						
Gizmo 1	Gizmos	1,500	1,450			
Gizmo 2	Gizmos	1,750	2,000			
Total Gizmos						
Total						

341

AP-7A LO 3

Garden Company uses the perpetual inventory system and its inventory consists of four products as at December 31, 2018. Selected information is provided below.

Required

a) Calculate the inventory value that should be reported on December 31, 2018, using the lower of cost and net realizable value applied on an individual-item basis.

Product	Number of Units	Cost (per unit)	Net Realizable Value (per unit)	LCNRV (individual)
1	15	$80	$120	
2	20	$80	$60	
3	40	$60	$50	
4	5	$120	$180	

Inventory Value: _____

b) Using the results from a), prepare the journal entry to adjust merchandise inventory to LCNRV (at individual-item level).

Date	Account Title and Explanation	Debit	Credit

AP-8A LO 3

MJ Corporation sells three categories of products: shirts, socks and pants. The following information was available at the year end of December 31, 2018.

	Shirts	Socks	Pants
	$ per unit	$ per unit	$ per unit
Original Cost	10	13	15
Estimated Selling Price (Net Realizable Value)	15	12	14
Inventory: Number of Units Held	300	380	240

Required

a) Calculate the value of inventory (apply the LCNRV at the category level).

	Shirts	Socks	Pants
Inventory: Units Held			
Lower of Cost and Market			
Value of Inventory			

b) Using the results from a), prepare the journal entry to adjust merchandise inventory to LCNRV (at category level).

Date	Account Title and Explanation	Debit	Credit

AP-9A LO 4

Tanner Radio Company has an inventory turnover of 4.5, while its competitor, Deej Radio, has an inventory turnover ratio of 1.0.

Required

a) What do these ratios mean for each company? Which company has the better ratio?

b) Calculate the days' sales in inventory for each company and interpret their meaning.

AP-10A LO 4

The following are relevant merchandise inventory numbers from ABC Company for the 2018 fiscal year.

	$ Millions
Merchandise Inventory—December 31, 2017	$108.5
Merchandise Inventory—December 31, 2018	169.7
Cost of Goods Sold	$1,452.5

Relevant merchandise inventory numbers from XYZ Company for the 2018 fiscal year are shown below.

	$ Millions
Merchandise Inventory—December 31, 2017	$221.7
Merchandise Inventory—December 31, 2018	209.6
Cost of Goods Sold	$1,432.0

Required

a) Calculate the inventory turnover ratio and days' sales in inventory for ABC Company.

_____

_____

b) Calculate the inventory turnover ratio and days' sales in inventory for XYZ Company.

_____

_____

c) Compare the results between the two companies. What conclusion can we draw about the performance of these two companies comparatively?

_____

_____

_____

_____

AP-11A LO 2

A company reported ending inventory of $100,000 in Year 1. It was discovered in Year 2 that the correct value of the ending inventory was $90,000 for Year 1 and a correction was made. Complete the following table based on this information. Assume the company uses the perpetual inventory system.

Item	Reported	Correct Amount
Merchandise Inventory	$100,000	
Current Assets	$150,000	
Total Assets	$500,000	
Owner's Equity Year 1	$200,000	
Sales	$1,000,000	
Cost of Goods Sold	$500,000	
Profit (Loss) for Year 1	$6,000	

AP-12A LO 7

Using the information provided from the general ledger, calculate the estimated closing inventory using the gross profit method.

Sales	$200,000
Opening Inventory	$67,000
Purchases	$90,000
Gross Profit Margin (from examination of prior years' statements)	30%

AP-13A LO 7

Use the following information to calculate the estimated closing inventory at cost by using the retail method.

	At Cost	At Retail
Cost of Goods Sold		
Opening Inventory	2,000	4,000
Purchases	42,000	90,000
Cost of Goods Available for Sale	44,000	94,000
Sales at Retail		50,000
Closing Inventory at Retail		44,000

Application Questions Group B

AP-1B LO 1

The following purchases and sales took place at YYY Co. during the month of June 2018. The company had no inventory on hand on June 1. YYY Co. uses the perpetual inventory system.

June 4	Purchased 260 units from CCC Co. for $12 per unit
June 8	Sold 160 units to QQQ Co.
June 14	Sold 37 units to NNN Co.
June 17	Purchased 117 units from LLL Co. for $13 per unit
June 28	Sold 100 units to VVV Co.

Required

a) Fill in the inventory schedule using the weighted-average cost inventory valuation method.

Date	Purchases			Sales			Balance		
	Quantity	Unit Cost	Value	Quantity	Unit Cost	Value	Quantity	Unit Cost	Value
June 1							0	$0	$0
June 4									
June 8									
June 14									
June 17									
June 28									
Ending Inventory									

b) Fill in the inventory schedule using the LIFO method.

Date	Purchases			Sales			Balance		
	Quantity	Unit Cost	Value	Quantity	Unit Cost	Value	Quantity	Unit Cost	Value
Jun 1							0	$0	$0
Jun 4									
Jun 8									
Jun 14									
Jun 17									
Jun 28									
Ending Inventory									

c) If the FIFO method had been used, what would the value of COGS have been for the sale to VVV Co.? Explain.

_____

_____

_____

_____

_____

d) If the specific identification method had instead been used, what would the value of COGS have been for the sale to VVV Co.? Assume that 32 of the units sold to VVV Co. were purchased from CCC Co. and the other 68 units were purchased from LLL Co.

_____

_____

_____

e) Complete the following table to compare the COGS figures for the different inventory valuation methods on the sale to VVV Co.

	Specific Identification	Weighted-Average Cost	FIFO	LIFO
COGS on sale to VVV				

AP-2B LO 6

Simplex Company has a fiscal year end on December 31. The company has only one product in inventory, and all units of that product are identical (homogenous). On January 1, Simplex has 15 units in inventory with a cost of $10 each. Complete the following schedule to calculate the value of ending inventory using the weighted-average cost method under the periodic inventory system in 2018.

Date	Purchases			Sales			Balance		
	Quantity	Unit Cost	Value	Quantity	Unit Cost	Value	Quantity	Unit Cost	Value
Jan 1							15		$150
Feb 13	25	$12							
Mar 26	16	$13							
Jul 25	34	$14							
Average Inventory									
Sales				65					
Ending Inventory									

AP-3B LO 1

LIME Suppliers is a wholesale company. It focuses primarily on office supplies, furniture and small electronic items. LIME Suppliers uses the perpetual inventory system. For one specific inventory item, it had the following transactions during the month of April 2018.

There were 10 items at the beginning of the month, with a cost of $10 each.

Date	Transaction	Quantity	Price
Apr 5	Purchased items	40	$12
Apr 7	Sold items	20	
Apr 15	Purchased items	50	$14
Apr 19	Purchased items	20	$16
Apr 27	Sold items	50	

Required

a) Calculate the value of COGS and ending inventory for April using the FIFO method.

Date	Purchases			Sales			Balance		
	Quantity	Unit Cost	Value	Quantity	Unit Cost	Value	Quantity	Unit Cost	Value
Apr 1									
Apr 5									
Apr 7									
Apr 15									
Apr 19									
Apr 27									
Ending Inventory									

Cost of Goods Sold:

b) Calculate the value of COGS and ending inventory using the LIFO method.

Date	Purchases			Sales			Balance		
	Quantity	Unit Cost	Value	Quantity	Unit Cost	Value	Quantity	Unit Cost	Value
Apr 1									
Apr 5									
Apr 7									
Apr 15									
Apr 19									
Apr 27									
Ending Inventory									

Cost of Goods Sold:

c) Calculate the value of COGS and ending inventory using the weighted-average cost method. Round the unit cost to two decimal places.

Date	Purchase			Sale			Balance		
	Quantity	Unit Cost	Value	Quantity	Unit Cost	Value	Quantity	Unit Cost	Value
Apr 1									
Apr 5									
Apr 7									
Apr 15									
Apr 19									
Apr 27									
Ending Inventory									

Cost of Goods Sold:

Analysis

In a period of rising inventory prices, which of the above methods results in the largest gross profit on the income statement? Explain.

_____

_____

_____

AP-4B LO 6

LifePros sells medical support products and records purchases at net amounts. It accounts for its inventory using the periodic system. In 2018, the following information was available from the company's inventory records for ankle support products.

	Units	Unit Cost
January 1 (beginning inventory)	1,600	$18
Purchases		
January 5	2,600	$20
January 25	2,400	$21
February 16	1,000	$22
March 15	1,400	$23

A physical count was taken on March 31, 2018 and showed 2,000 units on hand.

Required

a) Prepare a schedule to calculate the ending inventory at March 31, 2018 under the FIFO valuation method.

Date	Purchases			Sales			Balance		
	Quantity	Unit Cost	Value	Quantity	Unit Cost	Value	Quantity	Unit Cost	Value
Jan 1									
Jan 5									
Jan 25									
Feb 16									
Mar 15									
Sales									
Ending Inventory									

b) Prepare a schedule to calculate the ending inventory at March 31, 2018 under the LIFO valuation method.

Date	Purchases			Sales			Balance		
	Quantity	Unit Cost	Value	Quantity	Unit Cost	Value	Quantity	Unit Cost	Value
Jan 1									
Jan 5									
Jan 25									
Feb 16									
Mar 15									
Sales									
Ending Inventory									

c) Prepare a schedule to calculate the ending inventory at March 31, 2018 under the weighted-average cost method.

Date	Purchases			Sales			Balance		
	Quantity	Unit Cost	Value	Quantity	Unit Cost	Value	Quantity	Unit Cost	Value
Jan 1									
Jan 5									
Jan 25									
Feb 16									
Mar 15									
Average Inventory									
Sales									
Ending Inventory									

AP-5B LO 1

Handel Inc. uses a perpetual inventory system. It reported the following data related to beginning inventory and inventory purchases and sales for the month of August 2018.

Aug1   Beginning inventory consisted of 180 units at $6 per unit
Aug 10   Purchased 400 units at $4 per unit
Aug 17   Sold 250 units at $10 per unit
Aug 23   Purchased 700 units at $3 per unit
Aug 27   Sold 500 units at $9.50 per unit

Required

a) Fill in the inventory schedule and calculate the values of ending inventory, COGS and gross profit using the specific identification method. Assume that the 250 units sold on August 10 consist of 100 units from the beginning inventory and 150 units from the August 10 purchase. The 500 units sold on August 27 consist of 50 units from the beginning inventory, 100 units from the August 10 purchase and 350 units from the August 23 purchase.

Date	Purchases			Sales			Balance		
	Quantity	Unit Cost	Value	Quantity	Unit Cost	Value	Quantity	Unit Cost	Value
Aug 1									
Aug 10									
Aug 17									
Aug 23									
Aug 27									
Ending Inventory									

Cost of Goods Sold:

Gross Profit:

b) Fill in the inventory schedule and calculate the values of ending inventory, COGS and gross profit using the FIFO method.

Date	Purchases			Sales			Balance		
	Quantity	Unit Cost	Value	Quantity	Unit Cost	Value	Quantity	Unit Cost	Value
Aug 1									
Aug 10									
Aug 17									
Aug 23									
Aug 27									
Ending Inventory									

Cost of Goods Sold:

Gross Profit:

c) Fill in the inventory schedule and calculate the values of ending inventory, COGS and gross profit using the LIFO method.

Date	Purchases			Sales			Balance		
	Quantity	Unit Cost	Value	Quantity	Unit Cost	Value	Quantity	Unit Cost	Value
Aug 1									
Aug 10									
Aug 17									
Aug 23									
Aug 27									
Ending Inventory									

Cost of Goods Sold:

Gross Profit:

d) Fill in the inventory schedule and calculate the values of ending inventory, COGS and gross profit using the weighted-average cost method. Round value amounts to the nearest dollar. Round unit costs to two decimal places.

Date	Purchases			Sales			Balance		
	Quantity	Unit Cost	Value	Quantity	Unit Cost	Value	Quantity	Unit Cost	Value
Aug 1									
Aug 10									
Aug 17									
Aug 23									
Aug 27									
Ending Inventory									

Cost of Goods Sold:
Gross Profit:

Analysis

In a period of decreasing inventory prices, which inventory valuation method would be most preferable by a manager whose bonus is calculated based on a percentage of the gross profit? How would your answer change if inventory prices were rising?

_____

_____

_____

_____

AP-6B LO 3

A company has three types of products: gadgets, widgets and gizmos. The cost and NRV of each type is listed below. Complete the table by applying the lower of cost and net realizable value. The shaded areas do not require entries.

Description	Category	Cost	NRV	LCNRV Applied to		
				Individual	Category	Total
Gadget 1	Gadgets	$1,500	$1,390			
Gadget 2	Gadgets	4,830	5,430			
Total Gadgets		6,330	6,820			
Widget A	Widgets	890	470			
Widget B	Widgets	350	300			
Total Widgets		1,240	770			
Gizmo 1	Gizmo	1,350	1,960			
Gizmo 2	Gizmo	2,460	2,320			
Total Gizmos		3,810	4,280			
Total		$11,380	$11,870			

AP-7B LO 7

It is March 31, 2018 and Garden Company needs to present a set of financial statements showing the performance of the first quarter of 2018 to a local bank for a loan. To prepare the statements in a timely manner, Garden Company decided to estimate the inventory amount instead of doing a physical count. The following information is provided.

Accounts Receivable, January 1, 2018	$1,500
Accounts Receivable, March 31, 2018	2,200
Collections of accounts from January 1 to March 31	5,300
Merchandise Inventory, January 1, 2018	1,200
Purchases from January 1 to March 31	6,800

Assume all sales are made on account. Garden Company expects its gross margin percentage to be 30%.

Calculate the estimated cost of the inventory on March 31, 2018 using the gross profit method.

Sales Revenue		
Cost of Goods Sold		
Opening Inventory		
Purchases		
Cost of Goods Available for Sale		
Closing Inventory		
Cost of Goods Sold		
Gross Profit		

AP-8B LO 3

On December 31, 2018 Kranky Bike Shop has three types of bikes: mountain bikes, road bikes and hybrid bikes. The cost and NRV of each type is listed below.

Required

a) Complete the table by applying the lower of cost and net realizable value. The shaded areas do not require entries.

				LCNRV Applied to		
Description	Category	Cost	NRV	Individual	Category	Total
CCM	Mountain	$10,000	$8,000			
Mikado	Mountain	8,000	5,500			
Oryx	Mountain	2,000	3,100			
Total Mountain Bikes						
Giant	Road	7,000	12,500			
Norco	Road	6,000	8,100			
Total Road Bikes						
Electra	Hybrid	2,800	2,500			
Acquila	Hybrid	2,600	3,000			
Total Hybrid Bikes						
Total						

b) Prepare the adjusting entry, if required, if LCNRV was applied using
   i) individual products
   ii) category
   iii) total

	Date	Account Title and Explanation	Debit	Credit
i)				
ii)				
iii)				

AP-9B LO 7

A list of relevant inventory numbers from SI Company for the year ended December 31, 2018 is provided below.

Average Inventory—December 31, 2017	$90,000
Average Inventory—December 31, 2018	110,000
Cost of Goods Sold—2017	920,000
Cost of Goods Sold—2018	890,000

Required

a) Calculate the inventory turnover ratio and the days' sales in inventory for SI company for the two years.

	2018	2017
Inventory Turnover Ratio		
Days' Sales in Inventory		

b) Compare the results between two years. What conclusion can be drawn about the performance of the company regarding both years?

_____

_____

_____

_____

_____

_____

AP-10B LO 4

Delta Corporation reported the following amounts for ending inventory and cost of goods sold in the financial statements.

Ending Inventory		Cost of Goods Sold	
2018	$799,000	2018	$25,927,000
2017	$1,365,000	2017	$36,479,000
2016	$3,205,000	2016	$47,025,000

Required

a) Calculate the inventory turnover ratio and days' sales in inventory for 2018 and 2017.

_____

_____

_____

_____

b) Compare and discuss the results between the two years.

_____

_____

c) Delta Corporation is a software company in a rapidly changing industry. Evaluate the results from part a) by using this information and considering the amount of cost of goods sold.

_____

_____

_____

_____

_____

_____

AP-11B LO 2

Trevor and Arkady run Squash Stuff Company. The net income earned by their business during the year ended December 31, 2018 is $250,000. However, an inventory clerk realized that the ending inventory for 2018 was overstated by $10,000.

Required

a) If the error is not corrected, what is the effect on 2018 net income?

_____

_____

b) If the error is not corrected, what is the effect on the 2018 equity balance?

_____

_____

c) Record journal entries to correct the overstatement of merchandise inventory assuming the error was discovered on December 31, 2018.

Date	Account Title and Explanation	Debit	Credit

d) If the error is not corrected, how is the sum of 2018 and 2019 net income affected?

_____

_____

_____

_____

_____

e) There have been cases where companies applying for bank loans have intentionally overstated their closing inventory. Why would companies overstate their closing inventory and what are some of the methods of overstating closing inventory?

_____

_____

_____

_____

_____

AP-12B `LO 7`

During the month of January 2018, Fine Groceries lost inventory due to a fire. The following amounts have been extracted from the accounts of Fine Grocery Store.

Sales		$280,000
Beginning Inventory	$210,000	
Purchases	340,000	
Inventory in good condition after fire	300,000	
Gross Profit Margin		30%

Calculate the amount of inventory lost due to the fire by first calculating the amount of estimated ending inventory before the fire using the gross profit method.

Sales Revenue		
Cost of Goods Sold		
Opening Inventory	$210,000	
Purchases	340,000	
Cost of Goods Available for Sale		
Closing Inventory Before Fire		
Cost of Goods Sold		
Gross Profit		

AP-13B LO 7

The following information has been provided by AS Retailers for the month of August 2018. Calculate the estimated closing inventory at cost using the retail method.

	At Cost	At Retail
Cost of Goods Sold		
Opening Inventory	$3,000	$6,000
Purchases	32,000	80,000
Cost of Goods Available for Sale	$35,000	86,000
Sales at Retail		50,000
Closing Inventory at Retail		$36,000

Case Study

CS-1 LO 1 3 7

Monrose Park had the following transactions during the month of November 2018.

Nov 2   Purchased 1,000 widgets for $20 per unit on credit
Nov 5   Sold 900 widgets for $55 each for cash
Nov 10   Purchased 500 widgets for $25 per unit on credit
Nov 18   Sold 100 widgets for $60 each on credit
Nov 29   Sold 300 widgets for $50 each for cash

Monrose Park uses a perpetual inventory system and the FIFO inventory valuation method. There were no widgets in the company's opening inventory for November.

Required

a) Record the above transactions in the general journal.

Date	Account Title and Explanation	Debit	Credit

b) Prepare the schedule to calculate ending inventory after the above transactions.

Date	Purchases			Sales			Balance		
	Quantity	Unit Cost	Value	Quantity	Unit Cost	Value	Quantity	Unit Cost	Value
Nov 1									
Nov 2									
Nov 5									
Nov 10									
Nov 18									
Nov 29									
Ending Inventory									

c) Calculate the value of merchandise inventory using the lower of cost and net realizable value (LCNRV).

Description	Category	Cost	NRV	LCNRV Applied to	
				Individual	Category
Widget A	Widgets	$3,000	$2,300		
Widget B	Widgets	2,000	3,300		
Total Widgets					
Total					

d) Record the journal entry to adjust the value of merchandise inventory to the lower of cost and net realizable value based on individual items using the results from c).

Date	Account Title and Explanation	Debit	Credit

e) Prepare an excerpt of the multiple-step income statement for the month showing sales revenue, cost of goods sold, and gross profit.

f) Sales for December were $100,000 and purchases were $68,500. Using the gross profit method, estimate the closing value of inventory. Assume the gross profit margin from November will be the gross profit margin for December.

Sales Revenue		$100,000
Cost of Goods Sold		
Opening Inventory		
Purchases	68,500	
Cost of Goods Available for Sale		
Closing Inventory		
Cost of Goods Sold		
Gross Profit		

_____

_____

_____

_____

_____

Chapter 9

ACCOUNTING INFORMATION SYSTEMS

LEARNING OBJECTIVES

LO 1 Explain the flow of accounting information through the accounting paper trail

LO 2 Describe and record transactions in special journals and subsidiary ledgers

LO 3 Identify features of a computerized accounting system

Appendix

LO 4 Prepare special journals under a periodic inventory system

AMEENGAGE™ Access **ameengage.com** for integrated resources including tutorials, practice exercises, the digital textbook and more.

Assessment Questions

AS-1 LO 1

What is an accounting system?

_____

_____

_____

AS-2 LO 1

What are the features of an effective accounting information system?

_____

_____

_____

_____

_____

_____

AS-3 LO 1

Describe the paper trail in a manual accounting system.

_____

_____

_____

_____

_____

_____

_____

AS-4 LO 3

How do the elements in a computerized system differ from those in a manual system?

_____

_____

_____

AS-5 LO 3

What are special journals used for?

_____

_____

AS-6 LO 2

What type of information is found in the sales journal?

_____

_____

AS-7 LO 2

What are general journals used for?

_____

_____

AS-8 LO 2

Why are subsidiary ledgers used?

_____

_____

_____

AS-9 LO 2

What is the relationship between a controlling account and its corresponding subledgers?

_____

_____

_____

AS-10 LO 2

What type of information can be found in an accounts payable subsidiary ledger?

_____

_____

AS-11 LO 2

At the end of the accounting period what is done with the totals in the purchases special journal?

_____

_____

AS-12 `LO` `2`

When preparing a sales return in the general journal, what accounts are updated? How is the post reference column used to indicate the accounts are updated?

_____
_____
_____
_____

AS-13 `LO` `3`

Provide a few examples of reports that can be generated by QuickBooks.

_____
_____
_____
_____

AS-14 `LO` `3`

What is cloud accounting?

_____
_____
_____

AS-15 `LO` `3`

What are some advantages and disadvantages of cloud accounting?

_____
_____
_____
_____
_____
_____

AS-16 `LO` `3`

What are a few examples of cloud-based accounting services?

_____
_____

AS-17 `LO` `4`

How is using special journals in the periodic inventory system different from using special journals in the perpetual inventory system?

_____
_____
_____

Application Questions Group A

AP-1A LO 2

For each transaction, indicate in which journal it should be recorded.

- Sales Journal (SJ)
- Cash Receipts Journal (CR)
- Purchases Journal (PJ)
- Cash Payments Journal (CP)
- General Journal (GJ)

_____ Sold products for cash

_____ Received a loan from the bank

_____ Owner invested cash into the business

_____ Owner withdrew cash from the business

_____ Paid amount owing to a supplier

_____ Received a utility bill, which will be paid later

_____ Returned products to a supplier

_____ Recorded adjustment for depreciation

_____ Sold products on account

AP-2A LO 2

Hidson Inc. is a small retailer. The following is a list of sales transactions for the month of April.

Apr 2   Made a sale on account (Invoice #5703) to B. Fager for $450 (cost $300)

Apr 5   Made a sale on account (Invoice #5704) to J. Dryer for $1,150 (cost $900)

Apr 10   Made a sale on account (Invoice #5705) to T. Burton for $550 (cost $450)

Apr 12   Made a sale on account (Invoice #5706) to JB Inc. for $670 (cost $500)

Record these transactions in the sales journal.

Sales Journal					Page 1
Date	Account	Invoice #	PR	Accounts Receivable/ Sales (DR/CR)	COGS/Merchandise Inventory (DR/CR)

AP-3A LO 2

F. Benjamin owns a small clothing store. The following is the list of prices he charges for different types of products.

Product	Price	Cost
Blue cotton	$6 per sheet	$4 per sheet
Black silk	$20 per yard	$15 per yard
White tape	$10 per roll	$6 per roll
Green felt	$4 per yard	$2 per yard

During the month of July, the company made the following sales.

Jul 1   Sold 3 rolls of white tape, 5 sheets of blue cotton, and 1 yard of black silk to R. Grey, on account (Invoice #5739)

Jul 5   Sold 6 rolls of white tape and 30 yards of green felt to G. Abbott on account (Invoice #5740)

Jul 9   Sold 1 yard of black silk to E. Hines, on account (Invoice #5741)

Jul 11   Sold 10 rolls of white tape, 6 sheets of blue cotton, 3 yards of black silk and 11 yards of green felt to M. Allen, on account (Invoice #5742)

Jul 14   Sold 12 rolls of white tape, 14 sheets of blue cotton and 9 yards of green felt to B. Cooper, on account (Invoice #5743)

Record these transactions in the sales journal.

Sales Journal					Page 1
Date	Account	Invoice #	PR	Accounts Receivable/Sales (DR/CR)	COGS/Merchandise Inventory (DR/CR)

AP-4A LO 2

Riya Cosmetics has provided you with the following information about the transactions the company had during the month of June.

Jun 2   Received $2,000 from a cash sale to Faces Inc. (cost $1,500)

Jun 6   Received $840 from Beauty Breeze for outstanding accounts receivable

Jun 10   Received $650 for the cash sale of 5 facial scrubs (cost $540) to Seizers Salon

Jun 13   Received $325 in interest earned from Timberland Bank

Jun 25   Took out a loan of $3,000 from the bank

Record these transactions in the cash receipts journal.

Cash Receipts Journal							Page 1
Date	Account	PR	Cash (DR)	Accounts Receivable (CR)	Sales (CR)	Interest Revenue (CR)	Other (CR)	COGS/ Merchandise Inventory (DR/CR)

AP-5A LO 2

Lin Z is an owner-operated sporting goods retailer. The following is a list of the company's transactions for the month of June.

Jun 2   The owner, Lin Zarra, invested $16,500 into the business

Jun 6   Received a loan of $1,000 from the bank

Jun 10   Received $150 of interest earned on the savings account with Allmount Bank

Jun 13   Received $2,000 from cash sales to Dawn Sports (sold sports items costing $1,500)

Jun 25   Received $800 from AD Sports regarding outstanding accounts receivable

Record these transactions in the cash receipts journal.

Cash Receipts Journal								Page 1
Date	Account	PR	Cash (DR)	Accounts Receivable (CR)	Sales (CR)	Interest Revenue (CR)	Other (CR)	COGS/ Merchandise Inventory (DR/CR)

AP-6A LO 2

Peter's Pewter sells figurines. During the month of August 2018, the following transactions occurred.

Aug 3   Peter invested $4,000 into his business

Aug 7   Sold inventory to Joyce Fontane for $500 cash; the inventory had a cost of $240

Aug 16   Sold inventory to Carol Balsdon for $750 on account; the inventory had a cost of $310

Aug 17   Sold inventory to James Stewart for $820 on account; the inventory had a cost of $420

Aug 24   Received full payment from Carol Balsdon for the Aug 16 transaction

Assume zero opening balances for the subledger and general ledger accounts. Assume no entries were made directly to the accounts receivable general ledger from the general journal.

Use the following selected accounts to complete the posting references.

Account Description	Account #	Account Description	Account #
Cash	101	Pewter, Withdrawals	310
Accounts Receivable	110	Sales Revenue	400
Merchandise Inventory	120	Sales Discount	405
Office Supplies	130	Interest Revenue	410
Accounts Payable	200	Cost of Goods Sold	500
Notes Payable	220	Salaries Expense	520
Pewter, Capital	300	Telephone Expense	525

Required

a)   Record the above transactions in the sales journal and the cash receipts journal.

Sales Journal					Page 1
Date	Account	Invoice #	PR	Accounts Receivable/ Sales (DR/CR)	COGS/ Merchandise Inventory (DR/CR)

Cash Receipts Journal								Page 3
Date	Account	PR	Cash (DR)	Accounts Receivable (CR)	Sales (CR)	Notes Payable (CR)	Other (CR)	COGS/ Merchandise Inventory (DR/CR)

b)   Post the appropriate transactions from the journals to the subledger accounts. At the end of the month, total the journals and update the accounts receivable controlling account.

Account: Accounts Receivable					GL No:	
Date	Description	PR	DR	CR	Balance	

Account: Carol Balsdon				
Date	PR	DR	CR	Balance

Account: James Stewart				
Date	PR	DR	CR	Balance

AP-7A LO 2

Ryan Manufacturing sells flat-pack bookcases to retailers. The following transactions occurred during the month of September 2018. All sales on account come with terms of 2/10, net 30.

Sep 1   Received a loan from the bank for $15,000

Sep 5   Sold products for cash to Brock Retailer for $8,400; the products had a cost of $4,620

Sep 8   Sold products on account to Furniture Outlet for $10,600; the products had a cost of $6,360

Sep 12   Furniture Outlet paid the amount owing from Sep 8

Sep 21   Sold products on account to Brock Retailer for $6,200; the products had a cost of $3,410

Required

a) Record the transactions in the appropriate journal.

Sales Journal					Page 1
Date	Account	PR	Invoice #	Accounts Receivable/ Sales (DR/CR)	COGS/Merchandise Inventory (DR/CR)

Cash Receipts Journal								Page 1
Date	Account	PR	Cash (DR)	Sales Discount (DR)	Accounts Receivable (CR)	Sales (CR)	Other (CR)	COGS/ Merchandise Inventory (DR/CR)

b) Where appropriate, update the accounts receivable subledgers. At the end of the month, calculate the totals of the columns in the journals and update the controlling account.

Account:	Accounts Receivable				**GL No:** 110
Date	Description	PR	DR	CR	Balance

Account:	Furniture Outlet			
Date	PR	DR	CR	Balance

Account:	Brock Retailer			
Date	PR	DR	CR	Balance

AP-8A LO 2

J. Glen, a sports retailer, made the following purchases during the month of May.

May 2   Received a bill (Invoice #125) from F. Day for the purchase of 2 basketballs worth $100 each and 6 footballs worth $45 each

May 4   Received a bill (Invoice #135) from G. Smith for the purchase of 7 cricket bats worth $65 each, 5 pairs of ice skates worth $32 each and 4 rugby balls worth $32 each

May 10   Received a bill (Invoice #145) from L. Todd for the purchase of 6 cricket bats worth $55 each

May 12   Received a bill (Invoice #222) from M. Moore for the purchase of 9 packages of golf balls at $45 each

Record these transactions in the purchases journal.

Purchases Journal						Page 1
Date	Account	Invoice #	PR	Merchandise Inventory (DR)	Accounts Payable (CR)	

AP-9A LO 2

Vina Duckworth has provided the following information relating to her activities in the month of June 2018.

Jun 2   Paid amount owing of $650 (Invoice #780) to SK Depot (Check #195)
Jun 6   Paid back loan of $800 to the bank (Check #196)
Jun 10   Paid $3,000 to Nektel Inc. for purchase of inventory (Check #197)
Jun 13   Received a telephone bill for $350 and paid the amount owing to CasTech Inc. (Check #198)
Jun 25   Paid $205 to SFC Inc. for general expenses (Check #199)

Record these transactions in the cash payments journal.

Cash Payments Journal							Page 1
Date	Account	Check #	PR	Other (DR)	Merchandise Inventory (DR)	Accounts Payable (DR)	Cash (CR)

AP-10A LO 2

Medicines World, a medical store, makes all transactions in cash only. It has provided you with the following information about the transactions for the month of May.

May 2   Paid $1,000 rent for the month of May to Mrs. Elizabeth (Check #23)

May 4   Paid $800 salary to James Jones for the month of April (Check #24)

May 6   Paid repair and maintenance charges of $300 to Building Services Inc. (Check #25)

May 10   Paid $200 for internet charges to Castech (Check #26)

May 12   Bought medicine costing $8,000 from Medicines Inc. (Check #27)

Record these transactions in the cash payments journal.

	Cash Payments Journal						Page 1
Date	Account	Check #	PR	Other (DR)	Merchandise Inventory (DR)	Accounts Payable (DR)	Cash (CR)

AP-11A LO 2

Blossoming Gardens sells landscaping materials. During the month of May 2018, the following transactions occurred.

May 3	Purchased office supplies for $800 on account from Office Supply Shop
May 7	Purchased inventory for $1,200 cash from Rock Bottom with Check #456
May 10	Paid telephone bill for $350 with Check #457
May 17	Paid the amount owing to Office Supply Shop with Check #458
May 24	Purchased inventory for $3,500 from Paving Stones on account

Assume zero opening balances for the subledger and general ledger accounts. Assume no entries were made directly to the accounts payable general ledger from the general journal.

Use the following selected accounts to complete the posting references.

Account Description	Account #	Account Description	Account #
Cash	101	Owner's Withdrawals	310
Accounts Receivable	110	Sales Revenue	400
Merchandise Inventory	120	Sales Discount	405
Office Supplies	130	Interest Revenue	410
Accounts Payable	200	Cost of Goods Sold	500
Notes Payable	220	Salaries Expense	520
Owner's Capital	300	Telephone Expense	525

Required

a) Record the above transactions in the purchases journal and the cash payments journal.

	Purchases Journal						Page 6
Date	Account	Invoice #	PR	Merchandise Inventory (DR)	Office Supplies (DR)	Other (DR)	Accounts Payable (CR)

	Cash Payments Journal						Page 4
Date	Account	Check #	PR	Accounts Payable (DR)	Other (DR)	Merchandise Inventory (DR)	Cash (CR)

b) Post the appropriate transactions from the journals to the subledger accounts. At the end of the month, total the journals and update the accounts payable controlling account.

Account:	Accounts Payable				GL No:	
Date	Description	PR	DR	CR	Balance	

Account:	Office Supply Shop			
Date	PR	DR	CR	Balance

Account:	Paving Stones			
Date	PR	DR	CR	Balance

AP-12A LO 2

Cap It sells a variety of hats. The following is a list of transactions for the month of November 2018.

Nov 5	Received Invoice #2563 for $4,000 worth of office supplies from Office Outfitters
Nov 9	Received Invoice #8475 from Aqua for $180 for water
Nov 12	Paid amount on Invoice #2563 to Office Outfitters with Check #153
Nov 21	Purchased inventory from Fedora Company for $4,000 with Check 154
Nov 22	Paid amount on Invoice #8475 to Aqua with Check #155
Nov 25	Paid $260 to John Walker for repair expenses with Check #156
Nov 26	Received Invoice #563 from Total Hats for $3,700 worth of inventory

Required

a) Record the above entries in the appropriate journal.

Purchases Journal							Page 1
Date	Account	Invoice #	PR	Water Expense (DR)	Office Supplies (DR)	Merchandise Inventory (DR)	Accounts Payable (CR)

Cash Payments Journal							Page 1
Date	Account	Check #	PR	Other (DR)	Merchandise Inventory (DR)	Accounts Payable (DR)	Cash (CR)

b) Post the entries in the subledger accounts. At the end of the month, total the special journals and update the accounts payable controlling account.

Opening Balances

Office Outfitters	$400 (CR)
Aqua	$40 (CR)
Total Hats	$1,300 (CR)

Note that Cap It's accounts payable records consist of only these three subledgers. Assume no entries were made directly to accounts payable through the general journal. Update the PR columns in both the subledgers and special journals.

Account : Accounts Payable   **GL No:** 200

Date	Description	PR	DR	CR	Balance

Accounts Payable Subsidiary Ledger
Office Outfitters

Date	PR	DR	CR	Balance

Accounts Payable Subsidiary Ledger
Aqua

Date	PR	DR	CR	Balance

Accounts Payable Subsidiary Ledger
Total Hats

Date	PR	DR	CR	Balance

AP-13A LO 2

Gherry is a small shoe retailer. The following is a list of transactions for the month of May.

May 4	Received $6,000 from a cash sale to Teamster Inc. (sold sport shoes costing $700)
May 5	Received a bill (Invoice #5780) for $800 worth of office supplies from BZDepot Inc.
May 6	Received $840 from Jo-Ann regarding her outstanding accounts receivable
May 9	Received $650 for the cash sale of 5 pairs of shoes (costing a total of $85) to Sgt. Pepper
May 9	Received a telephone bill from ComTech Inc. (Invoice #167) for $150
May 10	Received $325 in interest from a loan to Lance Livestrong
May 12	Paid amount owing (Invoice #5780) to BZDepot Inc. (Check #201)
May 15	Received a loan of $1,000 from Method Bank
May 18	Made a sale on account (Invoice #2341) to Keith Ricardo, for $250 (with inventory costing $200)
May 21	Paid $2,000 to Nikel Inc. for the purchase of inventory (Check #202)
May 22	Paid amount owing (Invoice #167) to ComTech Inc. for telephone services with Check #203
May 25	Paid $205 to BFG Inc., for maintenance expenses (Check #204)
May 26	Received bill from Adibas Inc. (Invoice #113) for $5,500 worth of inventory
May 28	Made a sale on account (Invoice #2342), to Gary Lineker for $2,000 worth of shoes (costing $1,700)

Required

a) Record the transactions in the relevant journal.

Cash Receipts Journal									Page 1
Date	Account	PR	Cash (DR)	Accounts Receivable (CR)	Sales (CR)	Interest Revenue (CR)	Notes Payable (CR)	Other (CR)	COGS/ Merchandise Inventory (DR/CR)

Sales Journal					Page 1
Date	Account	Invoice #	PR	Accounts Receivable/ Sales (DR/CR)	COGS/Merchandise Inventory (DR/CR)

Purchases Journal							Page 1
Date	Account	Invoice #	PR	Telephone Expense (DR)	Office Supplies (DR)	Merchandise Inventory (DR)	Accounts Payable (CR)

Cash Payments Journal							Page 1
Date	Account	Check #	PR	Other (DR)	Merchandise Inventory (DR)	Accounts Payable (DR)	Cash (CR)

b) Post from the special journals to the accounts receivable subledger and then to the accounts receivable controlling account at the end of the month. Assume the following opening subledger balances.

Jo-Ann $940 (DR)
Keith Ricardo $600 (DR)
Gary Lineker $800 (DR)

Note that Gherry's accounts receivable records consist of only these three subledgers. Assume no entries were made directly to accounts receivable through the general journal. Update the PR columns in the subledgers and special journals.

Account : Accounts Receivable					**GL No:** 110	
Date	Description	PR	DR	CR	Balance	

Accounts Receivable Subsidiary Ledger Jo-Ann					
Date	PR	DR	CR	Balance	

Accounts Receivable Subsidiary Ledger Keith Ricardo					
Date	PR	DR	CR	Balance	

Accounts Receivable Subsidiary Ledger Gary Lineker					
Date	PR	DR	CR	Balance	

c) Post from the special journals to the accounts payable subledger and then to the accounts payable controlling account at the end of the month. Assume the following opening subledger balances.

BZDepot Inc. $1,000 (CR)
ComTech Inc. $1,200 (CR)
Adibas Inc. $1,400 (CR)

Note that Gherry's accounts payable records consist of only these three subledgers. Assume no entries were made directly to accounts payable through the general journal. Update the PR columns in both the subledgers and special journals.

Account : Accounts Payable					**GL No:** 110	
Date	Description	PR	DR	CR	Balance	

Accounts Payable Subsidiary Ledger
BZDepot Inc.

Date	PR	DR	CR	Balance	

Accounts Payable Subsidiary Ledger
ComTech Inc.

Date	PR	DR	CR	Balance	

Accounts Payable Subsidiary Ledger
Adibas Inc.

Date	PR	DR	CR	Balance	

AP-14A LO 4

Blossoming Gardens sells landscaping materials. During the month of May 2018, the following transactions occurred. Blossoming Gardens uses the periodic inventory system.

May 3   Purchased office supplies for $800 on account from Office Supply Shop
May 7   Purchased inventory for $1,200 cash from Rock Bottom with Check #456
May 10   Paid a telephone bill for $350 cash with Check #457
May 17   Paid the amount owing to Office Supply Shop with Check #458
May 24   Purchased inventory for $3,500 from Paving Stones on account

Assume zero opening balances for the subledger and general ledger accounts. Assume no entries were made directly to the accounts payable general ledger from the general journal.

Use the following selected accounts to complete the posting references.

Account Description	Account #	Account Description	Account #
Cash	101	Owner's Withdrawals	310
Accounts Receivable	110	Sales Revenue	400
Merchandise Inventory	120	Sales Discount	405
Office Supplies	130	Interest Revenue	410
Accounts Payable	200	Cost of Goods Sold	500
Notes Payable	220	Salaries Expense	520
Owner's Capital	300	Telephone Expense	525

Required

a)   Record the above transactions in the purchases journal and the cash payments journal.

Purchases Journal							Page 6
Date	Account	Invoice #	PR	Purchases (DR)	Office Supplies (DR)	Other (DR)	Accounts Payable (CR)

Cash Payments Journal							Page 4
Date	Account	Check #	PR	Accounts Payable (DR)	Other (DR)	Purchases (DR)	Cash (CR)

b) Post the appropriate transactions from the journals to the subledger accounts. At the end of the month, total the journals and udpate the accounts payable controlling account.

Account:	Accounts Payable				GL No:
Date	Description	PR	DR	CR	Balance

Account:	Office Supply Shop			
Date	PR	DR	CR	Balance

Account:	Paving Stones			
Date	PR	DR	CR	Balance

Application Questions Group B

AP-1B LO 2

For each transaction, indicate in which journal it should be recorded.

- Sales Journal (SJ)
- General Journal (GJ)
- Cash Receipts Journal (CR)
- Cash Payments Journal (CP)
- Purchases Journal (PJ)

_____ Received payment from a customer
_____ Paid salaries to employees
_____ Sold products on accounts
_____ A customer returned unused product
_____ Purchased inventory on account
_____ Recorded adjustment for unearned revenue
_____ Paid interest on a bank loan
_____ Purchased office supplies on account

AP-2B LO 2

SmartWays has provided you with the following information about its sales transactions during the month of September.

Sep 1	Made a sale on account (Invoice #1122) to Fatima Inc. for $1,450 (cost $1,200)
Sep 5	Made a sale on account (Invoice #1123) to Charisma Ltd. for $2,150 (cost $1,900)
Sep 9	Made a sale on account (Invoice #1124) to Hidendsa Inc. for $750 (cost $600)
Sep 11	Made a sale on account (Invoice #1125) to Henry Inc. for $1,270 (cost $1,080)
Sep 14	Made a sale on account (Invoice #1126) to Snoob Inc. for $970 (cost $800)
Sep 20	Made a sale on account (Invoice #1127) to Lime&Lemon for $ 1,150 (cost $1,020)

Record these transactions in the sales journal.

Sales Journal					Page 1
Date	Account	Invoice #	PR	Accounts Receivable/Sales (DR/CR)	COGS/Merchandise Inventory (DR/CR)

AP-3B LO 2

Jane Fisher is selling the following items at the prices listed below.

Product	Price	Cost
Plastic tubing	$1 per yard	$0.50 per yard
Polythene sheeting	$2 per yard	$1 per yard
Vinyl padding	$5 per box	$3 per box
Foam rubber	$3 per sheet	$2 per sheet

She has provided you the following data about sales transactions incurred during the month of August.

Aug 2   Sold 22 yards of plastic tubing, 6 sheets of foam rubber and 4 boxes of vinyl padding to A. Portsmouth, on account (Invoice #1240)

Aug 4   Sold 50 yards of polythene sheeting, 6 sheets of foam rubber and 4 boxes of vinyl padding to B. Butler, on account (Invoice #1241)

Aug 6   Sold 4 yards of plastic tubing to A. Gate, on account (Invoice #1242)

Aug 10   Sold 30 yards of plastic tubing to L. Makeson, on account (Invoice #1243)

Aug 12   Sold 32 yards of plastic tubing, 24 yards of polythene sheeting and 20 boxes of vinyl padding to M. Alison, on account (Invoice #1244)

Record these transactions in the sales journal.

				Sales Journal	Page 1
Date	Account	Invoice #	PR	Accounts Receivable/ Sales (DR/CR)	COGS/Merchandise Inventory (DR/CR)

AP-4B [LO 2]

Book World is a dealer for stationery items. The company has provided the following information about the transactions incurred in the month of March.

Mar 2   Received $3,500 from cash sale to Books & Books (cost $3,000)
Mar 9   Received $300 in interest earned from Hooper Bank
Mar 14   Received bank loan of $500 from Hooper Bank
Mar 19   Received $700 from cash sale to Book Ocean (cost $500)
Mar 21   Received $900 from cash sale to Beacon Books (cost $700)

Record these transactions in the cash receipts journal.

					Cash Receipts Journal			Page 1
Date	Account	PR	Cash (DR)	Sales (CR)	Accounts Receivable (CR)	Interest Revenue (CR)	Other (CR)	COGS/Merchandise Inventory (DR/CR)

AP-5B [LO 2]

Highway Interchange sells clothing to retailers. During the month of July 2018, the following transactions occurred.

Jul 7   Sold inventory to Fashion House (Invoice #526) for $5,600 cash; the inventory had a cost of $2,400
Jul 10   Received a loan from Kingsman Bank for $5,000
Jul 15   Sold inventory to Stella Lanes (Invoice #527) on account for $8,500; the inventory had a cost of $3,400
Jul 17   Sold inventory to Cover Me (Invoice #528) for $7,500 on account; the inventory had a cost of $3,100
Jul 24   Received full payment from Stella Lanes for the sale on July 15
Jul 31   Received $50 of interest earned on a savings account

Assume zero opening balances for the subledger and general ledger accounts. Assume no entries were made directly to the accounts receivable general ledger from the general journal.

Use the following selected accounts to complete the posting references.

Account Description	Account #	Account Description	Account #
Cash	101	Owner's Withdrawals	310
Accounts Receivable	110	Sales Revenue	400
Merchandise Inventory	120	Sales Discount	405
Office Supplies	130	Interest Revenue	410
Accounts Payable	200	Cost of Goods Sold	500
Notes Payable	220	Salaries Expense	520
Owner's Capital	300	Telephone Expense	525

Required

a) Record the above transactions in the sales journal and the cash receipts journal.

Sales Journal					Page 1
Date	Account	Invoice #	PR	Accounts Receivable/ Sales (DR/CR)	COGS/Merchandise Inventory (DR/CR)

Cash Receipts Journal								Page 1
Date	Account	PR	Cash (DR)	Accounts Receivable (CR)	Sales (CR)	Notes Payable (CR)	Other (CR)	COGS/ Merchandise Inventory (DR/CR)

b) Post the appropriate transactions in the sales journal and the cash receipts journal. At the end of the month, total the journals and update the accounts receivable controlling account.

Account: Accounts Receivable					GL No:
Date	Description	PR	DR	CR	Balance

Account: Stella Lanes				
Date	PR	DR	CR	Balance

Account: Cover Me				
Date	PR	DR	CR	Balance

AP-6B LO 2

Blip Wholesalers provides wholesale pastries to supermarkets. Since most customers are large retailers, Blip Wholesalers sells a lot of products on account and provides discounts for early payment. The following transactions occurred during the month of July 2018. All sales on account come with terms of 2/10, net 30.

Jul 3   Sold products on account to Farmer's Market for $5,200; the products had a cost of $3,120
Jul 7   Sold products for cash to Renfrew for $4,200; the products had a cost of $2,310
Jul 8   Received a loan from Stanley Bank for $3,000
Jul 10   Farmer's Market paid the amount owing from July 3
Jul 15   Sold products on account to Renfrew for $3,200; the products had a cost of $1,760

Required

a)   Record the transactions in the appropriate journal.

				Accounts Receivable/Sales (DR/CR)	COGS/Merchandise Inventory (DR/CR)
Date	Account	PR	Invoice #		

Sales Journal — Page 1

			Cash (DR)	Sales Discount (DR)	Accounts Receivable (CR)	Sales (CR)	Other (CR)	COGS/Merchandise Inventory (DR/CR)
Date	Account	PR						

Cash Receipts Journal — Page 1

b)   Where appropriate, update the accounts receivable subledgers. At the end of the month, calculate the totals of the columns in the journals and update the accounts receivable controlling account.

Account: Accounts Receivable — **GL No:** 110

Date	Description	PR	DR	CR	Balance

Account: Farmer's Market

Date	PR	DR	CR	Balance

Account: Renfrew

Date	PR	DR	CR	Balance

AP-7B LO 2

Bob123, a household items retailer, made the following purchases during the month of March.

Mar 2   Received a bill (Invoice #305) from D. Pope for the purchase of 4 DVDs, worth $240 each

Mar 4   Received a bill (Invoice #426) from F. Lloyd for the purchase of 2 washing machines worth $560 each and 5 vacuum cleaners worth $400 each

Mar 6   Received a bill (Invoice #765) from B. Sankey for the purchase of 1 wireless router worth $600 and 2 washing machines worth $320 each

Mar 10   Received a bill (Invoice #2132) from J. Wilson for the purchase of 6 blenders worth $45 each

Mar 12   Received a bill (Invoice #1234) from R. Freer for the purchase of 4 dishwashers worth $240 each

Record these transactions in the purchases journal.

Purchases Journal					Page 1
Date	Account	Invoice #	PR	Merchandise Inventory (DR)	Accounts Payable (CR)

AP-8B LO 2

Philips, a clothing store, made the following purchases for the month of September.

Sep 2   Received a bill (Invoice #723) from Smith Inc. for the purchase of $80 worth of silk, and $100 worth of cotton

Sep 7   Received a bill (Invoice #657) from Grantley Store for the purchase of Lycra goods worth $38 and woolen items worth $64

Sep 12   Received a bill (Invoice #498) from Henry Inc. for the purchase of silk worth $45, cotton worth $130 and Lycra worth $135

Sep 17   Received a bill (Invoice #342) from Kelly Inc. for the purchase of $98 worth of cotton and $56 worth of Lycra goods

Sep 22   Received a bill (Invoice #290) of $380 from Hamilton Inc. for the purchase of Lycra goods

Record these transactions in the purchases journal.

Purchases Journal					Page 1
Date	Account	Invoice #	PR	Merchandise Inventory (DR)	Accounts Payable (CR)

AP-9B LO 2

Ambassador uses a cash payments journal to record all the payments made by the company. Ambassador has provided you with the following information about the transactions incurred in the month of August.

Aug 2   Paid salary to Amanda Blythe, $1,600 cash (Check #241)

Aug 12   Paid $2,400 owing (Invoice #543) to Hargrave Inc. (Check #242)

Aug 14   Paid insurance premium of $300 (Check #243)

Aug 20   Paid newspaper bill of $150 to News & Paper (Check #244)

Aug 26   Paid $2,000 to JKL Company for the purchase of inventory (Check #245)

Record these transactions in the cash payments journal.

	Cash Payments Journal						Page 1
Date	Account	Check #	PR	Other (DR)	Merchandise Inventory (DR)	Accounts Payable (DR)	Cash (CR)

AP-10B LO 2

Put-A-Wrench-In-It sells tools. During the month of October 2018, the following transactions occurred.

Oct 3   Purchased inventory for $6,300 on account from Block and Deck

Oct 7   Paid salaries for $2,100 with Check #256

Oct 10   Purchased inventory for $4,100 cash from Malida Inc. with Check #257

Oct 17   Paid the full amount owing to Block and Deck from the Oct 3 transaction with Check #258

Oct 24   Purchased inventory for $7,700 on account from Debolt Inc.

Assume zero opening balances for the subledger and general ledger accounts. Assume no entries were made directly to the accounts payable general ledger from the general journal.

Use the following selected accounts to complete the posting references.

Account Description	Account #	Account Description	Account #
Cash	101	Owner's Withdrawals	310
Accounts Receivable	110	Sales Revenue	400
Merchandise Inventory	120	Sales Discount	405
Office Supplies	130	Interest Revenue	410
Accounts Payable	200	Cost of Goods Sold	500
Notes Payable	220	Salaries Expense	520
Owner's Capital	300	Telephone Expense	525

Required

a)   Record the above transactions in the purchases journal and the cash payments journal.

				Merchandise Inventory (DR)	Office Supplies (DR)	Other (DR)	Accounts Payable (CR)
Purchases Journal							**Page 6**
Date	**Account**	**Invoice #**	**PR**				

				Accounts Payable (DR)	Other (DR)	Merchandise Inventory (DR)	Cash (CR)
Cash Payments Journal							**Page 4**
Date	**Account**	**Check #**	**PR**				

b)   Post the appropriate transactions from the journals to the subledger accounts. At the end of the month, total the journals and update the accounts payable controlling account.

Account: Accounts Payable					**GL No:**
Date	**Description**	**PR**	**DR**	**CR**	**Balance**

Account: Block and Deck				
Date	**PR**	**DR**	**CR**	**Balance**

Account: Debolt Inc.				
Date	**PR**	**DR**	**CR**	**Balance**

AP-11B LO 2

Step On It is a small shoe retailer. The following is a list of transactions for the month of June 2018.

June 5   Received a bill (Invoice #5780) for $4,000 worth of office supplies from Runner

June 9   Received a telephone bill from Telly (Invoice #167) for $200

June 12   Paid amount owing (Invoice #5780) to Runner (Check #201)

June 21   Paid $3,500 to Jumper for purchase of inventory (Check #202)

June 22   Paid amount owing (Invoice #167) to Telly for telephone services with Check #203

June 25   Paid $300 to Daley Company for maintenance expenses (Check #204)

June 26   Received bill from The Walker (Invoice #113) for $4,200 worth of inventory

Required

a)   Record the above entries in the appropriate journal.

Purchases Journal							Page 1
Date	Account	Invoice #	PR	Telephone Expense (DR)	Office Supplies (DR)	Merchandise Inventory (DR)	Accounts Payable (CR)

Cash Payments Journal							Page 1
Date	Account	Check #	PR	Other (DR)	Merchandise Inventory (DR)	Accounts Payable (DR)	Cash (CR)

b)   Post the entries to the subledger accounts. At the end of the month, total the special journals and update the accounts payable controlling account.

Opening Balances

Runner	$1,000 (CR)
Telly	$1,200 (CR)
The Walker	$1,400 (CR)

Note that Step On It's accounts payable records consist of only these three subledgers. Assume no entries were made directly to accounts payable from the general journal. Update the PR columns in both the subledgers and special journals.

Account:	Accounts Payable				GL No: 200	
Date	**Description**	**PR**	**DR**	**CR**	**Balance**	

Accounts Payable Subsidiary Ledger					
Runner					
Date	**PR**	**DR**	**CR**	**Balance**	

Accounts Payable Subsidiary Ledger					
Telly					
Date	**PR**	**DR**	**CR**	**Balance**	

Accounts Payable Subsidiary Ledger					
The Walker					
Date	**PR**	**DR**	**CR**	**Balance**	

AP-12B LO 2

Horizon Company had the following transactions for the month of November 2018. They are recorded in the journals and posted to the ledger accounts.

Nov 1   Purchased inventory from Diagonal Company for $8,600 with Check #153

Nov 5   Received Invoice #2563 for $1,500 worth of office supplies from Max Supplies

Nov 9   Received Invoice #8475 from Vertical for $250 for hydro

Nov 10   Paid $320 to John Walker for repair expenses with Check #154

Nov 18   Paid amount owing to Vertical with Check #155

Nov 19   Paid amount owing to Max Supplies with Check #156

Nov 26   Received Invoice #563 from Total Hats for $4,600 worth of inventory

Purchases Journal							Page 1
Date	Account	Invoice #	PR	Hydro Expense (DR)	Office Supplies (DR)	Merchandise Inventory (DR)	Accounts Payable (CR)
Nov 1	Diagonal Company	153				8,600	8,600
Nov 5	Max Supplies	2563	✓			1,500	1,500
Nov 9	Vertical	8475	✓	250			250
Nov 26	Total Hats	563	✓			4,600	4,600
Nov 30	Total			250		14,700	14,950

Cash Payments Journal							Page 1
Date	Account	Check #	PR	Other (DR)	Merchandise Inventory (DR)	Accounts Payable (DR)	Cash (CR)
Nov 10	Repair Expense	154		320			320
Nov 18	Vertical	155	✓			250	250
Nov 19	Max Supplies	156	✓	1,500			1,500
Nov 30	Total			1,820		250	2,070

Opening Balances

Max Supplies	$200 (CR)
Vertical	$60 (CR)
Total Hats	$1,400 (CR)

Account:	Accounts Payable				GL No: 200	
Date	Description	PR	DR	CR	Balance	
Opening					1,660	CR
Nov 30		PJ1		14,950	16,610	CR
Nov 30		CP1	250		16,360	CR

Accounts Payable Subsidiary Ledger					
Max Supplies					
Date	PR	DR	CR	Balance	
Opening				200	CR
Nov 5	PJ1	1,500		1,300	DR
Nov 19	CP1		1,500	200	CR

Accounts Payable Subsidiary Ledger					
Vertical					
Date	PR	DR	CR	Balance	
Opening				60	CR
Nov 9	PJ1		250	310	CR
Nov 18	CP1	250		60	CR

Accounts Payable Subsidiary Ledger					
Total Hats					
Date	PR	DR	CR	Balance	
Opening				1,200	CR
Nov 26	PJ1		4,600	5,800	CR

Identify the errors made when the transactions were posted to the journals or when they were posted to the ledgers. What impact would these errors have on account balances?

_____

_____

_____

_____

_____

_____

_____

_____

_____

_____

_____

_____

_____

_____

AP-13B LO 1

TR Retailer has the following unadjusted trial balance at its year end, December 31, 2018.

TR Retailer Adjusted Trial Balance December 31, 2018		
Account Title	**DR**	**CR**
Cash	$12,800	
Accounts Receivable	32,400	
Merchandise Inventory	41,500	
Prepaid Insurance	2,400	
Equipment	65,000	
Accumulated Depreciation		$3,000
Accounts Payable		39,500
Interest Payable		0
Unearned Revenue		7,600
Notes Payable		20,000
Rogers, Capital		32,660
Rogers, Withdrawals	8,500	
Sales Revenue		164,800
Cost of Goods Sold	74,160	
Depreciation Expense	0	
Insurance Expense	0	
Interest Expense	0	
Rent Expense	26,000	
Telephone Expense	4,800	
Total	**$267,560**	**$267,560**

Regarding the notes payable, $10,000 will be paid by December 31, 2019.

TR Retailer also had the following adjusting entries that had to be entered into the books.
1. Interest accrued on the notes payable was $80.
2. Insurance used as of December 31, 2018 was $400.
3. TR Retailer had earned $1,000 of unearned revenue. Assume no accompanying COGS entry.
4. Depreciation for the year was $600.

Required

a) Complete the work sheet for TR Retailer for December 31, 2018.

Account Title	Unadjusted Trial Balance		Adjustments		Adjusted Trial Balance	
	DR	CR	DR	CR	DR	CR

b) Based on the values from the adjusted trial balance from part a), complete a multiple-step income statement and a classified balance sheet.

AP-14B LO 2

Highway Interchange sells clothing to retailers. During the month of July 2018, the following transactions occurred. Highway Interchange uses the periodic inventory system.

Jul 7   Sold inventory to Fashion House for $5,600 cash. The inventory had a cost of $2,400. The invoice number was #526.

Jul 10   Received a loan from Goldman Bank for $5,000.

Jul 15   Sold inventory to Stella Lanes on account for $8,500. The inventory had a cost of $3,400. The invoice number was #527.

Jul 17   Sold inventory to Cover Me for $7,500 on account. The inventory had a cost of $3,100. The invoice number was #528.

Jul 24   Received full payment from Stella Lanes for the sale on July 15.

Jul 31   Received $50 of interest earned on a savings account.

Required

a)   Record the above transactions in the sales journal and the cash receipts journal.

Sales Journal				Page 1
Date	Account	Invoice #	PR	Accounts Receivable/Sales (DR/CR)

Cash Receipts Journal							Page 1
Date	Account	PR	Cash (DR)	Accounts Receivable (CR)	Sales (CR)	Notes Payable (CR)	Other (CR)

b)   Post the appropriate transactions from the journals to the subledger accounts. At the end of the month, total the journals and update the accounts receivable controlling account.

Assume zero opening balances for the subledger and general ledger accounts. Assume no entries were made directly to the accounts receivable general ledger from the general journal.

Account: Accounts Receivable					GL No: 110
Date	Description	PR	DR	CR	Balance

Account: Stella Lanes				
Date	PR	DR	CR	Balance

Account: Cover Me				
Date	PR	DR	CR	Balance

Case Study

CS-1 LO 2 3

Easy Riser sells pre-fabricated staircases to builders for new homes and renovations. Lately, the owner has been receiving calls from suppliers regarding late payments. The owner is aware of the late payments because he has been holding back payments due to a shortage of cash. The company is having excellent sales, and earning a very good profit even though it has a cash shortfall.

After asking the bookkeeper about the cash shortage problem, the bookkeeper informed the owner about the accounting process. All transactions are entered into the general journal and posted to the general ledger. The supplier invoices are stored in one folder and the sales invoices in another folder in the bookkeeper's desk. When the owner asked to see a sales invoice from last month (to see if the amount had been collected), the bookkeeper had trouble finding it. When it was finally found, it was determined that it had not been collected yet.

a) What ethical and control issues does this company have?

_____

_____

_____

_____

_____

_____

_____

_____

b) What would you suggest to improve the bookkeeping for this company?

_____

_____

_____

_____

_____

_____

_____

_____

_____

_____

_____

_____

_____

_____

_____

_____

Notes

Chapter 10

CASH AND INTERNAL CONTROLS

LEARNING OBJECTIVES

LO 1 Describe and apply internal controls for a business

LO 2 Apply cash controls

LO 3 Prepare a bank reconciliation and related journal entries

LO 4 Prepare a petty cash fund and record related journal entries

AMEENGAGE *Access **ameengage.com** for integrated resources including tutorials, practice exercises, the digital textbook and more.*

——— Assessment Questions ———

AS-1 LO 3

What is a bank reconciliation?

_____

_____

AS-2 LO 3

List three typical reasons for a bank making additional deductions from a company's cash account.

_____

_____

_____

AS-3 LO 3

What are two typical reasons for a bank making additional deposits to a company's cash account?

_____

_____

AS-4 LO 3

In a typical bank reconciliation, what are the titles of the two column headers?

_____

_____

AS-5 LO 3

What are non-sufficient funds (NSF) checks?

_____

_____

AS-6 LO 3

What is an outstanding deposit?

_____

_____

AS-7 LO 3

When is a journal entry required during a bank reconciliation?

_____

_____

AS-8 LO 3

How are outstanding checks recorded on the bank reconciliation?

_____

_____

AS-9 LO 4

What is an imprest system for petty cash?

_____

_____

AS-10 LO 4

Briefly describe the responsibilities of the petty cash custodian.

_____

_____

AS-11 LO 4

What does an employee that requires petty cash need to present to the petty cash custodian?

_____

_____

AS-12 LO 4

What is a petty cash summary sheet?

_____

_____

AS-13 LO 4

Why do petty cash overages or shortages occur?

_____

_____

AS-14 LO 4

When does the cash over and short account behave like an expense account?

_____

_____

AS-15 LO 4

What are the only two times that the petty cash account in the ledger is debited or credited?

_____

_____

AS-16 LO 1 2

List two general controls that can be used for petty cash.

_____

_____

AS-17 LO 2

List two controls that can be used to prevent the misuse of cash.

_____

_____

AS-18 LO 2

Define cash equivalents.

_____

_____

AS-19 LO 2

Briefly describe what it means to be in bank overdraft.

_____

_____

AS-20 LO 2

Describe the position of cash equivalents on the balance sheet.

_____

_____

AS-21 LO 2

List two reasons why cash equivalents are entered with cash on the balance sheet.

_____

AS-22 LO 2

List three examples of cash equivalent items.

_____
_____
_____
_____

AS-23 LO 2

Why would a business invest in cash equivalents?

_____
_____

AS-24 LO 2

What are the two different ways a business usually receives cash from customers?

_____
_____
_____

AS-25 LO 2

When receiving a cash sale, why is it important for the customer to participate in the transaction?

_____
_____

AS-26 LO 2

Describe how a business can protect cash on its premises.

_____
_____
_____
_____

AS-27 LO 2

What is the overall goal of a business in managing its cash?

_____
_____

AS-28 LO 1

What are internal controls? Explain.

_____
_____
_____

AS-29 LO 1

List three reasons for designing internal controls in a company.

_____

_____

_____

AS-30 LO 1

What does section 404 of SOX require a company's senior management and auditors to do with regards to internal controls?

_____

_____

_____

AS-31 LO 1

Name the five key elements of internal control under the framework of Internal Control—Integrated Framework (2013).

_____

_____

AS-32 LO 2

What is a voucher system in regards to cash payments?

_____

_____

AS-33 LO 2

What is a remittance advice on an invoice?

_____

_____

_____

Application Questions Group A

AP-1A  3

Quality Electronic is preparing a bank reconciliation and has identified the following potential reconciling items. For each item, indicate in the action column if it is (i) added to the balance of the ledger, (ii) deducted from the balance of the ledger, (iii) added to the balance of the bank statement, or (iv) deducted from the balance of the bank statement.

Item	Action
a) deposits that are not shown on the bank statement	
b) interest deposited to the company's account	
c) bank service charges	
d) outstanding checks	
e) NSF checks returned	

AP-2A LO 3

The following data represents information necessary to assist in preparing the June 30, 2018 bank reconciliation for Trimore Company.

- The June 30 bank balance was $5,300.

- The bank statement indicated a deduction of $20 for all bank service charges.

- A customer deposited $1,200 directly into the bank account to settle an outstanding accounts receivable bill.

- Check #850 for $600 and Check #857 for $420 have been recorded in the company ledger but did not appear on the bank statement.

- A customer paid an amount of $4,534 to Trimore on June 30 but the deposit did not appear on the bank statement.

- The accounting clerk made an error and recorded a $200 check as $2,000. The check was written to pay the outstanding accounts payable account.

- Check #9574 for $100 was deducted from Trimore's account by the bank. This check was not written by Trimore and needs to be reversed by the bank.

- The bank included an NSF check in the amount of $820 relating to a customer's payment. The NSF service fee was $10.

- The general ledger cash account showed a balance of $6,764 on June 30.

Required

a) Complete the bank reconciliation for Trimore Company.

b)   Write the necessary journal entries to correct Trimore's records.

Date	Account Title and Explanation	Debit	Credit

AP-3A LO 3

Mike's Cleaning Service received its monthly bank statement for its business bank account, with a balance of $55,062 for the month of July 2018. The balance of the ledger account as at July 31, 2018 was $59,461.

After a comparison of the checks written by the company and those deducted from the bank account, Mike's accountant determined that three checks, totaling $2,806 (Check #256 for $606, Check #261 for $1,200, and Check #262 for $1,000), were outstanding on July 31. A review of the deposits showed that a deposit on July 1 for $12,610 was actually recorded in the company's ledger on June 30 and a July 31 deposit of $9,760 was recorded in the company's ledger but had not yet been recorded by the bank. The July bank statement showed a total service fee of $18, a customer's check in the amount of $70 that had been returned NSF, a loan payment of $857 that was deducted automatically by the bank, and a customer made a $3,500 payment that was deposited directly into the Mike's Cleaning bank account.

Required

a)   Prepare the bank reconciliation as at July 31, 2018.

b) How much cash does Mike's Cleaning Service actually have in its cash account on July 31?

_____

c) Prepare journal entries to record all necessary adjustments to bring the cash account to its adjusted balance.

Date	Account Title and Explanation	Debit	Credit

AP-4A LO 3

The following data represents information necessary to assist in preparing the January 31, 2018 bank reconciliation for Sellmore Company.

- The January 31 bank balance was $4,598.

- A customer deposited $900 directly into the bank account to settle an outstanding accounts receivable bill.

- The bank statement indicated a deduction of $33 for all bank service charges.

- Check #821 for $360 and Check #865 for $252 have been recorded in the company ledger but did not appear on the bank statement.

- A customer paid $4,589 to Sellmore on January 31 but the deposit did not appear on the bank statement.

- The accounting clerk made an error and recorded a $180 check as $1,800. The check was written to pay the outstanding accounts payable account.

- The bank included an NSF check in the amount of $710 relating to a customer's payment.

- Check #9504 for $153 was deducted from Sellmore's account by the bank. This check was not written by Sellmore and needs to be reversed by the bank.

- The general ledger cash account showed a balance of $6,951 on January 31.

Required

a) Complete the bank reconciliation for Sellmore Company.

b) Write the necessary journal entries to correct Sellmore's records.

Date	Account Title and Explanation	Debit	Credit

AP-5A LO 3

Use the following information to prepare the bank reconciliation for Jeremiah Motors.

- The bank balance on March 31 was $13,500.
- The general ledger cash account showed a balance of $14,950 on March 31.
- Received Check #80 from a customer for $950 but it has not been deposited yet.
- The bank statement shows a charge of $110 for all bank service fees.
- A customer transferred $800 directly into the company's bank account to pay their account.
- Recorded Check #94 to pay for supplies in the journal for $480 instead of $840.
- The bank statement showed an NSF check from a customer for $830.

Required

a) Complete the bank reconciliation for Jeremiah Motors.

b) Prepare any necessary journal entries to update the company's records for March 2018.

Date	Account Title and Explanation	Debit	Credit

AP-6A LO 3

The following cash ledger contains information about RJ Cosmetics' cash account.

GENERAL LEDGER

Account: Cash				GL No: 101	
Date	Description	Debit	Credit	Balance	
Feb 1	Opening Balance			4,000	DR
Feb 3	Check #1		800	3,200	DR
Feb 12	Deposit	2,500		5,700	DR
Feb 21	Check #2		1,200	4,500	DR
Feb 26	Check #3		950	3,550	DR
Feb 27	Check #4		600	2,950	DR
Feb 28	Deposit	1,300		4,250	DR

RJ Cosmetics' bank statement for the month of February is shown below.

BANK STATEMENT				
Date	Explanation	Withdrawal	Deposit	Balance
Feb 01	Opening Balance			4,000
Feb 03	Check #1	800		3,200
Feb 12	Deposit		2,500	5,700
Feb 14	NSF Check	500		5,200
Feb 14	NSF Charge	15		5,185
Feb 21	Check #2	1,200		3,985
Feb 25	EFT—Monthly rent expense	1,000		2,985
Feb 28	Service charges	25		2,960
Feb 28	Interest on bank account		20	2,980

Required

a) Prepare a bank reconciliation for RJ Cosmetics as at February 28, 2018.

b) Prepare the required journal entries for the corrections made in the bank reconciliation.

Date	Account Title and Explanation	Debit	Credit

c) Prepare the full reconciled cash ledger account for the month of February.

GENERAL LEDGER

Account: Cash				GL No: 101
Date	Description	Debit	Credit	Balance

d) Using last month's data along with the bank statement and the general ledger provided, prepare a bank reconciliation for RJ Cosmetics for March 31, 2018.

GENERAL LEDGER

Account: Cash				GL No: 101	
Date	**Description**	**Debit**	**Credit**	**Balance**	
Mar 1	Opening Balance			2,730	DR
Mar 7	Check #5		920	1,810	DR
Mar 13	Deposit	850		2,660	DR
Mar 18	Check #6		450	2,210	DR
Mar 28	Deposit	2,135		4,345	DR
Mar 29	Check #7		1,100	3,245	DR

BANK STATEMENT				
Date	**Explanation**	**Withdrawal**	**Deposit**	**Balance**
Mar 1	Opening Balance			2,980
Mar 2	Deposit		1,300	4,280
Mar 3	Check #4	600		3,680
Mar 7	Check #5	920		2,760
Mar 13	Deposit		850	3,610
Mar 18	Check #6	450		3,160
Mar 25	EFT—Monthly rent expense	1,000		2,160
Mar 28	Deposit		2,135	4,295
Mar 31	Service charges	25		4,270
Mar 31	Interest on bank account		13.65	4,283.65

Please note that the deposit from March 28 contains a check from the customer who provided an NSF check from the month before. The customer paid for the original amount of $500, plus the $15 charge.

AP-7A LO 3

Consider the following general ledger and bank statement for Meena Salon.

GENERAL LEDGER

Account: Cash					GL No: 101	
Date	Explanation	Debit	Credit	Balance		
Apr 1	Opening Balance			8,000	DR
Apr 6	Jimmy Supplies—Check #101		500	7,500	DR
Apr 10	HitHit Supplies—Check #102		1,000	6,500	DR
Apr 11	Mary Malony	250		6,750	DR
Apr 14	Inner Beauty Inc.—Check #103		757	5,993	DR
Apr 19	Shona Care Ltd.—Check #104		840	5,153	DR
Apr 29	Deposit	2,500		7,653	DR

BANK STATEMENT				
Date	Explanation	Withdrawal	Deposit	Balance
Apr 1	Opening Balance			8,000
Apr 6	Check #101	500		7,500
Apr 10	Check #102	1,000		6,500
Apr 10	EFT—Monthly rent	800		5,700
Apr 11	Mary Malony		250	5,950
Apr 11	NSF Check	250		5,700
Apr 11	NSF charge	5		5,695
Apr 14	Check #103	575		5,120
Apr 21	Check #1520	3,000		2,120
Apr 30	Service charges	25		2,095
Apr 30	Interest on bank account		20	2,115

Additional Information

1. On April 14, Meena Salon purchased $575 worth of salon supplies from Inner Beauty Inc.
2. The salon's check numbers are always three digits in length.

Required

a) Prepare a bank reconciliation for Meena Salon on April 30, 2018.

b)   Prepare the necessary journal entries.

Date	Account Title and Explanation	Debit	Credit

AP-8A LO 3

Shine Laundry's bank reconciliation is provided for the month of September 2018.
However, due to some errors on the bank reconciliation, the reconciled balance for the ledger and the bank are different from each other.

Shine Laundry Bank Reconciliation September 30, 2018		
	Ledger	**Bank**
Opening Balance	$5,100	$3,820
Add: Outstanding deposit—Sep 29	400	
Outstanding deposit—Sep 30	1,220	
Less: Outstanding Check #3—Sep 8		(1,000)
Outstanding Check #4—Sep 10	(600)	
EFT—Insurance—Sep 15		(400)
EFT—Monthly rent—Sep 18		(600)
NSF Check—Sep 19		(250)
Charges for NSF Check—Sep 19		(5)
Service charges—Sep 30	(15)	
Interest on bank account—Sep 30	(10)	
Reconciled Balance	$6,095	$1,565

Required

a) Prepare a reconciled bank reconciliation. Assume the dollar amounts of the individual items on the bank reconciliation are correct.

b) Prepare all journal entries required by Shine Laundry.

Date	Account Title and Explanation	Debit	Credit

AP-9A LO 3

The bookkeeper for Brose Industrial Supply has prepared a bank reconciliation for the month but, although it balances, it is not correct. Prepare a corrected bank reconciliation for Brose Industrial Supply. Assume that all figures show the correct dollar amounts, and that the opening balances are both correct.

Brose Industrial Supply Bank Reconciliation July 31, 2018		
	Ledger	Bank
Opening Balance	$14,630	$16,070
Add:		
Bank service charges		80
Interest earned	100	
Less:		
Outstanding checks		(1,600)
Outstanding deposits	(730)	
Unrecorded deposit		(550)
Reconciled Balance	$14,000	$14,000

Analysis

After preparing a bank reconciliation, journal entries must be prepared to record adjustments to cash. Name three items that require an adjusting entry. Why don't all items on the reconciliation require adjusting entries?

AP-10A LO 4

On June 7, 2018, Mary decided to set up a petty cash fund for her small business. A check of $125 was issued and cashed. The $125 cash was given to the store supervisor who was to act as petty cashier. The petty cashier was told to obtain authorized vouchers for all payments. Petty cash was to be replenished when the balance in the cash box reached $23.

Required

a) Record the establishment of the fund on June 7.

Date	Account Title and Explanation	Debit	Credit

b) On June 19, the following summary was prepared.

Delivery Expense	$50.90
Miscellaneous Expense	20.40
Office Expense	24.10
Postage Expense	6.60
Total	$102

Prepare the entry to replenish the petty cash.

Date	Account Title and Explanation	Debit	Credit

c) On June 23, it was decided to increase the amount of the petty cash fund from $125 to $175. A check of $50 was issued. Record the transaction.

Date	Account Title and Explanation	Debit	Credit

AP-11A LO 4

The petty cash fund was established on August 12, 2018 in the amount of $250. Expenditures from the fund by the custodian as of August 31, 2018, were evidenced by approved receipts for the following.

Postage Expense	$30.00
Supplies Expense	65.00
Maintenance Expense	42.00
Delivery Expense	58.20
Newspaper Advertising	21.95
Miscellaneous Expense	15.75

On August 31, 2018, the petty cash fund was replenished and increased to $300; currency and coin in the fund at that time totaled $15.60.

Prepare the journal entries to record the transactions related to the petty cash fund for the month of August.

Date	Account Title and Explanation	Debit	Credit

AP-12A LO 4

On June 29, 2018, Fire It Up Grill decided to establish a petty cash fund for the office. A check for $250 was issued and cashed. The $250 cash was given to the office manager who was to act as the petty cashier. He decided that the petty cash fund should be replenished when the balance in the cash box reached $70.

Required

a) Record the establishment of the petty cash fund on June 29.

Date	Account Title and Explanation	Debit	Credit

b) On July 31, the balance in the petty cash account was $70. A summary of the expenses was prepared.

Delivery Expense	$68
Office Supplies Expense	96
Miscellaneous Expense	10
Postage Expense	7
Total	$181

Determine the balance of the petty cash fund after all transactions have occurred for the month of July.

c) Prepare the journal entry to replenish the petty cash fund.

Date	Account Title and Explanation	Debit	Credit

d) Based on your response from part c), determine if the cash amount is over or short.

_____

e) On July 31, with input from the petty cashier, management decided to increase the amount of the petty cash fund from $250 to $350. This was based on the fact that more items were approved to be paid by petty cash. A check for $100 was issued and cashed. Record the transaction.

Date	Account Title and Explanation	Debit	Credit

AP-13A LO 4

On January 1, 2018, Hit Design set up a petty cash fund for $250. At the end of the first week, the petty cash fund contains the following items.

Cash on hand	$50
Receipt for the purchase of office supplies	40
Receipt for delivery charges	10
Receipt for the purchase of stamps	20
Receipt for travel to a client meeting	50
Receipt for the payment of newspaper advertising	75

Required

a) Calculate any cash overage or shortage.

_____

_____

b) Prepare the journal entries for setting up and replenishing the petty cash fund.

Date	Account Title and Explanation	Debit	Credit

Date	Account Title and Explanation	Debit	Credit

AP-14A LO 4

Eric Dravin Enterprises decided to establish a petty cash fund for the office on January 11, 2018. Management set up the fund, and appointed the office administrator as the petty cashier. A check was issued for the petty cash fund for $175, and was cashed. Management decided that the petty cash fund should be replenished when the balance in the cash box reaches $75.

Required

a)   Record the establishment of the petty cash fund on January 11.

Date	Account Title and Explanation	Debit	Credit

b)   On January 31, the balance in the petty cash account was $30. The totaled receipts showed the following information.

Delivery Expense	$89
Postage Expense	22
Office Supplies	13
Travel Expense	25
Total	$149

Determine the balance of the petty cash fund based on the receipts provided.

_____

c)   Prepare the journal entry to replenish the petty cash fund at the end of the month.

Date	Account Title and Explanation	Debit	Credit

d)   Based on your response from part c), determine if the cash amount is over or short.

_____

e)   On February 4, 2018, management determined that the petty cash fund's balance ran too low for the month of January. They suggested doubling the petty cash fund balance. A check for $175 was issued and cashed. Record the transaction.

Date	Account Title and Explanation	Debit	Credit

AP-15A LO 4

Sky Auctions set up a petty cash fund of $250 on January 1, 2018. The custodian found the following receipts in the cash box for the month.

$35 for food for the office employees
$63 for fuel for the company vehicle
$50 to pay a specialist to update the computer system
$46 to purchase supplies for the office

The custodian counted $81 cash remaining in the cash box. Prepare journal entries to establish the petty cash fund and replenish the petty cash fund on January 31, 2018.

Date	Account Title and Explanation	Debit	Credit

Analysis

What is the purpose of a petty cash system?

_____

_____

Application Questions Group B

AP-1B LO 3

For the month of September 2018, Jared Anitco noticed that the bank processed a check that he was not aware of. He called the bank and determined that the check belongs to another account. The following is the general ledger report for cash in the bank and the bank statement for Jared Anitco for the month of September.

GENERAL LEDGER

Account: Cash					GL No: 101	
Date	**Explanation**	**Debit**	**Credit**	**Balance**	
Sep 1	Opening Balance			7,000	DR
Sep 6	CandyMan—Check #200		500	6,500	DR
Sep 6	Supply Store—Check #201		754	5,746	DR
Sep 10	Jordan Lo—Check #1000	800		6,546	DR
Sep 25	Book Store—Check #202		200	6,346	DR

BANK STATEMENT				
Date	**Explanation**	**Withdrawal**	**Deposit**	**Balance**
Sep 1	Opening Balance			7,000
Sep 10	CandyMan—Check #200	500		6,500
Sep 10	Supply Store—Check #201	754		5,746
Sep 14	Jordan Lo—Check #1000		800	6,546
Sep 20	Mooris Mo—Check #1107	820		5,726
Sep 30	Book Store—Check #202	200		5,526

Identify the check that does not belong to Jared. Explain why a journal entry is not required to correct the mistake.

_____

_____

_____

AP-2B LO 3

The following financial information is related to a company called World's Computer..

- Cash balance per general ledger is $2,219

- Bank statement balance is $2,478.80

- These checks were recorded in the ledger but did not appear on the bank statement: Check #186 for $100; Check #193 for $57; Check #199 for $143

- A deposit for $368 dated July 31 was recorded in the ledger but did not appear on the bank statement

- Service charges of $18 are shown on the bank statement

- A check for $37.50 has been cashed (correctly) by the bank but was incorrectly recorded in the company's ledger as $375.50. The check was issued for the purchase of office supplies.

- The bank automatically deposited interest of $7.80 at the end of the month

Required

a)   Prepare the July 2018 bank reconciliation statement for World's Computer.

b)   Record any journal entries required to bring the company records up to date.

Date	Account Title and Explanation	Debit	Credit

AP-3B LO 3

The bank statement for Fashion Fly had an ending cash balance of $1,500 on December 31, 2018. On this date the cash balance in their general ledger was $2,000. After comparing the bank statement with the company records, the following information was determined.

•   The bank returned an NSF check in the amount of $320 that Fashion Fly deposited on December 20. The NSF service fee was $5.

•   A direct deposit was received from a customer on December 30 in payment of their accounts totaling $3,850. This has not yet been recorded by the company.

•   On December 30 the bank deposited $10 for interest earned.

•   The bank withdrew $15 for bank service charges.

•   Deposits in transit on December 31 totaled $4,020.

Required

a) Reconcile the ledger and bank statement.

b) Prepare the required journal entries.

Date	Account Title and Explanation	Debit	Credit

AP-4B LO 3

The bank statement for Flying Fashion had an ending cash balance of $1,640 on March 31, 2018. On this date the cash balance in the general ledger was $1,921. After comparing the bank statement with the company records, the following information was determined.

- The bank returned an NSF check in the amount of $264 that Flying Fashion deposited on March 20.

- A direct deposit was received from a customer on March 30 in payment of accounts totaling $3,900. This has not yet been recorded by the company.

- The bank withdrew $41 for all bank service charges.

- On March 30 the bank deposited $14 for interest earned.

- Deposits in transit on March 31 totaled $3,890.

Required

a) Reconcile the ledger and bank statement.

b) Create the required journal entries.

Date	Account Title and Explanation	Debit	Credit

AP-5B  LO 3

Lux Transportation Services has just received its bank statement for the month and has compared it to the general ledger cash account.

GENERAL LEDGER

Account: Cash				GL No: 101	
Date	Description	Debit	Credit	Balance	
Oct 1	Opening Balance			13,100	DR
Oct 2	Check #401		750	12,350	DR
Oct 5	Check #220	900		13,250	DR
Oct 8	Check #403		750	12,500	DR
Oct 16	Check #404		200	12,300	DR

BANK STATEMENT				
Date	Description	Withdrawal	Deposit	Balance
Oct 1	Opening Balance			13,100
Oct 2	Check #401	750		12,350
Oct 6	Check #220		900	13,250
Oct 6	EFT Rent Payment	750		12,500
Oct 10	Check #403	750		11,750
Oct 16	Check #88		445	12,195
Oct 30	Interest		50	12,245
Oct 31	Service Charge	110		12,135

Prepare the bank reconciliation for Lux Transportation as at October 31, 2018.

Analysis

After some investigation, it is discovered that Check #88 is not from a customer and should not have been deposited into the company's bank account by the bank. How does this discovery change the bank reconciliation and any necessary journal entries?

_____

_____

_____

AP-6B LO 3

Shelley Company had completed October's bank reconciliation with an exact reconciled balance on the last day of the month. Consider the bank reconciliation for October.

Shelley Company Bank Reconciliation October 31, 2018		
Explanation	**Ledger**	**Bank**
Opening Balance	$6,500	$4,725.63
Add: Outstanding deposit 1		700
Error on Check #366	189	
Outstanding deposit 2		950
Bank error Check #45928		1,000
Interest on bank account	23.63	
Less: Outstanding Check #354		(300)
Outstanding Check #367		(2,265)
Direct Insurance billing	(1,100)	
EFT—Monthly rent	(1,325)	
NSF Check	(875)	
NSF charges	(25)	
Outstanding Check #368		(1,463)
Service charges	(40)	
Reconciled Balance	$3,347.63	$3,347.63

The following items were discovered in November.

- An NSF check was entered by the bank for $570, it charged the bank account for $25.

- There are three deposits outstanding by the bank for $450, $200, and $1,465 respectively.

- Insurance is a preauthorized payment taken out every month for the same amount month.

- Shelley Company paid its monthly rent via an EFT.

- Checks #354 and #367 are still outstanding.

- Check #378 is outstanding for $675.

- Check #379 is outstanding for $1,110.96.

- Interest earned on the bank account $27.85.

- Total service charges for the bank account are $40.

- The balance of the ledger on November 30 is $6,284.95.

- The bank balance provided from the bank statement dated November 30 is $5,488.76.

Required

a)   Complete the bank reconciliation for Shelley Company for the month of November.

b)   Prepare the necessary journal entries.

Date	Account Title and Explanation	Debit	Credit

AP-7B LO 3

Consider the following general ledger and bank statement for Saleen Salon.

GENERAL LEDGER

Account: Cash				GL No: 101	
Date	Explanation	Debit	Credit	Balance	
Dec 1	Opening Balance			8,100	DR
Dec 6	Jonny Supplies—Check #120		660	7,440	DR
Dec 10	WalkWalk Supplies—Check #121		1,180	6,260	DR
Dec 11	Bethany Balony	230		6,490	DR
Dec 14	Salon Beauty Inc.—Check #122		686	5,804	DR
Dec 19	Shona Care Ltd.—Check #123		930	4,874	DR
Dec 29	Deposit	2,200		7,074	DR

BANK STATEMENT				
Date	Explanation	Withdrawal	Deposit	Balance
Dec 1	Opening Balance			8,100
Dec 6	Check #120	660		7,440
Dec 10	Check #121	1,180		6,260
Dec 10	EFT—Monthly rent	680		5,580
Dec 11	Bethany Balony		230	5,810
Dec 11	NSF Check	230		5,580
Dec 11	NSF charge	19		5,561
Dec 14	Check #122	866		4,695
Dec 21	Check #1470	3,700		995
Dec 31	Service charges	32		963
Dec 31	Interest on bank account		17	980

Additional Information

1. On Dec 14, Saleen Salon purchased $866 worth of salon supplies from Salon Beauty Inc.
2. The salon's check numbers are always three digits in length.

Required

a) Prepare a bank reconciliation for Saleen Salon on December 31, 2018.

b) Prepare the necessary journal entries.

Date	Account Title and Explanation	Debit	Credit

AP-8B LO 3

The owner of Lucy Learning has attempted to prepare the month-end bank reconciliation. However, she has noticed that the ending balances do not match.

Required

a) Prepare a corrected bank reconciliation for Lucy Learning, assuming all figures show the correct dollar amounts.

Lucy Learning		
Bank Reconciliation		
November 30, 2018		
Explanation	Ledger	Bank
Opening Balance	$3,400	$200
Add: Outstanding deposits	1,600	
EFT—monthly payment for Note Payable		1,500
Interest earned	250	
Less: NSF Check	(800)	
NSF charge		(40)
Bank service charge		(60)
Direct customer deposit for balance owed	(550)	
Reconciled Balance	$3,900	$1,600

b) Record any journal entries necessary to update the cash account.

Date	Account Title and Explanation	Debit	Credit

AP-9B LO 3

Tobias has been given the general ledger and bank statement for Eaton Company. Help him prepare the bank reconciliation based on the two documents on September 30, 2018.

GENERAL LEDGER

Account: Cash				GL No: 101	
Date	**Description**	**Debit**	**Credit**	**Balance**	
Sep 1	Opening Balance			8,400	DR
Sep 7	Check #412	500		8,900	DR
Sep 9	Check #900—Equipment		4,800	4,100	DR
Sep 16	Check #901—Inventory		405	3,695	DR
Sep 19	Check #81	2,300		5,995	DR
Sep 27	Check #902—Office Supplies		180	5,815	DR

BANK STATEMENT				
Date	**Description**	**Withdawal**	**Deposit**	**Balance**
Sep 1	Opening Balance			8,400
Sep 7	EFT—Rent payment	1,300		7,100
Sep 9	Check #900	4,800		2,300
Sep 16	Check #901	450		1,850
Sep 19	Check #81		2,300	4,150
Sep 19	NSF—Check #81	2,300		1,850
Sep 19	NSF Charge	40		1,810
Sep 30	Interest		80	1,890

Note: In case of any discrepency between dollar amounts, assume the bank statement is correct.

AP-10B LO 1 2 4

Last year, Holtzman Company established a petty cash fund of $100. The custodian complained that she had to reimburse the fund on a weekly basis, and suggested that the fund be increased to $400. That way, she would only have to summarize payouts and get a check from the cashier once per month.

Management agreed with the custodian, and on April 1, 2018, advised the cashier to increase the fund to $400.

Required

a) Write the journal entry to increase the fund to $400.

Date	Account Title and Explanation	Debit	Credit

b) List five internal controls that should be established around the use of petty cash.

AP-11B LO 4

On April 1, 2018, Clayton Company established a petty cash fund of $200.

During the month the custodian paid out the following amounts.

Apr 6   Purchased stamps for $40

Apr 8   Paid a $20 delivery charge on an outgoing package

Apr 10   Paid $25 for public transit fares for employees on company business

Apr 14   Purchased coffee and donuts for $8 for clients during a meeting

Apr 15   Bought a package of paper for $7 for the copy machine

The custodian counted the fund on April 16 and found $105 in the petty cash box.

Required

a)   Prepare the journal entry to record the establishment of the fund.

Date	Account Title and Explanation	Debit	Credit

b)   Prepare the journal entry to record the reimbursement of the fund on April 16, 2018.

Date	Account Title and Explanation	Debit	Credit

AP-12B LO 4

On March 20, 2018, Skyline Enterprises established a $300 petty cash fund.

Required

a)   Prepare the entry to record the establishment of the fund.

b)   At the end of the month, the petty cash custodian analyzed all the monthly transactions. She opened the petty cash box and counted $100 cash remaining. There were also two receipts in the petty cash box: receipt #1: $100—Entertainment and receipt #2: $98—Travel. Record the journal entries for this month's expenses and replenish the fund.

c)   At the end of the month, Skyline Enterprises wanted to increase the petty cash fund by $100. Prepare the journal entry to record the increase in petty cash fund.

Date	Account Title and Explanation	Debit	Credit

AP-13B LO 4

The following information was taken from the records of the JoJo Store.

Apr 14	Paid $25 for public transit
Apr 16	Paid $20 for food
Apr 17	Purchased stamps for $5
Apr 17	Paid $50 for window washing
Apr 19	Paid $15 for the delivery of packages
Apr 20	Purchased office supplies for $30

JoJo is the owner of the store and he established a petty cash fund of $200 on April 12, 2018.
All the transactions listed above were paid using petty cash. Petty cash needs to be replenished when $50 is left in the petty cash box. On April 21, there was $50 left in the petty cash box.

Prepare the journal entries for setting up and replenishing the petty cash fund.

Date	Account Title and Explanation	Debit	Credit

AP-14B LO 1 2 4

On September 24, 2018, Charlie decided to set up a petty cash fund for his small business. Charlie transferred $150 to a cash box and informed his employees that they could use the money for small expenses for the business. He told them to leave a short note with the reason for each withdrawal. Charlie decided to replenish the cash box when its balance reached $30.

The following events took place.

Sep 24   Petty cash fund was established

Oct 10   The following notes and cash were found inside the cash box.

Notes	
Travel	$94
Postage	4
Miscellaneous	17
Office Supplies	9
Total Notes	124
Cash Remaining	15
Total	$139

Nov 3 Charlie decided to increase the amount of the petty cash fund to $200

Record the transactions for the above three events.

Date	Account Title and Explanation	Debit	Credit

Analysis

Charlie has noticed quite a few significant shortages in the cash box since the fund was established. What are two controls that Charlie could implement around the use of petty cash to protect against shortages?

_____

_____

_____

AP-15B LO 4

On March 20, 2018, Michaelangelo's decided to establish a petty cash fund for the restaurant. A check of $350 was issued and cashed. The $350 cash was given to the manager, April, who was to act as the petty cashier, and the petty cash box could be locked in her office. With the suggestion from management, it was decided that the petty cash fund should be replenished when the balance in the cash box reached $85.

Required

a) Record the establishment of the petty cash fund on March 20.

Date	Account Title and Explanation	Debit	Credit

b) On March 31 the balance in the petty cash account was $84. A summary of the expenses was prepared.

Advertising Expense	$155
Delivery Expense	76
Miscellaneous Expense	18
Postage Expense	23
Total	$272

Determine the balance of the petty cash fund after all transactions have occurred for the month of April.

c) Prepare the journal entry to replenish the petty cash fund.

Date	Account Title and Explanation	Debit	Credit

d) Based on your response from part c), determine if the cash amount is over or short.

Case Study

CS-1

M & G Finances (M & G) is an incorporated tax preparation company. Most of its clients pay for the completion of their tax returns with either a debit or a credit card. The rest pay with cash.

M & G employs 20 tax preparers, two supervisors and one manager. The office collects thousands of dollars in cash every day. After a tax return is prepared by one of the 20 tax preparers, a supervisor is responsible for recording information (i.e. customer name, amount charged, payment method) related to the return in a log.

The receipt of cash is recorded immediately when it is received. Receipts are issued immediately, in numerical order. Copies of the receipts are also kept with the logs. The cash is kept in the drawer of the employee who prepared the tax return. At the end of the day, the cash being kept by the various employees is pooled together and then passed on to the supervisor, who keeps it in her drawer. The cash is deposited into the bank at the end of each work week.

Over the past few weeks, the manager has noted that the amount of cash on hand in the office has consistently been less than the amount recorded in the logs. In fact, the difference between the actual cash on hand and the recorded amount is increasing little by little over time.

Required

a) Is M & G exhibiting any positive aspects in its system of cash controls? Explain.

b) What are the negatives in M & G's cash control system? Explain. (You can refer to controls that do not exist, or controls that exist but are ineffective).

Notes

Chapter 11

ACCOUNTING FOR RECEIVABLES

LEARNING OBJECTIVES

LO 1   Explain the importance of accounts receivable

LO 2   Account for bad debt using the allowance method and the direct write off method

LO 3   Estimate bad debt using the income statement and balance sheet approaches

LO 4   Record promissory notes and notes receivable

LO 5   Utilize reports, including the accounts receivable subledger, to manage accounts receivable information

LO 6   Calculate financial ratios pertaining to accounts receivable

LO 7   Account for the disposal of receivables using factoring and pledging

LO 8   Apply internal controls relating to accounts receivable

LO 9   Apply ethics relating to accounts receivable and notes receivable

AMEENGAGE   *Access **ameengage.com** for integrated resources including tutorials, practice exercises, the digital textbook and more.*

Assessment Questions

AS-1 LO 1

Define accounts receivable.

_____

_____

AS-2 LO 1

Describe the presentation of accounts receivable on the balance sheet.

_____

_____

_____

AS-3 LO 1

What are the advantages and disadvantages to a company that sells on credit?

_____

_____

_____

AS-4 LO 1

What are payment terms? Where are payment terms usually indicated to customers?

_____

_____

AS-5 LO 1

How are sales through third-party credit cards (such as VISA or MasterCard) recorded in a vendor's books?

_____

_____

_____

AS-6 LO 1

For a vendor, what are some advantages and disadvantages of allowing customers to pay using third-party credit cards?

_____

_____

_____

_____

AS-7 LO 1

For retailers, what are some advantages and disadvantages of offering their own credit cards?

_____

_____

_____

_____

AS-8 LO 5

How can the accounts receivable subledger assist in managing a company's accounts receivable?

_____

_____

_____

AS-9 LO 5

Explain the relationship between the accounts receivable controlling account and individual customer accounts in the accounts receivable subledger.

_____

_____

_____

_____

AS-10 LO 1 4

What is the difference between accounts receivable and notes receivable?

_____

_____

_____

AS-11 LO 2

What is bad debt?

_____

_____

AS-12 LO 2

According to the expense recognition principle, in which period must bad debt expense be recorded?

_____

_____

_____

AS-13 LO 2

Explain the nature and purpose of the account called allowance for doubtful accounts, under the allowance method.

_____

_____

_____

AS-14 LO 3

What would cause the AFDA account to have a debit balance?

_____

_____

AS-15 LO 2

What does the net realizable value of accounts receivable refer to?

_____

_____

AS-16 LO 2

How is bad debt expense reported on the income statement?

_____

_____

AS-17 LO 2

Briefly outline the direct write off method for dealing with bad debt.

_____

_____

AS-18 LO 2

Explain the differences between the allowance method and the direct method in accounting for bad debt.

_____
_____
_____
_____
_____

AS-19 LO 2

Are both allowance and direct methods allowed under GAAP? Explain.

_____
_____
_____
_____

AS-20 LO 3

Name two different approaches for estimating bad debt expense. Briefly explain each approach.

_____
_____
_____
_____
_____

AS-21 LO 3

Which of the two approaches for estimating bad debt expense is better?

_____
_____
_____
_____

AS-22 LO 4

If Axon Company signs a promissory note to borrow from Blessa Company, which company is the maker of the note, and which company is the payee?

_____
_____

AS-23 LO 4

How is interest revenue on notes receivable reported on the income statement?

_____
_____

AS-24 LO 4

What is a dishonored note? What happens to the balance of notes receivable once the note is dishonored?

_____

_____

_____

AS-25 LO 6

In the space below, name two ratios used to assess accounts receivable, and state the formulas used to calculate the ratios.

AS-26 LO 6

How do you interpret the DSO number and the ART ratio?

_____

_____

_____

_____

AS-27 LO 5

Give two examples of accounting reports that can be generated involving accounts receivable.

_____

_____

_____

_____

AS-28 LO 7

What does factoring accounts receivable mean?

_____

_____

AS-29 LO 7

What are some advantages and disadvantages of factoring receivables?

_____

_____

_____

AS-30 LO 7

What does pledging accounts receivable mean?

_____

_____

AS-31 LO 7

Who has the ownership of factored receivables and pledged receivables?

_____

_____

AS-32 LO 8

What are some important internal control mechanisms relating to accounts receivable?

_____

_____

_____

_____

_____

AS-33 LO 9

What ethical problems are related to accounts receivable? Can they be avoided?

_____

_____

_____

_____

AS-34 LO 9

Suppose a company is in the middle of preparing its financial statements for the fiscal year, and finds out that its net income figure falls a little bit short of Wall Street earnings forecasts. How would management's desire to beat analysts' forecasts potentially influence the estimated amount of bad debt expense?

_____

_____

_____

_____

_____

_____

_____

Application Questions Group A

AP-1A LO 2

On December 31, 2018, Ghani Company discovered that one of its customers, Vince Suerty, had gone bankrupt. He owes the company $6,000. Prepare the journal entry to write off the amount due from Vince Suerty, assuming the direct method is used.

Date	Account Title and Explanation	Debit	Credit

AP-2A LO 2

Your company decides that an allowance for doubtful accounts is required in the amount of $6,000. There is a $4,000 credit balance in the account. Prepare the journal entry to set up the required allowance on December 31, 2018.

Date	Account Title and Explanation	Debit	Credit

AP-3A LO 3

Your company uses the income statement approach for estimating bad debt. For the year ending December 31, 2018, credit sales amounted to $1 million. The estimated bad debt is 0.5% of credit sales. Prepare the journal entry to record bad debt expense for the year.

Date	Account Title and Explanation	Debit	Credit

AP-4A LO 2

On July 31, 2018, Alou Company's accounts receivable ledger showed an ending balance of $50,000. The company estimates that $2,500 of accounts receivable will become uncollectible. Prepare a journal entry to record estimation of bad debt, assuming that the allowance for doubtful accounts has a zero balance.

Date	Account Title and Explanation	Debit	Credit

AP-5A LO 2 3

D&D Company uses the allowance method to account for uncollectible receivables. During 2018, the company made total credit sales of $1,370,000, of which $328,000 was currently owed by customers at year end. According to the company's historical sales, 2.5% of total credit sales will be uncollected. D&D Company uses an income statement approach to estimate the amount of uncollectible receivables. The company's year end is December 31. Prepare the journal entry to account for the amount deemed uncollectible.

Date	Account Title and Explanation	Debit	Credit

AP-6A LO 2 3

The Green Earth Company uses the allowance method to account for uncollectible receivables, and the income statement approach for estimating uncollectible receivables. During the fiscal year 2018, the company had credit sales of $2,300,000. It estimates that 1.5% of these sales will be uncollectible. Prepare the journal entry to record the uncollectible receivables on December 31, 2018, the company's year end.

Date	Account Title and Explanation	Debit	Credit

AP-7A LO 2

On June 15, 2018, you discover that your customer, Tyrone Huntzinger, has gone bankrupt. He owes you $1,000.

Required

a) Prepare the appropriate journal entry to write off bad debt assuming AFDA has already been estimated and recorded in the past.

Date	Account Title and Explanation	Debit	Credit

b) Tyrone Huntzinger's situation changed and he paid you in full on August 20, 2018. Prepare the journal entries to record this transaction.

Date	Account Title and Explanation	Debit	Credit

AP-8A LO 2

A customer's account in the amount of $2,000 was previously written off. Amazingly, on December 31, 2018, you receive a check in the mail from the customer with a letter of apology for not paying sooner (the account is two years old). Prepare the journal entries using the allowance method.

Date	Account Title and Explanation	Debit	Credit

AP-9A LO 2 3

During 2018, Jaime Company made total credit sales of $500,000, of which $25,000 was owed by customers at year end. On the basis of historical sales, 1% of sales will be uncollectible. Jaime Company uses the allowance method to account for uncollectible receivables, and the income statement approach to estimate the amount of receivables that will not be collected.

Required

a) Prepare the journal entry on December 31, 2018 to account for the amount deemed uncollectible.

Date	Account Title and Explanation	Debit	Credit

b) On January 20, 2019, Mrs. L. Green, who owes the company $500, informs Jaime Corporation that she is unable to pay the amount. Prepare the necessary journal entry.

Date	Account Title and Explanation	Debit	Credit

c) On February 14, 2019, Mrs. L. Green wins a lottery and decides to repay the full amount owing to Jaime Corporation. Prepare the necessary journal entries.

Date	Account Title and Explanation	Debit	Credit

AP-10A LO 3

The 2017 and 2018 sales and accounts receivable information for Velcary Company are shown below.

At the beginning of 2017, the AFDA account had a $0 balance. During 2017, sales for the year totaled $1,200,000 with 60% on credit. At December 31 year end, accounts receivable had a debit balance of $55,000. Management estimated that 0.5% of all credit sales would be uncollectible. The company wrote off $3,100 worth of accounts receivable at the end of the year.

During 2018, sales totaled $1,630,000 with 60% on credit. On December 31, 2018, accounts receivable has a debit balance of $76,000. During the year, the company wrote off a number of accounts receivable, leaving the allowance for doubtful accounts with a debit balance of $4,500. The estimate for bad debt expense for the year has not been determined or recorded. After reviewing the write offs, the company decided that the estimated percentage for AFDA should be increased from 0.5% to 0.75%.

Required

a) Prepare the journal entry to record the bad debt expense for 2018.

Date	Account Title and Explanation	Debit	Credit

b) Prepare a T-account for the allowance for doubtful accounts and enter all related transactions for years 2017 and 2018.

c) What are the net accounts receivable at the end of 2018?

AP-11A LO 2 3

The chart in part a) is prepared by the accountant of Happy Shoes. The percentages are based on historical performance. Happy Shoes uses the balance sheet approach to estimate uncollectible receivables.

Required

a) Calculate the company's bad debt.

Aging Category	Bad Debt %	Balance	Estimated Bad Debt
30 days	1%	$80,000	
31–60 days	3%	40,000	
More than 60 days	5%	20,000	
Total		$140,000	

b)   Assume that allowance for doubtful accounts has a credit balance of $1,000. Calculate the amount of bad debt expense the company will record.

AP-12A LO 2 3

Your company uses the balance sheet approach to estimate bad debt. Details of the accounts receivable balances owing on December 31, 2018 are shown in part a).

Required

a)   Calculate the required allowance.

Aging Category	Bad debt %	Balance	Required Allowance
Under 30 days	1%	$90,000	
31–60 days	20%	90,000	
More than 60 days	50%	30,000	
Total		$210,000	

b)   Write the journal entry to record bad debt expense for the year, assuming that the allowance account has a $20,000 credit balance.

Date	Account Title and Explanation	Debit	Credit

AP-13A LO 2 3

The chart in part a) was prepared by the accountant of Outdoor Apparel. The percentages are based on historical performance. Outdoor Apparel uses the balance sheet approach to estimate uncollectible receivables.

Required

a)   Calculate the company's bad debt.

Aging Category	Bad Debt %	Balance	Estimated Bad Debt
30 days	2%	$76,000	
31–60 days	3.5%	45,000	
More than 60 days	10%	25,000	
Total		$146,000	

b)   Assume that allowance for doubtful accounts has a debit balance of $1,100. Calculate the amount of bad debt expense the company will record.

AP-14A LO 2 3

Whitney Fabricators uses the balance sheet approach to estimate uncollectible receivables. The aging of receivables on December 31, 2018 is shown in part a).

Required

a) Calculate the required allowance for doubtful accounts.

Aging Category	Bad Debt %	Balance	Allowance for Doubtful Accounts
Under 30 days	2%	$175,000	
31–60 days	4%	40,000	
61–90 days	10%	10,000	
More than 90 days	60%	3,000	
Total		$228,000	

b) Prepare the journal entry on December 31, 2018 to record bad debt expense assuming the allowance account has a $3,700 credit balance.

Date	Account Title and Explanation	Debit	Credit

c) Prepare the journal entry on December 31, 2018 to record bad debt expense assuming the allowance account has a $10,000 credit balance.

Date	Account Title and Explanation	Debit	Credit

d) Prepare the journal entry to record bad debt expense assuming the allowance account has a $2,000 debit balance.

Date	Account Title and Explanation	Debit	Credit

AP-15A LO 6

Wechsler Company has a net accounts receivable opening balance of $250,000 and an ending balance of $300,000. The total sales amount for the year is $1,700,000, of which 80% are on credit. Normal credit terms are 30 days. Calculate the days' sales outstanding and the accounts receivable turnover. Comment on the calculated ratios.

_____

_____

_____

_____

_____

_____

_____

_____

AP-16A LO 6 7

The following information relevant to accounts receivable is presented for Dommar Company (in thousands of dollars).

	2018	2017	2016
Accounts Receivable	$319	$422	$501
Allowance for Doubtful Accounts	19	18	20
Net Credit Sales	4,377	3,598	2,937

Required

a) Calculate the accounts receivable turnover ratio for the years 2017 and 2018.

_____

_____

_____

_____

b) Calculate the days' sales outstanding for the years 2017 and 2018.

_____

_____

_____

c) On January 2, 2019, Dommar Company agreed to sell $200,000 of its accounts receivable with a 7% fee paid to the factor. Why do you think a company would pay a factoring fee to sell its accounts receivable?

_____

_____

d) Prepare the journal entry to record the factoring of accounts receivable in part c).

Date	Account Title and Explanation	Debit	Credit

AP-17A LO 4

Lakisha Ogata operates a proprietorship selling machinery. Because of the high value of the machinery sold, Lakisha often requires customers to sign a note. Lakisha sold a Gadget machine to Neil Marcin for $10,000 on November 14, 2018. The sale was initially recorded as an account receivable, but now Lakisha asks Neil to sign a note. On December 1, 2018, Neil signs a one-year note to be paid on maturity, plus 5% interest. Lakisha's company has a year end of April 30. Prepare the journal entries to reflect the transactions related to the receivable, note and its related interest.

Date	Account Title and Explanation	Debit	Credit

AP-18A LO 4

On January 1, 2018, Beta Company determined that it would not be able to pay the accounts receivable that was owed to Star Company. Beta Company believed that it would have sufficient cash one year later, and signed a one-year note receivable for the $10,000 that was owed. The annual interest rate is 9%, payable on July 1 and January 1. Star Company has a year end of June 30. On January 1, 2019, Beta Company dishonored the note because it went bankrupt. Star Company assessed that the debt will never be collected and decided to immediately write off the note.

Required

a) Record journal entries for Star Company when the note is signed.

Date	Account Title and Explanation	Debit	Credit

b) Prepare journal entries for the year end adjustment.

Date	Account Title and Explanation	Debit	Credit

c) Prepare journal entries for the receipt of the first interest payment.

Date	Account Title and Explanation	Debit	Credit

d) Prepare journal entries to write off Beta Company's note on January 1, 2019 using the allowance for doubtful accounts.

Date	Account Title and Explanation	Debit	Credit

AP-19A LO 4

On February 1, 2018, the Success Company accepted a six-month note receivable as an extension of time for a balance of $15,000 owing from Summit Company. The note has an annual interest rate of 7%. Success Company has a June 30 year end.

Required

a) Prepare the journal entry on February 1, 2018.

Date	Account Title and Explanation	Debit	Credit

b) Prepare the journal entry for the year-end adjustment, if required.

Date	Account Title and Explanation	Debit	Credit

c) Summit Company honored the note. Record the entry upon payment.

Date	Account Title and Explanation	Debit	Credit

AP-20A LO 4

On January 1, 2018, Ashley Manufacturing sold equipment to Henry Company for $200,000, with a cost of $140,000. Henry Company signed a nine-month note for the purchase. The note is due on September 30, 2018 with an annual interest rate of 9%. Ashley Manufacturing has an April 30 year end and uses a perpetual inventory system. On September 30, Henry Company dishonored the note due to insolvency. Ashley believes that Henry will eventually pay when things get better.

Required

Prepare the following journal entries for Ashley Manufacturing.

a) Prepare the journal entry to record the sale of the equipment.

Date	Account Title and Explanation	Debit	Credit

b) Prepare the journal entry for the year-end adjustment, if required.

Date	Account Title and Explanation	Debit	Credit

c) Prepare the journal entry to record the dishonored note by Henry Company on September 30, 2018.

Date	Account Title and Explanation	Debit	Credit

d) On April 30, 2019, Ashley decided to write off the amount outstanding from Henry Company. Prepare the journal entry to record the transaction, assuming that allowance for doubtful accounts has already been estimated and recorded in the past.

Date	Account Title and Explanation	Debit	Credit

AP-21A LO 7

AlpacaYarn Company sold $150,000 of its accounts receivable on March 19, 2018. The factor charged AlpacaYarn an 8% factoring fee. Prepare the journal entry to record the factoring of accounts receivable.

Date	Account Title and Explanation	Debit	Credit

Application Questions Group B

AP-1B LO 2

On December 31, 2018, Zaw Inc. informed Mann Company that its business was closing down and it would not be able to pay the $2,000 debt it still owed.

Required

a) Prepare the journal entry for Mann Company to write off the amount due from Zaw Inc., assuming the direct method is used.

Date	Account Title and Explanation	Debit	Credit

b) On February 16, 2019, Zaw Inc. informed Mann Company that after selling all of the company's assets, it had enough money left over to pay its debt. Mann Company received payment of $2,000 from Zaw Inc. on February 20, 2019. Prepare journal entries to reinstate Zaw Inc.'s account on February 16 and to record cash received on February 20.

Date	Account Title and Explanation	Debit	Credit

AP-2B LO 2

On December 31, 2018, your company decides that an allowance for doubtful accounts is required in the amount of $6,000. There is a $1,000 debit balance in the account. Prepare the journal entry to set up the required allowance.

Date	Account Title and Explanation	Debit	Credit

AP-3B LO 2 3

B&B Company uses the allowance method to account for uncollectible receivables. During 2018, the company made total credit sales of $1,250,000, of which $300,000 was owed by customers at year end. Following the company's historical sales data, 1.5% of credit sales is estimated to be uncollectible. B&B Company uses the income statement approach to estimate the amount of uncollectible receivables. The company's year end is December 31. Prepare the journal entry to account for the amount deemed uncollectible.

Date	Account Title and Explanation	Debit	Credit

AP-4B LO 2

After analyzing the current accounts receivable, your company decides that the allowance for doubtful accounts should have an ending normal balance of $5,870. There is an $850 credit balance in the account. Prepare the journal entry to set up the required allowance.

Date	Account Title and Explanation	Debit	Credit

AP-5B LO 2 3

Mayflower Company uses the allowance method to account for uncollectible receivables. During 2018, the company had total sales of $750,000, all on credit. The company uses the income statement approach to estimate uncollectible receivables. Historically, the company estimates that 1% of credit sales will be uncollectible. Mayflower Company has a December 31 year end. Prepare the journal entry to record the uncollectible receivables on December 31, 2018.

Date	Account Title and Explanation	Debit	Credit

AP-6B LO 2 3

Johnson Company uses the allowance method to account for uncollectible receivables. During 2018 the company had total sales of $2,500,000, including $300,000 in cash sales. On December 31, 2018 the company had an accounts receivable balance of $165,000 and a credit balance in allowance for doubtful accounts of $7,000. Johnson Company has a December 31 year end.

Required

a) Assume the company uses the income statement approach to estimate uncollectible receivables. Historically the company estimates 0.5% of credit sales will be uncollectible. Prepare the journal entry to record bad debt expense on December 31, 2018.

Date	Account Title and Explanation	Debit	Credit

b) Assume the company uses the balance sheet approach and estimates uncollectible receivables to be 7.5% of accounts receivable. Prepare the journal entry to record bad debt expense on December 31, 2018.

Date	Account Title and Explanation	Debit	Credit

c) Assume the AFDA has a debit balance of $2,000 on December 31, 2018. Using the balance sheet approach and estimating that 7.5% of receivables will be uncollectable, prepare the journal entry to record the bad debt expense on December 31, 2018.

Date	Account Title and Explanation	Debit	Credit

AP-7B LO 2

Jane Lee is the owner of a small consulting firm called Lee Solutions. Lee Solutions uses the allowance method to account for bad debt. On April 14, 2018, Lee Solutions' accounts receivable account balance was $10,000 and allowance for doubtful accounts balance was $2,000. A week later, it was discovered that Joe Black, who owed the firm $1,500, would not be able to make the payment.

Required

a) Prepare a journal entry to write off the amount deemed uncollectible.

Date	Account Title and Explanation	Debit	Credit

b) On May 26, 2018, Joe Black was able to repay 50% of the amount he owed, which had been previously written off. Prepare the journal entries required to record this transaction.

Date	Account Title and Explanation	Debit	Credit

AP-8B LO 2

On February 8, 2018, you discover that your customer, Gerome Linger, has gone bankrupt. He owes you $910. Prepare the appropriate journal entry to write off bad debt assuming AFDA has already been estimated and recorded in the past.

Date	Account Title and Explanation	Debit	Credit

AP-9B LO 2 3

In 2018, Upper Machine Sales Company sold equipment on credit in the amount of $950,000. Total cash collections during the year were $820,000. Using the allowance method, the company determined that $7,000 of accounts receivable would not be collected and wrote them off. At the end of 2018, management decided to increase its allowance percentage from 0.5% to 1% of credit sales because of the amount of accounts receivable that proved to be uncollectible during the year. At the end of 2017, the company had $135,000 in accounts receivable and a credit balance of $6,000 in allowance for doubtful accounts. Assume the company has a year end of December 31.

Required

a) Prepare the necessary journal entries to record all 2018 transactions including sales, collection, the write off and the new allowance amount. Disregard the dates when recording the transactions.

Date	Account Title and Explanation	Debit	Credit

b) Show the amount of net accounts receivable on the balance sheet as at December 31, 2018.

AP-10B LO 2 3

Dalton Company has the following unadjusted balances on December 31, 2018. All amounts shown are in their normal balance.

Accounts Receivable	$425,750
Allowance for Doubtful Accounts	25,000
Sales (10% of sales are cash sales)	950,000
Sales Discounts	15,000

Required

a) Dalton estimates that 1.5% of net credit sales will be uncollectible. Prepare the journal entry to record the uncollectible receivables on December 31, 2018.

Date	Account Title and Explanation	Debit	Credit

b) Prepare the balance sheet presentation of accounts receivable on December 31, 2018.

AP-11B LO 2 3

Fishy uses the balance sheet approach to estimate uncollectible receivables. Use the following table to determine the amount of bad debt expense, and prepare the journal entry on June 30, 2018 to record the bad debt expense. The allowance account has a zero balance.

Aging Category	Bad Debt %	Balance	Estimated Bad Debt
30 days	2%	$25,000	
31–60 days	3%	10,000	
More than 60 days	4%	2,000	
Total		$37,000	

Date	Account Title and Explanation	Debit	Credit

AP-12B LO 2 3

Elm Row operates in an industry that has a high rate of bad debt. Before the year end adjustments, accounts receivable has a debit balance of $536,000 and the allowance for doubtful accounts had a credit balance of $20,000. The December 31, 2018 year end balance reported on the balance sheet for the allowance for doubtful accounts is based on the aging schedule shown in part a).

Required

a) What is the balance for the allowance for doubtful accounts at year end?

Aging Category	Bad Debt %	Balance	Estimated Bad Debt
Less than 16 days	2%	$300,000	
16–30 days	3%	100,000	
31–45 days	5%	75,000	
46–60 days	10%	32,000	
61–75 days	20%	18,000	
More than 75 days	40%	11,000	

b) Prepare the journal entry to record bad debt expense for the year.

Date	Account Title and Explanation	Debit	Credit

AP-13B LO 2 3

Innovision Inc. operates in an industry that has a high rate of bad debts. Before the year end adjustments on April 30, accounts receivable has a debit balance of $485,000 and the allowance for doubtful accounts has a credit balance of $15,700. The year-end balance reported on the balance sheet for the allowance for doubtful accounts is based on the aging schedule shown below.

Required

a) Fill in the table to calculate the balance for the allowance for doubtful accounts.

Aging Category	Bad Debt %	Balance	Estimated Bad Debt
Less than 16 days	2%	$270,000	
16–30 days	4%	84,000	
31–45 days	7%	71,000	
46–60 days	12%	30,000	
61–75 days	21%	17,000	
More than 75 days	44%	13,000	
Total		$485,000	

b) Prepare the journal entry to record bad debt expense for the year.

Date	Account Title and Explanation	Debit	Credit

AP-14B LO 2

On January 1, 2018, Jay Company's allowance for doubtful accounts had a credit balance of $30,000. During 2018, Jay charged $64,000 to bad debt expense, and wrote off $46,000 of uncollectible accounts receivable. What is the balance of allowance for doubtful accounts on December 31, 2018?

AP-15B LO 6

A company's relevant accounts receivable information for the years 2017 and 2018 is provided below.

	2018	2017
Average Net Accounts Receivable	$1,486,739	$1,769,032
Net Credit Sales	23,075,635	22,107,539

Required

a) Calculate the accounts receivable turnover ratio for 2017 and 2018.

b) Calculate the days' sales outstanding for 2017 and 2018.

c) Compare and discuss the results from parts a) and b).

AP-16B LO 6 7

The following information is taken from the records of Hanlan Corporation. Normal credit terms are 30 days.

	2019	2018	2017
Net Credit Sales	$250,000	$200,000	$190,000
Account Receivable	17,500	24,000	32,300
Allowance for Doubtful Accounts	1,050	960	1,292

Required

a) Calculate the accounts receivable turnover ratio for 2018 and 2019. Round your answers to two decimal places.

b) Calculate the days' sales outstanding for the years 2018 and 2019. Round your answers to the nearest whole number.

c) Comment on the accounts receivable ratios calculated from 2018 and 2019.

_____

_____

_____

_____

d) On January 5, 2019, Hanlan Corporation signed a note to borrow $80,000 from the bank, and pledged $100,000 of its receivables as collateral for the loan. Prepare the journal entry to record the notes payable.

Date	Account Title and Explanation	Debit	Credit

e) In addition to the journal entry in part d), does Hanlan Corporation need to provide any additional disclosure regarding the pledging of accounts receivable? Explain.

_____

_____

_____

AP-17B LO 4

On May 1, 2018, People's Networks sold computer networking supplies to American Autos for $36,000. The cost of the supplies is $15,000. Instead of paying immediately, American Autos signed a note receivable with 11% annual interest, payable in eight months. People's Networks has a year end of October 31.

Required

a) Record the journal entry when the sale is made; assume People's Networks uses the perpetual inventory system.

Date	Account Title and Explanation	Debit	Credit

b) Prepare the journal entry for the year end adjustment.

Date	Account Title and Explanation	Debit	Credit

c)   Prepare the journal entry for receipt of payment from American Autos on January 1, 2019.

Date	Account Title and Explanation	Debit	Credit

d)   What items would be included on the balance sheet and income statement of People's Networks as at October 31, 2018 with respect to this note?

_____

_____

_____

AP-18B LO 4

On January 1, 2018, Delta Company determined that it would not be able to pay the accounts receivable that was owed to Star Company. Delta Company was confident that it would have sufficient cash one year later, and signed a one-year notes receivable for the $16,100 that was owed. The annual interest rate is 10%, payable on July 1 and January 1. Star Company has a year end of June 30.

Required

a)   Record the journal entry for Star Company when the note is signed.

Date	Account Title and Explanation	Debit	Credit

b)   Prepare the journal entry for the year end adjustment.

Date	Account Title and Explanation	Debit	Credit

c)   Prepare the journal entry for the receipt of the first interest payment.

Date	Account Title and Explanation	Debit	Credit

d)   Prepare the journal entries for receipt of payment from Delta Company on January 1, 2019.

Date	Account Title and Explanation	Debit	Credit

AP-19B LO 4

On March 1, 2018, Asper Company accepted a $100,000, six-month note from Arctic Company as a time extension on a past-due amount in accounts receivable. The note has an interest rate of 5%.

Required

a) Prepare the journal entry for Asper Company on March 1, 2018.

Date	Account Title and Explanation	Debit	Credit

b) Prepare the journal entry for Asper Company to record the payment of the note in full with interest on August 31, 2018.

Date	Account Title and Explanation	Debit	Credit

AP-20B LO 4

On September 1, 2018, Highlander Truck Company sold two heavy duty trucks to Zebra Corporation for $160,000. Highlander's cost for the trucks was $135,000. Zebra Corporation signed a seven-month note for the purchase. The note is due on April 1, 2019 with an annual interest rate of 6%. Highlander Truck Company has a December 31 year end and uses a perpetual inventory system. On April 1, 2019, Zebra dishonored the note because the company was going through a tough period and could not afford to pay the balanced owed. Highlander Truck Company believes that Zebra Corporation will eventually make the payment when the economy improves.

Required

a) Prepare the journal entry to record the sale.

Date	Account Title and Explanation	Debit	Credit

b) Prepare the journal entry for the year end adjustment, if required.

Date	Account Title and Explanation	Debit	Credit

c) Prepare the journal entry to record the dishonored note by Zebra Corporation on April 1, 2019.

Date	Account Title and Explanation	Debit	Credit

AP-21B LO 7

On December 1, 2018, Fai Tan Inc. had an accounts receivable balance of $300,000. On December 9, 2018, the company sold $50,000 of its accounts receivable to a financial institution, which charges a 5% factoring fee. On December 20, 2018, the company borrowed $100,000, pledging $120,000 of accounts receivable as security for the loan. Prepare journal entries to record the factoring of accounts receivable and the notes payable. Also prepare any notes to the December 31, 2018 financial statements that result from these transactions.

Date	Account Title and Explanation	Debit	Credit

Notes to the financial statement resulting from accounts receivable transactions:

_____

_____

_____

_____

_____

_____

_____

_____

Case Study

CS-1

Softbed Hotel (Softbed) owns and manages a large hotel on the east coast of the US. The hotel is close to a few popular tourist attractions, and is usually fully booked in the summer. Business is relatively slower in other seasons, when the company gains most of its revenues from business clients organizing events, such as trade shows and conferences.

The hotel has established a credit policy. For individual guests, Softbed requires a cash deposit or credit card up front. For large groups of guests and corporate clients, Softbed extends credit selectively, based on the amount of revenue they will generate for the hotel and on their credit information obtained from a reliable independent source. For the clients that Softbed decides to extend its credit to, the credit term is n/30.

Detailed examination of the accounts receivable aging report reveals that because Softbed completes credit checks before extending its credit, there are only rare cases where customers are unable to pay. However, bill dispute is the cause of most long outstanding accounts receivable balances. The billing process is complicated because guests have multiple purchase points (their rooms, restaurants, business centre, spa and souvenir shop). Hotel guests can buy products and services from any of the purchase points and ask for the costs to be billed to their rooms.

Sometimes billing mistakes arise due to wrong room numbers being recorded, or the purchase information for each customer not being compiled properly from different purchase points. Also, customers often make last-minute changes to their room arrangements or other arrangements from what they booked prior to their arrival. These changes are recorded manually before being transferred to Softbed's centralized accounts receivable department. Sometimes these changes are improperly recorded or transferred, resulting in incorrect invoices being billed to customers. Once customers dispute their bills, the hotel starts an investigation to validate the customers' claims. The investigation involves checking internal records, and asking various hotel staff about what actually happened with a particular customer. Unfortunately, usually by the time the investigation gets started, the hotel staff has forgotten details. The customers usually refuse to pay, or pay only partially, until the disputes involving their bills are resolved, resulting in long outstanding accounts receivable.

Required

a) To account for bad debt, Softbed estimates that 2% of its gross accounts receivable balance will become uncollectible. Use the information provided in the table below to calculate allowance for doubtful accounts balances for 2016 to 2018, and the days' sales outstanding and accounts receivable turnover for the years 2017 and 2018. Compare the results of ratio calculations and comment on whether the company's performance has improved or weakened.

	2018	2017	2016
Net Credit Sales	$4,500,000	$4,200,000	$4,000,000
Gross Accounts Receivable	490,000	400,000	770,000
Allowance for Doubtful Accounts			
Days' Sales Outstanding			
Accounts Receivable Turnover			

b) What are other methods that Softbed can use to estimate its bad debt? Which method do you think would be most suitable for Softbed?

_____

_____

_____

_____

_____

_____

_____

c) Following Softbed's seasonal business fluctuations, should the company adopt a seasonal credit policy? In other words, should Softbed Hotel use different credit policies for different seasons? Explain.

_____

_____

_____

_____

_____

_____

_____

d) Analyze and identify strengths and weaknesses of Softbed's accounts receivable controls.

_____

_____

_____

_____

_____

_____

_____

_____

_____

_____

_____

_____

_____

_____

_____

Critical Thinking

CT-1 LO 1 2 3 5 6 8 9

You are the Chief Financial Officer for Stanton Feery and Company. Mr. Feery's friend, Shad Baxtor, is starting up a new company, and needs some advice on accounts receivable and bad debt accounting practices. Mr. Feery has asked you to meet with Mr. Baxtor and answer a few questions. He hands you a list of things that Shad Baxtor wants clarified.

Required

Answer the following questions for Shad Baxtor.

a) What are accounts receivable?

b) What are bad debts?

c) When are amounts considered bad debt?

d) How is bad debt estimated?

e) How is bad debt shown on the financial statements?

f) How can bad debt be minimized?

g) Which reports are helpful in analyzing a company's accounts receivable?

h) What is an aging list?

_____

_____

_____

i) What is the difference between a credit sale and a cash sale?

_____

_____

j) How can you assess the quality of accounts receivable?

_____

_____

k) What is an upside of selling on credit and what is the potential risk involved?

_____

_____

_____

l) How would one determine if the bad debt estimate for a new company is reasonable? Should desired net income be used as the basis for estimating bad debt?

_____

_____

_____

_____

_____

_____

_____

_____

_____

_____

_____

_____

_____

_____

_____

_____

_____

_____

Notes

Chapter 12

NONCURRENT ASSETS

LEARNING OBJECTIVES

LO 1   Identify the characteristics of noncurrent assets

LO 2   Record the acquisition and changes in the value of property, plant and equipment

LO 3   Apply and compare the three methods of depreciation of property, plant and equipment

LO 4   Account for disposal of assets and changes in depreciation estimates

LO 5   Account for natural resources

LO 6   Define and account for intangible assets and describe the different types of intangible assets

LO 7   Calculate and interpret asset turnover and return on assets ratios

LO 8   Describe controls related to noncurrent assets

LO 9   Describe ethical approaches related to noncurrent assets

Appendix

LO 10   Account for trading of noncurrent assets

AMEENGAGE   Access **ameengage.com** *for integrated resources including tutorials, practice exercises, the digital textbook and more.*

Assessment Questions

AS-1 LO 1

Where are noncurrent assets listed on the balance sheet?

_____

_____

AS-2 LO 1

Define noncurrent assets. Give an example of a noncurrent asset.

_____

_____

_____

_____

AS-3 LO 1

What are the three characteristics of noncurrent assets?

_____

_____

_____

_____

_____

_____

AS-4 LO 2

In addition to the purchase price, what other expenditures need to be included as the cost of a plant asset when it is purchased? Provide an example.

_____

_____

_____

_____

AS-5 LO 2

What is meant by a lump sum purchase of assets? How are costs allocated in a lump sum asset purchase?

_____

_____

_____

_____

AS-6 LO 2

What is a capital expenditure? On which financial statement is it reported?

_____

_____

_____

AS-7 LO 2

What is a revenue expenditure? On which financial statement is it reported?

_____

_____

AS-8 LO 2

What is a betterment? Is it a capital expenditure or a revenue expenditure?

_____

_____

AS-9 LO 2

What is an extraordinary repair? Is it a capital expenditure or a revenue expenditure?

_____

_____

AS-10 LO 2

What are ordinary repairs and maintenance? Are they capital expenditures or revenue expenditures?

_____

_____

_____

AS-11 LO 3

What is depreciation?

_____

_____

_____

AS-12 LO 3

What is the residual value of a noncurrent asset?

_____

_____

AS-13 LO 3

Name three different methods of calculating depreciation.

_____

_____

_____

AS-14 LO 3 4

Does a company always receive the estimated residual value of an asset on disposal? Assuming the asset is fully depreciated, how is the difference between the estimated residual value and the actual proceeds from asset disposal treated?

_____

_____

_____

AS-15 LO 3

Explain the nature of the accumulated depreciation account.

_____

_____

AS-16 LO 3

What does the net book value of a noncurrent asset represent? Does the net book value represent the market value of the asset?

_____

_____

_____

AS-17 LO 3

What is the equation to calculate the per unit amount for the units-of-production depreciation method?

_____

_____

_____

AS-18 LO 6

In which section of the balance sheet are intangible assets found?

_____

_____

AS-19 LO 6

What is the primary difference between intangible assets and tangible assets?

_____

_____

AS-20 LO 6

Define intangible assets and describe the costs that are included in their book value.

_____

_____

_____

_____

AS-21 LO 6

Define goodwill.

_____

_____

_____

AS-22 LO 6

How is the value of goodwill calculated?

_____

_____

AS-23 LO 6

What is the major difference between goodwill and other intangible assets?

_____

_____

AS-24 LO 6

List three examples of intangible assets.

_____

_____

AS-25 LO 8

How can a company protect the value of its intangible assets?

_____

_____

_____

AS-26 LO 9

True or False: In the year that a company has high taxable income, its accountant should help to minimize the company's tax obligations by classifying noncurrent asset items as expense items.

AS-27 LO 4

What is impairment?

AS-28 LO 4

Where does an impairment loss appear on the income statement?

AS-29 LO 4

What is the Modified Accelerated Cost Recovery System (MACRS)?

AS-30 LO 5

Which depreciation method is usually used to calculate the depletion of natural resources?

AS-31 LO 5

In a natural resource company, what do assets under construction mainly represent?

AS-32 LO 5

True or False: Depletion of assets should start as soon as the asset is under construction.

AS-33 LO 7

What does the asset turnover ratio measure?

AS-34 LO 7

What does the return on assets ratio measure?

_____

_____

AS-35 LO 10

What does commercial substance mean in the context of noncurrent asset exchange?

_____

_____

_____

Application Questions Group A

AP-1A LO 2

Prepare the journal entry for the purchase of machinery worth $200,000 (on credit) on March 6, 2018.

Date	Account Title and Explanation	Debit	Credit

AP-2A LO 2

On March 28, 2018, Turbo Delivery Inc. brought its delivery truck to a garage, which upgraded the truck's exhaust system to increase its fuel efficiency. An engine was also replaced to extend the useful life of the truck by three years. In addition, the garage completed an oil change on the truck. The oil change is part of routine maintenance, which takes place every few months. The invoice from the garage shows the exhaust system upgrade cost $1,000, the engine replacement cost $500, and the oil change cost $100. Turbo Delivery Inc. will pay for this invoice next month.

Prepare the journal entries to record the exhaust system upgrade, engine replacement and oil change on March 28.

Date	Account Title and Explanation	Debit	Credit

AP-3A LO 3

On January 1, 2018, Parts2U purchased a van for $34,000. The company plans to retire the van after it has been driven for 150,000 miles, at which time the residual value is expected to be $4,000. The van was driven 10,000 miles in 2018. Prepare the journal entry to record depreciation of the van on December 31, 2018, using the units-of-production method.

Date	Account Title and Explanation	Debit	Credit

AP-4A LO 3

On July 1, 2017, Earth Corporation purchased factory equipment for $150,000. The equipment has a residual value of $3,000 and is to be depreciated over eight years using the double-declining-balance method. Earth Corporation's year end is on September 30. Calculate the depreciation expense to be recorded for the fiscal years ending September 30, 2017 and September 30, 2018. Earth Corporation depreciates its assets based on the number of months it owned the asset during the year.

AP-5A LO 2

Land, building and equipment were purchased for a total amount of $800,000 on May 25, 2018. The assessed values of these purchases were, Land—$600,000; Building—$300,000; Equipment—$100,000. Calculate the cost of each asset by filling in the following table, and write the journal entry that records the purchase.

Item	Assessment	Percent	Applied to Cost

Date	Account Title and Explanation	Debit	Credit

AP-6A LO 3 4

On December 31, 2012, Tiesto Company purchased equipment worth $150,000. The equipment has a useful life of six years and no residual value. Depreciation is recorded beginning the month after acquisition and will be recorded up until the month of disposal. The company uses the straight-line method of depreciation.

Required

a) Given that the company's year end is December 31, complete the following table.

Year	Cost of Noncurrent Asset	Depreciation Expense	Accumulated Depreciation To Date	Net Book Value

b) On June 30, 2018, Tiesto Company sold the equipment for $3,000. Prepare a journal entry to record the depreciation on the disposal and the sale. You will need to recalculate the depreciation expense for 2018 from part a) to account for the sale part-way through the year.

Date	Account Title and Explanation	Debit	Credit

Analysis

The owner of Tiesto Company believes that the loss on sale of equipment indicates that the company has made a mistake while calculating depreciation. Do you agree or disagree? Explain.

_____

_____

_____

AP-7A LO 3 4

Equipment was purchased on January 1, 2015 for $50,000. The asset is expected to last for four years, at which time the estimated residual value will be $10,000.

Required

a) Prepare a table showing the year, the cost of the asset, the amount of depreciation expense each year, accumulated depreciation to date and net book value. The company uses straight-line depreciation.

Year	Cost of Noncurrent Asset	Depreciation Expense	Accumulated Depreciation To Date	Net Book Value

b) The asset was sold for $12,000 cash on January 1, 2019. Prepare the journal entry to record the sale.

Date	Account Title and Explanation	Debit	Credit

c) Using the same purchase information from the beginning of the question, complete the table assuming that the company uses double-declining-balance depreciation.

Year	Net Book Value at the Beginning of the Year	Depreciation Expense	Accumulated Depreciation To Date	Net Book Value at the End of the Year

d) Using the same purchase information and residual value as the beginning of the question, assume that the company uses the units-of-production method. The asset can produce one million units. Record of production: 2015—300,000 units; 2016—250,000 units; 2017—300,000 units; and 2018—100,000 units. Complete the table showing the year, cost of the asset, amount of depreciation expense each year, accumulated depreciation to date and net book value. (Hint: Depreciate the cost of the asset minus its residual value.)

Year	Cost of Noncurrent Asset	Depreciation Expense	Accumulated Depreciation To Date	Net Book Value

Analysis

Since the double-declining-balance method for depreciation allows charging higher depreciation in the first few years, some business owners may want to use this method for all assets. Is it appropriate to use this method for all assets?

_____

_____

AP-8A LO 3

A new machine for a bottle factory was purchased in February 2015 for $900,000. The machine has an estimated production capacity of 1,500,000 bottles and no residual value. The machine produced the following number of bottles over the past four years: 2015—420,000 bottles; 2016—405,000 bottles; 2017—390,000 bottles; and 2018—315,000 bottles. Assuming the company uses the units-of-production method, complete the following table.

Year	Cost of Noncurrent Asset	Depreciation Expense	Accumulated Depreciation To Date	Net Book Value

AP-9A LO 3 4

On January 1, 2015, a noncurrent asset was purchased for $50,000. The asset was expected to last for four years (with an estimated residual value of $10,000). For the first two years, the company used the double-declining-balance method. Suppose the company decides to switch to the straight–line method after recording the depreciation expense for 2016. Calculate the depreciation expense for the years 2017 and 2018.

AP-10A LO 2 3

At the beginning of 2017, an entrepreneur purchased a basket of assets at an auction sale. The entrepreneur paid $250,000 "as is" for two automobiles, a widget machine, a forklift truck and a trailer. The items were valued by a professional appraiser as follows.

Item	Estimated Value	Percentage	Estimated Remaining Life
Auto 1	$10,000	3.22%	3 Years
Auto 2	15,000	4.84%	5 Years
Widget Machine	258,000	83.23%	15 Years
Forklift	15,000	4.84%	5 Years
Trailer	12,000	3.87%	10 Years
Total	$310,000	100%	

After the auction, the entrepreneur had the machine moved to the factory. Moving the widget machine cost $2,000. After the machine was placed in the factory, an electrician was contracted to install additional power lines and hook up the machine at a cost of $1,000. A plumber was also needed to connect the machine to the water mains. This cost $500. A gas fitter was required to connect the widget machine to the gas line at a cost of $200.

Before placing Auto 1 and 2 into use, the entrepreneur took both autos to the local repair shop. The mechanic said that Auto 1 needed a new engine that would cost $2,000 and Auto 2 needed a major tune-up at a cost of $500 (the tune-up is required to get the car working). The entrepreneur paid cash for the repairs. Early in 2018, the entrepreneur sold Auto 1 for $8,000 and replaced the front brakes on Auto 2 for $300. The new front brakes are expected to last until the end of the same year.

The entrepreneur's company uses a half-year method for depreciation (i.e. a half-year's depreciation in the year of purchase, and a half-year's depreciation in the year of sale). The company uses the straight-line method of depreciation, with an estimated residual value of 10% of cost for all assets.

Required

Write the journal entries to record the following.

a) Using the straight-line depreciation method, record all journal entries for 2017 and journal entries related to Auto 1 and Auto 2 in 2018. When allocating a bulk purchase, round up to the nearest dollar. If necessary, adjust the largest number up or down to avoid journal entry imbalance due to rounding. Note: The exact journal entry dates can be omitted for the purpose of this exercise. Simply indicate if each transaction belongs to 2017 or 2018.

Date	Account Title and Explanation	Debit	Credit
	Account Title and Explanation	Debit	Credit

Date	Account Title and Explanation	Debit	Credit

b) Using the double-declining-balance depreciation method, redo the journal entries for the depreciation of the trailer for 2017 and 2018. Note: The exact journal entry dates can be omitted for the purpose of this exercise. Simply indicate if each transaction belongs to 2017 or 2018.

Date	Account Title and Explanation	Debit	Credit

AP-11A LO 6

John Partington purchased assets ($500,000) and liabilities ($400,000) of a company, for which he paid $150,000 on August 6, 2018. The company owns the rights to a unique product.

Required

a) Record the purchase transaction.

Date	Account Title and Explanation	Debit	Credit

b) Subsequent to the purchase of the company, a competitor appeared. On December 31, 2018, John assessed that the value of the goodwill that his company owned was now worth $20,000. Record the appropriate journal entry to reflect the reduction in the value of goodwill.

Date	Account Title and Explanation	Debit	Credit

AP-12A LO 6

Feggins Company purchased a patent from Marquette Limited for $200,000 on January 1, 2018. The patent has a remaining life of six years.

Required

a) Prepare the journal entry to record the purchase.

Date	Account Title and Explanation	Debit	Credit

b) Prepare the journal entry to record amortization for one year on December 31, 2018.
   The company does not use the half-year rule. Assume the straight-line method of depreciation is used.

Date	Account Title and Explanation	Debit	Credit

AP-13A LO 5

Turpen Corporation purchased a large forest for $12 million on January 1, 2018. Turpen estimates that 10 million board feet (BF) of lumber can be harvested. After 10 years, Turpen will sell the land and expects it to be worth $2 million.

Required

a) Record the journal entry for the purchase of the forest.

Date	Account Title and Explanation	Debit	Credit

b) Calculate the depletion rate for each BF to be extracted.

_____

_____

_____

_____

_____

c) During the current year, the company harvested and sold 500,000 board feet. Record the journal entry to record the harvesting on December 31, 2018.

Date	Account Title and Explanation	Debit	Credit

AP-14A LO 6

Mirabella Manufacturing spent several years developing a process for producing widgets. Its lawyer suggested patenting the process. The company obtained the patent on January 1, 2018. The company paid $100,000 to the lawyer, $25,000 to the government for the patent and $10,000 in additional fees.

Required

a) Prepare the journal entries to record the cost of the patent.

Date	Account Title and Explanation	Debit	Credit

b) The patent has a life of 20 years. Prepare the journal entry to amortize the patent for one year on December 31, 2018.

Date	Account Title and Explanation	Debit	Credit

AP-15A LO 6

On February 1, 2018, Eastern Company acquired the assets ($800,000) and liabilities ($500,000) of Newton Corporation. The agreed purchase price is $500,000 in cash. Prepare a journal entry to record the purchase.

Date	Account Title and Explanation	Debit	Credit

AP-16A LO 6

On February 1, 2018 Canning Corporation bought assets and liabilities of Linus Inc. for $300,000. Canning paid a premium for the purchase because Linus Inc. is a recognizable brand in the market. Linus had assets of $600,000 and liabilities of $400,000.

Required

a) Prepare the journal entry for Canning Corporation to record the purchase of Linus Inc.

Date	Account Title and Explanation	Debit	Credit

b) Due to an increase in the number of competitors in the market, on December 31, 2018, Canning Corporation reviewed all assets for any impairment. It was discovered that the goodwill has a fair market value of only $85,000. Prepare the journal entry to record this impairment to goodwill.

Date	Account Title and Explanation	Debit	Credit

AP-17A LO 6

On January 1, 2018, Lava Company purchased a $90,000 patent for a new consumer product. However, the patent's useful life is estimated to be only 10 years due to the competitive nature of the product.

Required

a) Prepare a journal entry to record the purchase.

Date	Account Title and Explanation	Debit	Credit

b) Prepare a journal entry to record the amortization on December 31, 2018.

Date	Account Title and Explanation	Debit	Credit

AP-18A LO 7

The following data pertains to Frost Company for the year ended December 31, 2018.

Net Sales	$60,000
Net Income	15,000
Total Assets (January 1, 2018)	200,000
Total Assets (December 31, 2018)	300,000

Calculate Frost Company's return on assets for 2018. Explain what the ratio means.

_____

_____

_____

_____

_____

_____

_____

_____

AP-19A LO 3 4

Details of some of Stark Corporation's noncurrent assets are listed below.

Date of Purchase	Asset	Cost	Residual Value	Estimated Useful Life
Feb 1, 2015	Equipment	$370,600	$25,000	8 years
Sep 1, 2015	Truck	$51,400	$4,600	6 years

On August 1, 2018, Stark Corporation decides to dispose of both of these assets. The total proceeds received for the assets were $246,000. Both assets use the straight-line depreciation method based on the number of months owned in the year. Stark Corporation has a December 31 year end. Round all answers to the nearest whole number.

Required

a) Prepare the depreciation table.

Year	Cost of Noncurrent Asset	Depreciation Expense	Accumulated Depreciation	Net Book Value
Equipment				
Truck				

b) Prepare the journal entry to record the disposal of the assets. Assume that the journal entry to update the depreciation before disposal has already been made.

Date	Account Title and Explanation	Debit	Credit

Analysis

What is a drawback of using the straight-line depreciation method?

_____

_____

_____

_____

AP-20A LO 2

On September 8, 2018, Swanway Corporation purchased the following assets: land, machinery and a building. The appraised values of the assets were $1,000,000 for land, $200,000 for machinery and $800,000 for the building. The total purchase price of all three assets was $1,700,000. Swanway paid $365,400 in cash and signed a note payable for the remaining balance.

Required

a) Complete the table to determine the cost of the assets.

Item	Appraised	Percent	Applied to Cost

b) Prepare the journal entry to record the purchase.

Date	Account Title and Explanation	Debit	Credit

AP-21A LO 2 3 4

On January 1, 2018, Brantley Company purchased a machine for $56,000 cash. The company plans to use the machine for 10 years before selling it at its estimated residual value of $6,000. The machine is depreciated using the straight-line method.

a) Journalize the entry to record the machine purchase.

Date	Account Title and Explanation	Debit	Credit

b) Prepare the journal entry to record depreciation expense of the machine on December 31, 2018.

Date	Account Title and Explanation	Debit	Credit

c) On January 1, 2019, an upgrade was installed to increase the machine's useful life by three years. The company paid $3,000 cash for the upgrade. Journalize the entry to record the machine upgrade.

Date	Account Title and Explanation	Debit	Credit

d) Prepare the journal entry to record depreciation expense of the machine on December 31, 2019.

Date	Account Title and Explanation	Debit	Credit

e) Brantley Company sold the machine for $6,000 cash at the end of its useful life on December 31, 2030. Prepare the journal entry to record the disposal of the machine. Assume that the journal entry to update the depreciation before disposal has already been made.

Date	Account Title and Explanation	Debit	Credit

AP-22A LO 4

On December 31, 2018, a company had the following information reported on its balance sheet.

Equipment	$400,000
Accumulated Depreciation—Equipment	(320,000)

The equipment was donated to a charity. The equipment was valued at its current net book value. Prepare the journal entry to record the donation.

Date	Account Title and Explanation	Debit	Credit

AP-23A LO 5

Metallic Inc. is an international producer of aluminum through bauxite mining. On January 1, 2018, it spent $5,000,000 cash to purchase a mine with an estimated residual value of zero. The company also incurred additional expenditures of $700,000 to prepare the mine for the extraction of bauxite. Metallic Inc. expects to use this mine for eight years with an expected capacity of 200,000 tons of bauxite over that time.

Required

a) Prepare the journal entry to record the purchase of the bauxite mine.

Date	Account Title and Explanation	Debit	Credit

b) Calculate the depletion rate for each ton of bauxite to be extracted.

c) Metallic Inc. extracted 15,000 tons of bauxite in the first year; 11,000 tons of bauxite were sold during the year, while the remaining 4,000 tons were kept as inventory. Prepare the journal entry to record the depletion for this year.

Date	Account Title and Explanation	Debit	Credit

AP-24A LO 3 4

ReHear Company produces and sells hearing aid technology. As a result of recent advances in this type of technology, the company decided to test its factory equipment for impairment. Four years ago, the equipment was purchased for $520,000 with an estimated residual value of $40,000. The equipment is expected to have a useful life of 15 years and four years of depreciation have been recorded up to the impairment test. The company uses the straight-line method of depreciation.

Required

a) What is the net book value of the equipment at the end of this year?

b) Was it required for ReHear to implement an impairment test for its equipment? Why?

c) Assume ReHear company finds out that the equipment's fair value is $390,000. Is the equipment impaired? If yes, how much is the impairment loss?

d) Record the journal entry for the impairment loss, if any.

Date	Account Title and Explanation	Debit	Credit

AP-25A LO 7

The following financial data is given for two companies, TIX and SUBA. They are both in the business of selling fresh produce to large supermarkets across North America. Both companies have a year end of December 31.

TIX Company	December 31, 2018	December 31, 2017
Net Sales	$2,500,000	$2,250,000
Total Assets	$4,700,000	$4,200,000
Net Income	$310,000	$300,000
Gross Profit	$1,000,000	$900,000

SUBA Company	December 31, 2018	December 31, 2017
Net Sales	$1,900,000	$2,200,000
Total Assets	$1,500,000	$1,800,000
Net Income	$400,000	$421,000
Gross Profit	$855,000	$990,000

Required

Based on the information provided, answer the following questions. Round your answers to two decimal places.

a) Calculate the asset turnover of each company for 2018.

b) In 2018, which company performed better when it comes to managing assets? Explain.

Analysis

TIX uses the straight-line method of depreciation and SUBA uses the double-declining-balance method of depreciation. Does this affect your ability to compare these two companies?

_____

_____

_____

AP-26A LO 3 10

On July 1, 2010, Bob's Juice Factory purchased a bottle-sealing machine for $102,000. The machine has an estimated useful life of 10 years and is expected to have no residual value. Assume that the company has adopted a partial-year depreciation policy, where depreciation is applied on a monthly basis.

Required

a) Fill in the table below using the following facts.

- The company uses straight-line depreciation.
- The company's fiscal year end is December 31.
- The company stopped using this machine on November 1, 2018, when it was traded for a new machine.

Year	Cost of Noncurrent Asset	Depreciation Expense	Accumulated Depreciation To Date	Net Book Value

b) On November 1, 2018, Bob's Juice Factory traded the old bottle-sealing machine for a new machine. The price tag on the new machine is $130,000. In return for the old machine that Bob's Juice Factory is giving up, the supplier of the new machine agrees to take $30,000 off the price of the new machine even though the fair value of the old machine on the day of the trade is only $20,000. Record the journal entry for the machine exchange, assuming that the exchange has commercial substance.

Date	Account Title and Explanation	Debit	Credit

Application Questions Group B

AP-1B LO 2

On March 1, 2018, Lime Corp. bought machinery for $250,000 on credit from Super Machines Inc. Prepare the journal entry to record the transaction.

Date	Account Title and Explanation	Debit	Credit

AP-2B LO 2

In 2018, Phoenix Manufacturing Co. Ltd. decided to invest some money to improve and fix some of its noncurrent assets. Journalize the following transactions.

a) On February 15, the company paid $30,000 cash to replace the roof for its building. The new roof is expected to extend the useful life of the building past the original estimate by 10 years.

Date	Account Title and Explanation	Debit	Credit

b) One of the company's machines was making a loud noise. On May 4, the company paid $120 cash to lubricate its machine and successfully fixed the noise problem.

Date	Account Title and Explanation	Debit	Credit

c) On August 21, the company invested $14,000 cash to upgrade an engine for the existing machine, which will increase the machine's productivity by 15%.

Date	Account Title and Explanation	Debit	Credit

AP-3B LO 3

On June 1, 2015, new equipment was purchased for use in the factory. The equipment cost $1,200,000 and has a residual value of $180,000. The equipment has an estimated production capacity of 800,000 units. The equipment produced the following number of units over the past four years: 2015—224,000 units; 2016—216,000 units; 2017—208,000 units; and 2018—168,000 units. Assuming the company uses the units-of-production method, complete the following table. Do not round the per unit cost of depreciation in your calculations.

Year	Cost of Noncurrent Asset	Depreciation Expense	Accumulated Depreciation To Date	Net Book Value

AP-4B LO 3

On January 1, 2018, Howling Corp. purchased a truck for $40,000. The truck is expected to last eight years, at which time its estimated residual value is $5,000. Howling decided to depreciate the truck using the double-declining-balance method. Round all amounts to the nearest dollar.

a)   Complete the following chart to calculate the truck's depreciation for each year.

Year	Beginning Book Value	Depreciation	Ending Book Value
2018			
2019			
2020			
2021			
2022			
2023			
2024			
2025			

b)   Prepare the journal entry to record depreciation expense for the truck on December 31, 2018.

Date	Account Title and Explanation	Debit	Credit

AP-5B LO 2

On September 5, 2018, land, building and equipment were purchased for a total amount of $1,300,000. The assessed value of each asset at the time of acquisition is as follows: Land—$845,000; Building—$325,000; Equipment—$455,000. Write the journal entry to record the purchase.

Date	Account Title and Explanation	Debit	Credit

AP-6B LO 3 4

On April 1, 2010, Bob's Juice Factory purchased a new bottle sealing machine for $99,000. The machine has an estimated useful life of 10 years and is expected to have no residual value. Assume that the company has adopted a partial-year depreciation policy, where depreciation is taken on a monthly basis.

Required

a) Prepare the table using the following facts.
    • The company uses straight-line depreciation.
    • The asset is sold on April 30, 2018 for $31,000.
    • The company's fiscal year end is December 31.

Year	Cost of Noncurrent Asset	Depreciation Expense	Accumulated Depreciation To Date	Net Book Value

b) Record the journal entry for the sale, assuming that the depreciation for 2018 has already been recorded.

Date	Account Title and Explanation	Debit	Credit

AP-7B LO 3 4

Equipment was purchased on January 1, 2018 for $86,000. The asset is expected to last for four years, at which time the estimated residual value will be $7,000.

Required

a) Fill in the following table, assuming the company uses straight-line depreciation.

Year	Cost of Noncurrent Asset	Depreciation Expense	Accumulated Depreciation To Date	Net Book Value

b) Fill in the following table, assuming that the company uses the units-of-production method and that the estimated residual value will be $7,000. The asset is expected to produce a total of 1,010,000 units over four years. The number of units that the asset is expected to produce for each year is: 2018—202,000 units; 2019—252,500 units; 2020—303,000 units; and 2021—252,500 units.

Year	Cost of Noncurrent Asset	Depreciation Expense	Accumulated Depreciation To Date	Net Book Value

c) Continuing from part b), the business sold the equipment on December 31, 2021 for $9,000 cash. The sale happened after the journal entry to record the year's depreciation. Prepare the journal entry to record the sale of the equipment.

Date	Account Title and Explanation	Debit	Credit

AP-8B LO 3 4

On January 1, 2016, South Company purchased a machine for $40,000. The residual value was estimated to be $5,000. The machine will be depreciated over five years using the straight-line method. The company's year end is December 31.

Required

a) Prepare a depreciation schedule for the machine's useful life using the following table.

Year	Cost of Noncurrent Asset	Depreciation Expense	Accumulated Depreciation To Date	Net Book Value

b) At the end of 2020, the company stopped using this machine. Since no one was interested in buying it, the machine was simply discarded. Prepare a journal entry to record the machine's retirement.

Date	Account Title and Explanation	Debit	Credit

c) Assume that South Company uses the double-declining-balance depreciation method. At the end of 2020, new technology emerged, making the product manufactured by this machine obsolete. After testing for impairment, South Company determines that the fair value of the machine has permanently declined to $50. Prepare a depreciation schedule for the machine's useful life using the following table. Determine whether impairment has incurred, and if so, calculate the amount of impairment loss.

Year	Net Book Value (beginning of year)	Depreciation Expense	Accumulated Depreciation to Date	Net Book Value (end of year)

d) Assume that the company uses the units-of-production method, and the machine can produce 350,000 units. Record of production: 2016—20,000 units; 2017—60,000 units; 2018—70,000 units; 2019—100,000 units; and 2020—100,000 units. Prepare a depreciation schedule for the machine's useful life using the following table.

Year	Cost of Noncurrent Asset	Depreciation Expense	Accumulated Depreciation To Date	Net Book Value

e) Compare the pattern of depreciation expense resulting from three different depreciation methods in parts a), c) and d).

AP-9B LO 3 4

MNO Company purchased equipment worth $35,000 on January 1, 2018. The equipment has an estimated five-year service life with no residual value. The company's policy for five-year assets is to use the double-declining-balance method for the first two years of the asset's life and then switch to the straight-line depreciation method. The company's year end is December 31.

Required

a) Calculate the depreciation expense on December 31, 2020.

b) Assume that MNO Company's depreciation policy recognizes only half a year's depreciation in the year of purchase and half a year's depreciation in the year of disposal. The company uses the straight-line method. The asset was sold for $15,000 on May 15, 2020. Prepare a depreciation schedule using the following table.

Year	Cost of Noncurrent Asset	Depreciation Expense	Accumulated Depreciation To Date	Net Book Value

c) Prepare the journal entry to record the depreciation on the disposal and sale.

Date	Account Title and Explanation	Debit	Credit

AP-10B LO 3 4

Leonard Corporation acquired a machine in the first week of October 2017 and paid the following bills.

Invoice Price	$40,000
Freight-In	5,000
Installation Cost	7,000

The estimated useful life of the machine is eight years with no residual value. The company has December 31 as its year end and uses a straight-line depreciation method for noncurrent assets. Leonard Corporation depreciates its assets based on the number of months it owned the asset during the year.

Required

a) Calculate the net book value of the machine on December 31, 2018.

_____

_____

_____

_____

b) On December 31, 2018, the business sold the machine for $40,000. The sale happened after the journal entry to record the year's depreciation. Prepare the journal entry to record the sale of the machine.

Date	Account Title and Explanation	Debit	Credit

AP-11B LO 6

On September 1, 2017, Pat Jarvis purchased assets ($492,000) and liabilities ($422,000) of a company, for which he paid $200,000. The extra amount was paid because the company sells a superior product.

Required

a) Record the purchase transaction.

Date	Account Title and Explanation	Debit	Credit

b) Subsequent to the purchase of the company, a competitor appeared. On August 31, 2018, Pat assessed the value of the goodwill that his company owned was now worth $113,000. Record the appropriate journal entry to reflect the reduction in the value of goodwill.

Date	Account Title and Explanation	Debit	Credit

AP-12B LO 6

Higgins Company purchased a patent from Marquette Limited for $283,000 on August 1, 2017. The patent has a remaining life of six years.

Required

a) Prepare the journal entry to record the purchase.

Date	Account Title and Explanation	Debit	Credit

b) Prepare the journal entry to record amortization for one year on July 31, 2018. The company does not use the half-year rule.

Date	Account Title and Explanation	Debit	Credit

AP-13B LO 5

On March 1, 2018, Bowser Mining purchased an ore mine for $3,000,000. The company expects to use the mine for five years and extract 100,000 tons of ore over that time. At the end of five years, the residual value is estimated to be $500,000. For the year ended December 31, 2018, the company extracted 16,000 tons of ore; 12,000 tons were sold during the year, and the remaining 4,000 tons were kept as inventory. Prepare the journal entry to record the depletion for 2018.

Date	Account Title and Explanation	Debit	Credit

AP-14B LO 6

On August 1, 2018, Watertown Inc. purchased a trademark from Savannah Corp. for $410,000. The company paid $265,000 cash and issued a note payable for the remaining balance. The trademark has a legal life of 12 years but Watertown plans to stop using the trademark after eight years because it anticipates technological changes in the market that will render the trademark obsolete.

Required

a) Prepare the journal entry for the purchase of the trademark and the entry required to record amortization for the first year on December 31, 2018.

Date	Account Title and Explanation	Debit	Credit

b) Prepare the journal entry to record amortization for the second year on December 31, 2019.

Date	Account Title and Explanation	Debit	Credit

AP-15B LO 6

On January 1, 2018, Singleton Corporation purchased the assets and liabilities of Twinning's Inc. for a total purchase price of $215,800. Singleton paid a premium for the purchase, because Twinning's products are a recognizable brand name in the market. Twinning's had assets of $847,000 and liabilities of $674,900.

Required

a) Prepare the journal entry for Singleton to record the purchase.

Date	Account Title and Explanation	Debit	Credit

b) Due to an increase in the number of competitors in the market, on December 31, 2018, Singleton reviewed all assets for any impairment. It was discovered that the goodwill had a fair market value of only $36,500. Record the journal entry to record this impairment to goodwill.

Date	Account Title and Explanation	Debit	Credit

AP-16B LO 6

Turnbull Inc. purchased the assets ($516,800) and liabilities ($407,600) of Chappie Inc. on May 1, 2018 for a total purchase price of $315,000. Turnbull paid $105,000 in cash and signed a note payable for the remaining balance. This is an exciting transaction for Turnbull, as it will be acquiring Chappie's employees, a very experienced and skilled workforce.

Required

a) Prepare the journal entry for Turnbull to record the purchase.

Date	Account Title and Explanation	Debit	Credit

b) Over the year, a number of key personnel have left the company, and through a review of its assets on December 31, 2018, Turnbull has noted impairment to goodwill of $23,000. Record the journal entry to record this impairment to goodwill.

Date	Account Title and Explanation	Debit	Credit

AP-17B LO 6

Gamma Inc. purchased a copyright from Sigma Corporation for $60,000 cash on March 1, 2018. The copyright allows the owners' rights for five years. Gamma uses the straight-line method to amortize intangible assets and has a December 31 year end.

Required

a) Prepare the journal entry for the purchase of the copyright and the entry required to record amortization for the first year on December 31, 2018.

Date	Account Title and Explanation	Debit	Credit

b) Prepare the journal entry to record amortization for the second year on December 31, 2019.

Date	Account Title and Explanation	Debit	Credit

Analysis

Intangible assets do not have any physical form. Why are they considered assets?

_____

_____

_____

_____

AP-18B LO 7

Joe Corporation's selected financial data is given below.

Net Sales for 2018	$180,000
Cost of Goods Sold for 2018	99,000
Average Total Assets for 2018	120,000

Calculate the company's asset turnover. Explain what the ratio means.

_____

_____

_____

_____

_____

_____

_____

_____

_____

_____

AP-19B LO 3 4

Details of some of Lannister Inc.'s noncurrent assets are listed below.

Date of Purchase	Asset	Cost	Residual Value	Estimated Useful Life
Mar 30, 2015	Equipment	$127,800	$18,000	10 years
Jul 1, 2015	Machinery	$95,800	$25,000	12 years

On April 30, 2018, Lannister Inc. decides to dispose of both of these assets. The total proceeds received for the assets were $180,000. Both assets use the straight-line depreciation method based on the number of months owned in the year. Lannister Inc. has a December 31 year end. Round all answers to the nearest whole number.

Required

a) Prepare the depreciation table.

Year	Cost of Noncurrent Asset	Depreciation Expense	Accumulated Depreciation	Net Book Value
Equipment				
Machinery				

b) Prepare the journal entry to record the disposal of the assets. Assume that the journal entry to update the depreciation before disposal has already been made.

Date	Account Title and Explanation	Debit	Credit

AP-20B LO 2

Patterson Inc. purchased land, equipment and a truck on May 15, 2018 from StarGen Inc. The appraised values of the assets were $740,000 for land, $100,000 for equipment and $160,000 for the truck. Patterson paid $530,000 in cash and signed a note payable for the remaining balance of $370,000.

Required

a) Complete the table to determine the cost of the assets.

Item	Appraised	Percent	Applied to Cost

b) Prepare the journal entry to record the purchase.

Date	Account Title and Explanation	Debit	Credit

AP-21B LO 3 4

On January 1, 2015, Cutie Company purchased a piece of equipment for $90,000 and depreciated it by using the straight-line method. The company estimated that the equipment had a useful life of eight years with no residual value. On January 1, 2018, Cutie determined that the equipment only had a useful life of six years from the date of acquisition with no residual value.

Calculate the accumulated depreciation as of December 31, 2018. Explain why the yearly depreciation for 2018 is different from the three preceding years.

AP-22B LO 3 4

On January 1, 2016, a company purchased equipment for $22,400. It is expected to last for four years and have a residual value of $9,600. The equipment is donated to a local charity on December 31, 2018 after depreciation expense has been recorded for the year. Prepare the journal entry required to record the donation. The company uses straight-line depreciation.

Date	Account Title and Explanation	Debit	Credit

AP-23B LO 5

On January 1, 2017, WeOil Company installed an oil well at a purchase price of $40 million in addition to an installation cost of $5 million, all for cash. The residual value of the oil well is $3 million. WeOil Company estimates that the total predicted output is 75,000 barrels of oil. The company only pumped out and sold 2,000 barrels in 2017 and 3,500 barrels in 2018.

Required

a) Prepare the journal entry to record the purchase of the oil well.

Date	Account Title and Explanation	Debit	Credit

b) Calculate the depletion rate for each barrel to be extracted.

_____

_____

_____

_____

c) Prepare the journal entries to record the depletion for 2017.

Date	Account Title and Explanation	Debit	Credit

d) Prepare the journal entries to record the depletion for 2018.

Date	Account Title and Explanation	Debit	Credit

Analysis

If the total estimated barrels of oil extracted changes during the life of the natural resources, is it still suitable to use the units-of-production method? Explain why.

_____

_____

_____

_____

_____

AP-24B LO 3 4

AIT Company is a well-known producer of activeware including sports shirts and fleeces. On April 2, 2017, AIT Company bought an item of machinery for $120,000 with an expected useful life of 10 years and residual value of zero. AIT Company uses straight-line depreciation and its year end is December 31. The impairment test was done on December 31, 2020, after taking into account the depreciation expense for the year. After conducting an impairment test on its machinery, AIT realized that the asset has been impaired by $5,000.

Required

a) Record the journal entry for the impairment loss.

Date	Account Title and Explanation	Debit	Credit

b) Calculate the fair value of the machinery on December 31, 2020.

_____

_____

_____

_____

_____

_____

_____

_____

_____

_____

_____

Analysis

How might AIT Company determine the fair value of the machinery at December 31, 2020? When does the company need to test the assets for impairment?

_____

_____

AP-25B LO 7

The following financial data is given for two companies, LIN and WOK. They both manufacture and sell office furniture across the US and Canada. Both companies have a year end of June 30.

LIN Company	June 30, 2018	June 30, 2017
Net Sales	$3,500,000	$3,000,000
Total Assets	$2,200,000	$1,150,000
Net Income	$590,000	$500,000
Gross Profit	$1,575,000	$1,350,000

WOK Company	June 30, 2018	June 30, 2017
Net Sales	$4,500,000	$4,120,000
Total Assets	$5,500,000	$4,800,000
Net Income	$840,000	$620,000
Gross Profit	$1,575,000	$1,442,000

Required

Based on the information provided, answer the following questions. Round your final answers to the nearest whole percentage.

a) Calculate the return on assets for each company in 2018.

b) In 2018, which company performed better when it comes to managing assets? Explain.

c) Assume LIN Company's total assets in 2016 were the same as its total assets in 2017. Did LIN perform better in managing its noncurrent assets in 2017 or 2018? Why?

_____

_____

_____

_____

_____

_____

_____

_____

_____

AP-26B LO 3 10

A company purchased a machine for $50,000 on March 1, 2017. It is expected to last for four years and have a residual value of $10,000. Assume that the company has adopted a partial-year depreciation policy, for which half a year's depreciation is taken in the year of purchase, and half a year's depreciation is recorded in the year of disposal. The old machine is exchanged for the new machine on January 18, 2019 for an additional cash payment of $25,000. The price tag on the new machine is $60,000. The fair market value of the old machine on the day of the exchange is $33,000. Assume that this exchange has no commercial substance.

Required

a) Prepare the depreciation table for the old machine from the date it was purchased to the date it was exchanged for the new machine. The company uses straight-line depreciation.

Year	Cost of Noncurrent Asset	Depreciation Expense	Accumulated Depreciation To Date	Net Book Value

b) Prepare the journal entry to record the machine exchange. Assume the depreciation expense for the old machine has not been recorded for the year 2019.

Date	Account Title and Explanation	Debit	Credit

Case Study

CS-1 LO 3 6 7

Upmount Inc. reported the following information on their annual financial statements (all numbers are in millions).

	Year End September 30, 2018	Year End September 30, 2017
Net Sales	$233,715	$182,795
Net Income	53,394	39,510

An excerpt from its balance sheet and notes to the financial statements is presented below.

CONSOLIDATED BALANCE SHEETS

(In millions, except number of shares which are reflected in thousands and per value)

	September 30, 2018	September 30, 2017
Assets		
Current assets		
Cash and cash equivalents	$21,120	$13,844
Short-term marketable securities	20,481	11,233
Accounts receivable, less allowances of $82 and $86, respectively	16,849	17,460
Inventories	2,349	2,111
Deferred tax assets	5,546	4,318
Vendor non-trade receivables	13,494	9,759
Other current assets	9,539	9,806
Total current assets	89,378	68,531
Long-term marketable securities	164,065	130,162
Property, plant and equipment, net	22,471	20,624
Goodwill	5,116	4,616
Acquired intangible assets, net	3,893	4,142
Other assets	5,556	3,764
Total Assets	$290,479	$231,839

Property, Plant and Equipment

Property, plant and equipment are stated at cost. Depreciation is calculated using the straight-line method over the estimated useful lives of the assets, which for buildings is the lesser of 30 years or the remaining life of the building; between one to five years for machinery and equipment; and the shorter of lease terms or 10 years for leasehold improvements. Depreciation and amortization expenses on property and equipment was $9.2 billion, $6.9 billion and $5.8 billion during 2018, 2017 and 2016, respectively.

Noncurrent Assets Including Goodwill and Other Acquired Intangible Assets

Upmount reviews property, plant and equipment, and certain identifiable intangibles, excluding goodwill, for impairment. If property, plant and equipment, and certain identifiable intangibles are considered to be impaired, the impairment to be recognized equals the amount by which the carrying value of the assets exceeds its fair value.

Upmount does not amortize goodwill and intangible assets with indefinite useful lives, rather such assets are required to be tested for impairment at least annually or sooner whenever events or changes in circumstances indicate that the assets may be impaired. Upmount performs its goodwill and intangible asset impairment tests in the fourth quarter of each year. Upmount did not recognize any impairment charges related to goodwill or indefinite lived intangible assets during 2018, 2017 and 2016.

Upmount amortizes its intangible assets with definite useful lives over their estimated useful lives and reviews these assets for impairment. Upmount typically amortizes its acquired assets with definite useful lives over periods from three to seven years.

Note 3 – Consolidated Financial Statement Details

The following tables shows Upmount's consolidated financial statement details as of September 30, 2018 and September 30, 2017 (in millions):

Property, Plant and Equipment, Net

	2018	2017
Land and buildings	$6,956	$4,863
Machinery, equipment and internal-use software	37,038	29,639
Leasehold improvements	5,263	4,513
Gross property, plant and equipment	49,257	39,015
Accumulated depreciation and amortization	(26,786)	(18,391)
Total property, plant and equipment	$22,471	$20,624

Required

a) Noncurrent assets make up what percentage of total assets in 2018?

_____

_____

b) What method of depreciation does Upmount use? How many years does Upmount depreciate machinery and equipment?

_____

_____

c) What is the value of goodwill in Upmount at the end of 2018? Did Upmount write off any impairment on goodwill in 2018?

_____

_____

d) Calculate the return on assets for 2018. What does it mean?

_____

_____

e) Calculate the asset turnover for 2018. What does it mean?

_____

_____

_____

Critical Thinking

CT-1 LO 2 3 6

Grain Eagle Company manufactures and sells pet food. The company has adopted a partial-year depreciation policy, where depreciation is taken on a monthly basis. The company's accounting intern treated the following events that occurred in 2018 as follows.

1. On March 31, 2018, Grain Eagle spent $16 million to purchase land that already comes with a building, which the company will use as a warehouse. The land has a fair value of $12 million and the building has a fair value of $8 million on the date of the purchase. The building has a residual value of $2 million and is expected to bring future economic benefits to the company evenly over its expected useful life of 20 years. Because land and building are acquired together as a bulk purchase and because the building is attached to the land, the intern recorded the $16 million purchase simply as a debit to building and credit to cash.

2. On July 1, 2018, the company purchased a patent at a cost of $500,000. The patent has a legal life of 20 years even though its useful life is expected to be only 10 years. The intern recorded the purchase as a debit to patent and credit to cash for $500,000.

3. On November 30, 2018, the building incurred some water damage. The company spent $30,000 to repair the damage. The intern capitalized this cost by debiting building and crediting cash for $30,000.

4. On December 31, 2018, the intern recorded depreciation and amortization for all noncurrent assets, including the building and the patent listed above, and a machine that Grain Eagle acquired on December 31, 2017. The machine costs $200,000, has no residual value, and is expected to produce 2 million pounds of pet food over its 10 years of useful life. The future economic benefit of the machine depends on the number of pounds of food it produces, which is expected to vary substantially from year to year. The machine produced 250,000 pounds of pet food in 2018. Since the intern was not sure which depreciation method she should use, she decided to use the straight-line method for all assets because that is easiest. She recorded depreciation expenses of $20,000 for the machine and $600,000 for the building in 2018. She amortized the patent over the patent's legal life of 20 years. The patent's amortization expense from her calculation is $12,500. The intern recorded depreciation and amortization expenses separately for each asset by debiting depreciation/amortization expenses and crediting accumulated depreciation/amortization.

Required

a) For each of the above events, comment whether the intern's treatment of the event correctly follows GAAP. If the intern was wrong, suggest what she should have done.

_____

_____

_____

_____

_____

_____

_____

_____

_____

_____

_____

_____

_____

b) Prepare a partial balance sheet as at December 31, 2018 to present the noncurrent assets and their accumulated depreciation and amortization listed in the events above. Use the correct numbers (not the intern's numbers) in preparing the balance sheet. Assume that the company has no other noncurrent assets.

c) If Grain Eagle's most important competitor uses the double-declining-balance method to depreciate its noncurrent assets, should Grain Eagle also use this method for comparability purpose? Also, discuss whether accounting standards should allow only one method rather than allowing multiple methods of depreciation for improved comparability.

_____

_____

_____

_____

_____

_____

_____

_____

CT-2 LO 6

Since intangible assets have no physical existence, they cannot be seen. Stockholders may question showing an amount on the balance sheet for an "invisible" asset. Companies have staff with many years of experience who would be difficult to replace, and are therefore deemed valuable. However, the value of such staff is not reflected in the financial statements. Discuss.

_____

_____

_____

_____

_____

_____

_____

_____

_____

_____

_____

_____

_____

_____

_____

_____

_____

_____

_____

Chapter 13

CURRENT LIABILITIES

LEARNING OBJECTIVES

LO 1   Define and differentiate between determinable and non-determinable liabilities

LO 2   Record accounts payable

LO 3   Record transactions with sales tax

LO 4   Record unearned revenue

LO 5   Record short-term notes payable

LO 6   Record transactions related to the current portion of long-term liabilities

LO 7   Record payroll liabilities

LO 8   Record estimated liabilities

LO 9   Explain the accounting treatment for contingent liabilities

LO 10   Apply internal controls relating to current liabilities

AMEENGAGE™ *Access **ameengage.com** for integrated resources including tutorials, practice exercises, the digital textbook and more.*

Assessment Questions

AS-1 LO 1

What are current liabilities?

AS-2 LO 1

How are long-term liabilities different from current liabilities?

AS-3 LO 1

Explain the main difference between the way assets and liabilities are listed on the balance sheet.

AS-4 LO 1

Should notes payable be presented on the balance sheet as current liabilities or long-term liabilities?

AS-5 LO 1

Define determinable (known) liabilities.

_____
_____
_____

AS-6 LO 1

List at least three examples of determinable (known) liabilities.

_____
_____
_____
_____

AS-7 LO 1

Define non-determinable (unknown) liabilities.

_____
_____

AS-8 LO 1

List at least two examples of non-determinable (unknown) liabilities.

_____
_____
_____

AS-9 LO 1

What is a bank overdraft?

_____
_____

AS-10 LO 1

What is an operating line of credit?

_____
_____

AS-11 LO 2

What business transaction must have occurred for a company to debit merchandise inventory and credit accounts payable in its books?

_____
_____
_____

AS-12 LO 7

Why are accrued liabilities considered known liabilities?

AS-13 LO 7

Give an example of accrued liabilities that is common to most businesses.

AS-14 LO 7

How are gross pay and net pay different? Should a company record salaries expense using gross pay or net pay?

AS-15 LO 7

Define statutory deductions, and identify the statutory deductions in the United States.

AS-16 LO 7

Define voluntary deductions, and provide three examples of voluntary deductions.

AS-17 LO 3

Define sales tax.

AS-18 LO 3

Why is sales tax not recorded as part of revenue or expenses on a retailer's income statement?

AS-19 LO 3

Explain the use of clearing accounts in the context of sales tax.

_____
_____
_____

AS-20 LO 4

What is unearned revenue? Why is it a liability? Give two examples of unearned revenue.

_____
_____
_____
_____
_____
_____

AS-21 LO 5

Explain what a short-term note payable is. List the items you would expect to find on a note payable.

_____
_____
_____
_____
_____
_____
_____
_____
_____

AS-22 LO 4

Describe the journal entries that would be made by the borrower during the period of a short-term note payable.

_____
_____
_____
_____
_____
_____
_____

AS-23 LO 5 6

Northing Company has an outstanding 10-year, 5%, $1,000,000 note payable, which was issued on October 31, 2018. Northing must pay $100,000 to the lender on October 31 of each year, starting in 2019. In addition, it must pay interest to the lender semi-annually on April 30 and October 31 of each year. Describe how the note payable and accrued interest should be presented on Northing's financial statements for the year ended December 31, 2018.

AS-24 LO 8

Define "estimated liabilities" and give two examples of them.

AS-25 LO 3

Why have customer loyalty programs gained popularity in recent years?

AS-26 LO 8

Because it is impossible to predict with 100% certainty the amount of money that a company will have to spend repairing warrantied products, should warranty expense be recorded only when the products are returned for repair? Explain.

AS-27 LO 9

Define "contingent liabilities" and give an example of one.

AS-28 LO 9

Describe how a company accounts for contingent liabilities in its accounting records.

AS-29 LO 10

List some basic practices that a company can implement to control its current liabilities.

Application Questions Group A

AP-1A LO 2

A company has repairs completed on the heating system. The service man hands the accountant an invoice for $1,000 dated May 25, 2019, due in one month. Write the journal entry the company must prepare to record this transaction.

Date	Account Title and Explanation	Debit	Credit

AP-2A LO 8

A company uses substantial amounts of utilities (electricity and water) with an average cost of $6,000 per monthly billing period. It receives and pays the actual bill on the 15th of each month. In January 2019, the company received its bill in the amount of $6,207 for the period December 15 to January 15. The bill was paid right away. Assume the company prepares monthly financial statements.

Required

a) Record the journal entry on December 31, 2018 for the estimate of utilities expense for the period December 16–31, 2018.

b) Record the journal entry required for payment of the bill on January 15, 2019.

Date	Account Title and Explanation	Debit	Credit

AP-3A LO 6

On January 1, 2019, Cervera Company borrowed $100,000 from the local bank. The note is payable in equal installments over five years. Write the journal entry to record the note payable. How much of the note payable would be considered current on January 1, 2019?

Date	Account Title and Explanation	Debit	Credit

AP-4A LO 6

On December 31, 2018, Zaharah Company negotiates a note payable from the bank for $60,000 with a term of six years, bearing an annual interest rate of 6%. For this note payable, $10,000 plus interest is payable every December 31. Zaharah has a December 31 year end, and it prepares adjusting entries and financial statements only once a year.

Required

a) Prepare the journal entry to record the cash receipt from the note payable.

Date	Account Title and Explanation	Debit	Credit

b) Prepare the journal entry to record the payment of the first installment plus interest on December 31, 2019.

Date	Account Title and Explanation	Debit	Credit

c) What would be the total note payable balance on December 31, 2019? How much would be considered current?

_____

_____

_____

AP-5A LO 5

NOTE PAYABLE

For the Value Received, the undersigned promises to pay to the order of

_____U. Paymee_____ the sum of

_____ ***** $5,000 and 00/100 Dollars *********************** ($5,000.00) _____

with annual interest of 5% on any unpaid balance. This note shall mature and be payable,

along with accrued interest on:

_____July 31, 2019_____

_____February 1, 2019_____   _____A. Notemaker_____

Issue Date   Borrower Signature

Required

Answer the following questions regarding the note shown on the previous page.

a) Who is the lender?

_____

b) Who is the borrower?

_____

c) When is payment due?

_____

d) When was the note issued?

_____

e) When is interest payable?

_____

f) What amount must the borrower pay to the lender?

_____

AP-6A LO 5

On May 1, 2019, ACME Bank agreed to lend Mirza Enterprises $100,000. Mirza signed a $100,000, 10-month, 12% per annum note. Mirza Enterprises has a year end of December 31.

Required

Prepare the journal entries for Mirza Enterprises for the following.

a) On the date the note was signed
b) At year end
c) On March 1, 2020, when the note is repaid

Date	Account Title and Explanation	Debit	Credit

AP-7A LO 5

On June 15, 2019, Actor Surplus agreed to lend Wei Hong Enterprises $250,000. Wei signed a $250,000, eight-month, 10% per annum note. Wei Hong Enterprises has a year end of November 30.

Required

Prepare the journal entries for Wei Hong Enterprises for the following.

a) On the date the note was signed

b) At year end

c) On February 16, 2020, when the note is repaid

Date	Account Title and Explanation	Debit	Credit

AP-8A LO 5

Darren Spoon from Carding Company signed a 7%, half-year note payable for $100,000 on November 1, 2019. The note is due with interest on May 1, 2020. Carding Company has a year end of December 31.

Required

Prepare the journal entries for Carding Company for the following.

a) Record the receipt of cash

b) Record accruing interest at the year end

c) Record ultimate payment of the note in the new year

Date	Account Title and Explanation	Debit	Credit

Date	Account Title and Explanation	Debit	Credit

AP-9A LO 4

A transit company offers special transit passes to local students. The passes are sold for $200 each and for the fall semester are good from September 1 to December 31 (i.e. the passes cost $50 per month). The transit company sold 1,000 passes on August 1, 2019.

Required

Record the journal entries for the following.

a) The sale of the passes

b) The entry to be recorded on September 30

Date	Account Title and Explanation	Debit	Credit

AP-10A LO 7

Identify the following items as statutory or voluntary deductions by placing an "X" in the appropriate column.

Description	Statutory	Voluntary
Federal income taxes		
Dental benefits		
Union dues		
Social security tax		
Uniform allowance		
Medicare tax		
State income taxes		
Prescription coverage		
Retirement deduction		
Federal unemployment taxes		
Purchase of company stock		
Professional dues		
Charitable donations		
Tools and safety apparel		

AP-11A LO 7

Saleem Enterprises is a graphic design company. The accountant needs to prepare the relative journal entries to determine items related to salaries, deductions, and contributions.

Required

a) On May 31, Saleem Enterprises had gross pay for employees of $42,500. Total employee contributions to the retirement savings plan is $1,700. The appropriate deduction rates are provided. Record the entry for salaries expense on May 31.
- Federal income tax rate is 9%
- State income tax rate is 6%
- FICA is 7.65%
- FUTA is 0.6%
- SUTA is 5.4%

Date	Account Title and Explanation	Debit	Credit

b) Using the data from above and assuming Saleem Enterprises contributes the same amount toward the employee retirement savings plan, prepare the journal entry for the employer's payroll contributions.

Date	Account Title and Explanation	Debit	Credit

c) What is the total amount of cash that Saleem Enterprises will pay? How much will Saleem Enterprises pay for every $1.00 of gross pay earned by employees?

AP-12A LO 7

Answer the following questions related to Morales Inc.

a) On September 30, Morales Inc. had gross pay for employees of $37,000.00. Withholdings for employees are $1,367.00 for state income taxes, $2,960.00 for federal income taxes, $2,830.50 for FICA, $1,300.00 for the retirement savings plan and $400.00 for charitable donations.

Record the entry for salaries expense on September 30.

Date	Account Title and Explanation	Debit	Credit

b) Using the given information and assuming Morales Inc. does not contribute toward the employee retirement savings plan, prepare the journal entry for the employer's taxes and benefit costs. Assume FUTA is $222.00 and SUTA is $1,998.00.

Date	Account Title and Explanation	Debit	Credit

c) What is the total amount of cash that Morales Inc. will pay? How much will Morales Inc. pay for every $1.00 of gross pay earned by employees?

_____

_____

AP-13A LO 8

Lee-Yau Enterprises sells heavy-duty lawnmower equipment. On May 4, 2019, it sold a lawnmower (on account) for $45,000, which included a four-year unlimited warranty. The corporation's accountant estimates that $3,000 will be paid out in warranty obligations. The cost of goods sold is $17,000. Assume Lee-Yau uses a perpetual inventory system. Prepare the journal entries relating to these transactions.

Date	Account Title and Explanation	Debit	Credit

AP-14A LO 8

After recording an estimated warranty liability on the sale of a lawnmower, Lee-Yau is required to repair the lawnmower sold (there is a faulty wire) and Lee-Yau spends $500 in cash on October 15, 2019 remedying the problem. Record the journal entry for this transaction.

Date	Account Title and Explanation	Debit	Credit

AP-15A LO 8

Shining Star Corporation produces and sells washing machines, and provides customers with a one-year warranty on all its products. It is estimated that the company incurs approximately $50 of warranty expense on each machine sold. During 2018, the company sold 400 washing machines. All warranty transactions are recorded on December 31.

Required

a) Prepare a journal entry to record the estimated warranty liability.

Date	Account Title and Explanation	Debit	Credit

b) During 2019, the company used $5,000 worth of inventory parts and paid $10,000 for maintenance staff salaries. Prepare a journal entry to record this transaction.

Date	Account Title and Explanation	Debit	Credit

c) At the end of 2019, the company decided to decrease its estimated liability by the remaining balance. Prepare a journal entry to record this transaction.

Date	Account Title and Explanation	Debit	Credit

AP-16A LO 8

Shining Star Corporation provides its customers with an option to purchase a three-year warranty on washing machines. On March 1, 2019, Shining Star received $30,000 cash from customers who purchased the extended warranty for their washing machines.

Required

a) Prepare a journal entry to record the sale of extended warranty on March 1, 2019.

Date	Account Title and Explanation	Debit	Credit

b) Prepare the journal entry required on March 1, 2020.

Date	Account Title and Explanation	Debit	Credit

AP-17A LO 8

Inline Company sells Spartan laptops for $3,500 each. Each laptop comes with a three-year warranty that requires the corporation to replace defective parts and provide labor. Assume the warranty is honored equally over the three years. During 2018 the corporation sold 300 laptops. Based on past experience, the estimated average cost for repairs under warranties is $150 for parts and $200 for labor per laptop sold. During 2019, actual repair costs were $12,000 for parts and $24,000 for labor.

Required

a) Prepare a journal entry on December 31, 2018 to record the estimated warranty liability in 2018.

Date	Account Title and Explanation	Debit	Credit

b) Explain how the warranty liability and expense will appear on the balance sheet and income statement on December 31, 2018.

_____

_____

_____

c) Prepare the journal entry on December 31, 2019 to record the warranty costs for 2019.

Date	Account Title and Explanation	Debit	Credit

d) Explain how the warranty liability and expense will appear on the balance sheet and income statement on December 31, 2019.

_____

_____

_____

_____

Analysis

Discuss why product warranties are recorded as expenses (estimated) at the same time that products are sold, while extended warranties sold to customers are recognized as revenue over several periods.

_____
_____
_____
_____
_____

AP-18A LO 5

On September 1, 2019, Express Company purchased a delivery truck from MJ Trucks, costing $80,000. However, due to cash flow problems, Express Company is currently unable to make the payment. Therefore, to assure MJ Trucks that it will be paid, Express Company signed a one-year note with 3% interest per annum, to be payable at maturity on August 31, 2020. Express Company's year end is on December 31. Prepare all the necessary journal entries related to the notes payable from the time it is signed to the maturity date.

Date	Account Title and Explanation	Debit	Credit

Analysis

Businesses are supposed to accrue expenses (such as interest expense) at the end of their fiscal years to report them on their financial statements. Why do you think businesses should not wait until cash is paid to record the expenses?

_____
_____
_____
_____
_____
_____

AP-19A LO 6

On February 1, 2018, Red Ball signed a note payable for $30,000. The note bears an interest rate of 2.5% per annum, and is due in two years. Red Ball has a December 31 year end. The partial principal of $15,000 plus interest is payable every January 31. Prepare the necessary journal entries from February 1, 2018 to January 31, 2020.

Date	Account Title and Explanation	Debit	Credit

AP-20A LO 2 4 8

GoodJob Company buys and sells home appliances and uses the perpetual inventory system. GoodJob has a year end of December 31. During 2019, the company had the following transactions.

Jan 15   Purchased vacuum cleaners worth $60,000 from V Wholesalers, on account.

Feb 4   Sold vacuum cleaners for $45,000 cash, which includes a three-year warranty. GoodJob originally bought these vacuum cleaners for $30,000.

Feb 4   Recorded $15,000 of estimated warranty liability for the year.

Feb 15   Paid the full amount owing to V Wholesalers.

May 8   Received a utilities bill for $3,000, to be paid in exactly 15 days.

May 23   Paid the utilities bill received on May 8.

Jul 11   Received $42,000 cash for the sale of vacuum cleaners, which cost the company $30,000. The delivery is to be made on August 31.

Aug 31   Delivered the vacuum cleaners from the July 11 transaction.

Prepare journal entries to record the above transactions.

Date	Account Title and Explanation	Debit	Credit

AP-21A LO 3

Porch Living sells outdoor furniture and accessories. It operates in a state that has a 5% sales tax. The following transactions occurred during May 2019.

May 5   Sold inventory to a customer for $2,000 plus sales tax on account. The inventory costs $1,200.

May 25   Sold inventory to a customer for $6,000 plus tax for cash. The inventory costs $3,200.

May 27   Received the total amount owing from the customer from May 5.

May 31   Remitted the sales tax to the government.

Record the transactions for May 2019. The company uses a perpetual inventory system.

Date	Account Title and Explanation	Debit	Credit

AP-22A LO 3

Signet Sales operates in a state with a 7% sales tax. During July 2019, it had the following sales.

Jul 10   Sold inventory to a customer for $1,000 plus sales tax on account. The inventory costs $700.

Jul 12   Sold inventory to a customer for $4,000 plus sales tax for cash. The inventory costs $2,900.

Record the transactions for July 2019. The company uses a perpetual inventory system.

Date	Account Title and Explanation	Debit	Credit

AP-23A LO 8

Office File is a retail company that sells stationary in several eastern states. The company offers a customer loyalty program whereby customers are rewarded one cent of "Office File Money" (OFM) for every $1 purchase. The OFM has no expiry date and can be used by customers as a discount toward future purchases at any Office File store. In January 2018, Office File made sales of $400,000. Historically, an average of 75% of OFM issued is redeemed.

Required

a)   Prepare the journal entry to record the issuance of OFM in January 2018.

Date	Account Title and Explanation	Debit	Credit

b) In February, Office File had sales of $500,000, of which $498,000 was received in cash and $2,000 was redeemed using OFM. Prepare the journal entry to record the sales through cash and OFM redemption in February.

Date	Account Title and Explanation	Debit	Credit

Analysis

In this question, Office File uses a 75% redemption rate to calculate the amounts for sales discount and redemption rewards liability. What happens if 100% of the rewards were redeemed this year?

_____

_____

_____

AP-24A LO 6

Ricotta Company has the following selected items and balances on its trial balance at December 31, 2018. Ricotta offers a one-year warranty on its products and does not sell extended warranties.

Accounts Payable	$9,700
Accounts Receivable	4,200
Cash	5,000
Equipment	65,000
Estimated Warranty Liability	2,500
Merchandise Inventory	18,400
Prepaid Rent	8,500
Salaries Payable	6,300
Notes Payable, Current Portion	21,000
Unearned Revenue	8,400

Required

a) Prepare the current liabilities portion of the balance sheet.

b)   Based on the information available, calculate the current ratio and comment on the liquidity of the company.

_____

_____

_____

_____

Analysis

It is recommended to make use of any purchase discounts that are available. Suppose a company is offered a discount of 2% for a total payable of $100,000 if payment is made within 30 days. The company does not have enough cash to pay for it within the discount period. What would you suggest the company do?

_____

_____

_____

_____

Application Questions Group B

AP-1B LO 2

Corrose Company bought equipment worth $10,000 on credit from a supplier. On June 20, the supplier delivered the equipment and sent an invoice, which is due on July 20. Write the journal entry the company must prepare to record the purchase of equipment on June 20.

Date	Account Title and Explanation	Debit	Credit

AP-2B LO 6

On May 1, 2018, Verico Company borrowed $98,000 from the local bank. The note is payable in equal installments over five years.

Required

a) Write the journal entry to record the note.

Date	Account Title and Explanation	Debit	Credit

b) How much of the note payable would be considered long-term on May 1, 2018?

AP-3B LO 6

On July 1, 2018, Merrit Company borrowed a $200,000 note payable with a term of four years, bearing an annual interest rate of 5%. Of this note, $50,000 plus interest is payable every June 30. Merrit has a June 30 year end, and it prepares adjusting entries and financial statements only once a year.

Required

a) Prepare the journal entry to record the cash receipt from the arranged note.

Date	Account Title and Explanation	Debit	Credit

b) Prepare the journal entry to record the payment of the first installment plus interest on June 30, 2019.

Date	Account Title and Explanation	Debit	Credit

c) What would be the total note payable balance on June 30, 2019? How much of the loan would be considered current?

_____

_____

AP-4B LO 6

On July 1, 2018, Express Company purchased a delivery truck from DW Trucks, costing $85,000. However, due to cash flow problems, Express Company is currently unable to make the payment. To assure DW Trucks of payment, Express signed a one-year note with 6% interest per annum, to be payable at maturity on June 30, 2019. Express Company's year end is on December 31. Prepare all the necessary journal entries related to the notes payable from the time it is signed to the maturity date.

Date	Account Title and Explanation	Debit	Credit

AP-5B LO 6

On August 1, 2018, DEBTS Bank agreed to lend Zirkula Enterprises $110,000. Zirkula signed a $110,000, 10-month, 12% per annum note. Zirkula Enterprises has a year end of December 31. Interest is payable at maturity.

Required

Prepare the journal entry for Zirkula Enterprises for the following.

a) On the date the note was signed

b) At year end

c) On May 31, 2019, when the note is repaid

Date	Account Title and Explanation	Debit	Credit

AP-6B LO 5

On May 1, 2018, Cool Water signed a $50,000, six-month note payable with a 7% annual interest rate. Cool Water has a September 30 year end.

Required

Prepare the necessary journal entries to record the following.

a)   The signing of the note payable on May 1, 2018
b)   The required adjusting entry on September 30, 2018
c)   The payment of interest and repayment of the note on November 1, 2018

Date	Account Title and Explanation	Debit	Credit

AP-7B LO 5

On November 1, 2018, Compression Company signed a $100,000, eight-month note payable with a 5% annual interest rate. Compression Company has a December 31 year end.

Required

Prepare the necessary journal entries to record the following.

a)   The signing of the note payable on November 1, 2018
b)   The required adjusting entry on December 31, 2018
c)   The payment of interest and repayment of the note on July 1, 2019

Date	Account Title and Explanation	Debit	Credit

Analysis

The accounting practice of estimating and recording accrued expense is part of accrual-based accounting. This process is different from cash-based accounting, which is an accounting practice that records expenses and revenue only when cash is paid or received. What benefit does accrual-based accounting have over cash-based accounting?

_____

_____

_____

_____

AP-8B LO 4

A local transit company sells monthly transit passes for $150 each. Each pass is valid for six months and the value of the pass decreases month by month. The company sold 1,200 units on February 1, 2018.

Required

Write the entry for the following transactions.

a) The sale of the transit passes

b) The entry to be recorded on June 30, the company's year end

Date	Account Title and Explanation	Debit	Credit

AP-9B LO 7

The records of Magic Delivery Inc. show the following figures.

Employee Earnings	
Monthly Salary	?
Overtime Pay	2,200
Total Gross Pay	?
Deductions and Net Pay	
Withheld Statutory Deductions	990
Charitable Contributions	?
Medical Insurance	780
Total Deductions	2,270
Net Pay	6,630

Calculate the missing amounts.

AP-10B LO 7

Rippling Waters rents canoes and other water crafts to campers and hikers. On May 15, 2018, Rippling Waters prepared its semi-monthly payroll for its employees. Payroll information for May 15, 2018 is listed below.

Employee	Total Hours	Hourly Rate	Health Insurance (employee portion)
M. Swift	87.5	$14.50	$18.00
S. Current	85.5	15.00	20.00
B. Wavey	73.5	13.50	14.00

The employer pays half of the health care premium, and the employees pay the other half. The appropriate deduction rates are as follows.

- Federal income tax rate is 9%
- State income tax rate is 6%
- FICA is 7.65%
- FUTA is 0.6%
- SUTA is 5.4%

Required

a) Prepare the payroll journal entries for May 15, 2018 to record the salaries payable to the employees and accrue the employer contributions.

Date	Account Title and Explanation	Debit	Credit

b) Prepare the entry to pay the employees on May 17, 2018.

Date	Account Title and Explanation	Debit	Credit

c) Prepare the entry to pay the liability to the health insurance company on May 31, 2018.

Date	Account Title and Explanation	Debit	Credit

d) Prepare the entry to pay the liabilities to the government on June 15, 2018.

Date	Account Title and Explanation	Debit	Credit

AP- 11B LO 7

Tristan Industries has the following numbers for its payroll for November 15.
- Gross pay is $42,000
- Federal income tax is $3,780
- State income tax is $2,100
- FICA is $3,213
- FUTA is $252
- SUTA is $2,268

Prepare the journal entries to accrue the employee's payroll and the payroll tax expense on November 15.

Date	Account Title and Explanation	Debit	Credit

AP-12B LO 8

Los Amigos Manufacturing builds and sells cars. On January 1, 2018, the company sold 150 cars for $30,000 each, on account. The cost to build each car is $7,000. Los Amigos does not automatically include warranties with the purchase of the car; however, the customer has the option to purchase the warranty separately. Los Amigos sold a four-year warranty for each car sold. Each warranty costs $2,000. Prepare the journal entries for the sale of the cars and warranties. Assume the cars were purchased on account and that the warranties were paid for in cash. Los Amigos uses a perpetual inventory system.

Date	Account Title and Explanation	Debit	Credit

AP-13B LO 8

PanPress Company sold four-year extended warranties on January 1, 2018 and received $300,000 cash. Record the journal entry related to unearned warranty revenue required at the end of the first year, on December 31, 2018.

Date	Account Title and Explanation	Debit	Credit

AP-14B LO 8

SASA, a manufacturer of photocopying machines, offers customers a three-year warranty on the purchase of each machine. If a machine breaks down during this warranty period, SASA is required to repair or replace the machine. On the basis of historical experience, SASA determines that an average of $80 worth of parts per machine will be used for warranty obligations. SASA sold 300 machines during 2018. All journal entries related to warranties are recorded on December 31.

Required

a) Prepare the journal entry to record the estimated warranty liability for 2018.

b) Prepare the journal entry recorded in 2019 assuming SASA uses $5,000 in parts for warranty claims.

Date	Account Title and Explanation	Debit	Credit

c) How would the 2019 income statement be affected if SASA used $5,000 in parts in 2019 for warranty claims?

_____

_____

AP-15B LO 8

Solace produces and sells sunglasses and provides customers with a one-year warranty on all products. It is estimated that the company incurs approximately $10 of warranty expense on each pair sold. During 2018, the company sold 400 pairs of sunglasses. All journal entries related to warranties are recorded on December 31.

Required

a) Prepare a journal entry to record the estimated warranty liability.

b) During the year 2018, the company used $200 worth of inventory parts and paid $100 cash for staff salaries toward warranty claims. Prepare a journal entry to record this transaction.

Date	Account Title and Explanation	Debit	Credit

AP-16B LO 8

Spinicker sells in-home stereo systems. The corporation also sells a four-year warranty contract as a separate service. Spinicker sold 40,000 warranty contracts at $100 each in 2018. Spinicker recognizes warranty revenue evenly over the warranty period.

Required

a) Prepare a journal entry on December 31, 2018 to record the sale of the warranty contracts for the year.

Date	Account Title and Explanation	Debit	Credit

b) Explain how the unearned warranty revenue will appear on the balance sheet at the end of 2018.

_____

_____

c) Prepare the journal entry on December 31 to record warranty revenue in 2019.

Date	Account Title and Explanation	Debit	Credit

Analysis

Why do you think businesses record the full amount of warranty expenses concurrently as products are sold even though the amount of warranty liabilities are reduced over the life of warranty period, which can be as long as several years?

_____

_____

_____

_____

_____

AP-17B LO 5

On April 1, 2018, Sinister Toys signed a $600,000, six-month note payable with a 12% annual interest rate. Sinister Toys has a June 30 year end.

Required

a) Record the signing of the note payable on April 1, 2018.

b) Prepare the required adjusting entry on June 30, 2018.

c) Record the payment of interest and repayment of the note on October 1, 2018.

Date	Account Title and Explanation	Debit	Credit

AP-18B LO 2 4 5

Shawn Clarity owns a consulting firm called Clarity Solutions. Clarity Solutions has a year end of December 31. The firm had the following transactions during 2018.

Jan 1	Received $10,000 cash for consulting fees from a client. To date, $5,000 worth of services have been provided, and the rest will be provided on February 16.
Feb 16	Provided the services outstanding from the January 1 transaction.
Mar 11	Purchased office equipment worth $500, on account.
Apr 1	Purchased new office furniture for $7,000 from JJ Store by signing a six-month note with 4% annual interest. Interest and principal payment is due at maturity.
May 11	Paid $500 cash for the purchase of equipment on March 11.
Jun 12	Received a $600 invoice for repair services, to be paid after 45 days.
Jul 27	Paid cash for the invoice received on June 12.
Sep 30	Recorded any payments and interest accrued related to the notes payable from April 1.
Oct 19	Received $2,000 cash from a client for consulting services provided.

Prepare journal entries to record the above transactions.

Date	Account Title and Explanation	Debit	Credit

AP-19B LO 2 4 6

During 2019, FitnessFirst Ltd. had the following transactions.

Feb 1 | Signed a five-year note payable for $150,000 with an interest rate of 5% per annum. Annual principal payment of $30,000 and interest is payable at the end of January.

Mar 1 | Sold 100 three-month club membership to customers for a total $6,000 cash. Regardless of the number of times a customer visits the club, the monthly memberships are not refundable.

Mar 31 | Recorded revenue earned from the March 1 transaction.

Apr 14 | Purchased treadmills worth $20,000 from RunRun Company, on account.

Apr 30 | Recorded revenue earned from the March 1 transaction.

May 25 | Received a utilities bill for $1,000, to be paid within 30 days.

May 31 | Recorded revenue earned from the March 1 transaction.

Jun 14 | Paid $10,000 cash to RunRun Company to reduce the balance owing.

Jun 24 | Paid the utilities bill received on May 25.

Sep 1 | Received $10,000 cash from customers for the sale of one-month memberships. Once the customer has paid the membership fees, it cannot be refunded.

Prepare journal entries to record the above transactions during 2019. FitnessFirst Ltd. has a year end of December 31.

Date	Account Title and Explanation	Debit	Credit

Date	Account Title and Explanation	Debit	Credit

AP-20B LO 3

Tasty Cafe has recorded all its transactions for September 2018. As of September 30, the balance of the sales tax payable account was $3,500.

Prepare the journal entry that Tasty Cafe will prepare on September 30 to remit the sales tax to the government.

Date	Account Title and Explanation	Debit	Credit

AP-21B LO 2 3

Toy Retailer operates in a city where the combined state and local sales tax rate is 8%. During August 2018, it had the following transactions.

Aug 12   Sold inventory to a customer for $2,000 plus sales tax for cash; the inventory costs $1,100

Aug 15   Sold inventory to a customer for $5,000 plus sales tax on account; the inventory costs $2,800

Record the transactions for August 2018. The company uses a perpetual inventory system.

Date	Account Title and Explanation	Debit	Credit

AP-22B [LO 8]

Safe Sound Airlines is a low-cost airline operating in North America. The company offers a customer loyalty program whereby customers are rewarded 1 "Safe Mile" for every 10 miles traveled with the airline. One Safe Mile can be redeemed for a two-cent discount toward future flights. In March 2018, customers flew 6,000,000 miles with Safe Sound Airlines. Historically, customers redeem an average of 55% of Safe Miles issued.

Required

a) Prepare the journal entry to record the issuance of Safe Miles in March 2018.

Date	Account Title and Explanation	Debit	Credit

b) Safe Sound Airlines' total ticket sales in April was $640,000, of which $636,000 was received in cash and $4,000 was redeemed using Safe Miles. Prepare the journal entry to record the sales through cash and Safe Miles redemption in April.

Date	Account Title and Explanation	Debit	Credit

Analysis

If the redemption rate for the rewards program has decreased to 50% this year, should the company use the lower rate to record its redemption rewards liability?

_____

_____

_____

AP-23B [LO 6]

Brisbane Company has the following selected items and balance on its trial balance at its year end on October 31, 2018. Brisbane offers a one-year warranty on its products and does not sell extended warranties.

Accounts Payable	$6,200
Accounts Receivable	8,700
Cash	9,200
Notes Payable, Current Portion	15,000
Estimated Warranty Liability	6,700
Merchandise Inventory	32,400
Notes Payable, Long-Term Portion	80,000
Prepaid Insurance	2,600
Salaries Payable	5,400
Unearned Revenue	4,700

Required

a) Prepare the current liabilities portion of the balance sheet.

b) Based on the information available, calculate the current ratio and comment on the liquidity of the company.

_____

_____

_____

Analysis

A company is offered a discount of 2% if payment of a $100,000 invoice is made within 30 days of the invoice date. However, the company realized that it would not have sufficient funds until 59 days after the invoice date. The company has an operating line of credit arranged with its bank for $1,000,000 at an annual interest rate of 5% on any outstanding balance at the beginning of each month. Should the company borrow from its operating line of credit to pay off the amount to its supplier and receive the discount?

_____

_____

_____

_____

_____

_____

_____

_____

_____

_____

_____

_____

_____

_____

Case Study

CS-1 LO 2 3 4 5 6 7 8

Fulton Electronics sells televisions and other electronics. All the electronics come with a default one-year warranty against defects. Warranty estimates are recorded every month. Fulton estimates that warranty repairs or replacements are 2% of the sales price. Customers are also able to purchase a two-year extended warranty. The warranty revenue is spread evenly over the two-year period. During September 2018, the following transactions occurred. The company uses the perpetual inventory system and operates in a state that has a sales tax rate of 6%. Sales tax amounts on purchases are added to the value of the item purchased.

Sep 1　Purchased store fixtures for $300,000 plus sales tax. Since Fulton does not have the cash, it signed a three-year note payable with a rate of 5%. Payment of $50,000 plus interest is due each March 1 and September 1 until the note matures.

Sep 1　Sold extended two-year warranties on products sold last month. Received $4,800 cash.

Sep 10　Incurred warranty costs of $500 to replace defective products sold last month. The warranty costs were taken from inventory.

Sep 14　Prepared the payroll for employees for the first half of the month. The actual payment will be made at a later date. Details of the payroll are shown below.

Gross Pay	$5,000
Federal Income Tax	$500
State Income Tax	$250
FICA	$383
FUTA	$30
SUTA	$270

Sep 15　Cash sales for the first half of the month totaled $400,000 plus sales tax. Cost of goods sold was $240,000. Estimated warranty costs must also be recorded. There is no sales tax recorded on warranty estimates.

Sep 15　Paid the amount of payroll owing to employees from September 14.

Sep 20　Purchased inventory on account for $150,000 plus sales tax.

Sep 29　Prepared the payroll for employees for the second half of the month. The actual payment will be made at a later date. Details of the payroll are shown below.

Gross Pay	$6,000
Federal Income Tax	$600
State Income Tax	$300
FICA	$459
FUTA	$36
SUTA	$324

Sep 30　Sales for the second half of the month amount to $350,000 plus sales tax. Cost of goods sold was $210,000. Estimated warranty costs must also be recorded. There is no sales tax recorded on warranty estimates.

Sep 30　Paid the amounts of payroll owing to employees from September 29.

Sep 30　Paid the sales tax owing for the month of September.

Sep 30　Paid the payroll remittance for the amount owing from payroll for the month of September.

Sep 30　Accrued one month of interest on the note payable from September 1.

Sep 30　Earned one month of extended warranty revenue from September 1.

Required

a)　Complete journal entries for the above transactions for the month of September 2018.

Date	Account Title and Explanation	Debit	Credit
Date	Account Title and Explanation	Debit	Credit

Date	Account Title and Explanation	Debit	Credit

b) Are liabilities reported as current or long-term on the balance sheet on September 30, 2018?

_____

_____

_____

_____

_____

Critical Thinking

CT-1 LO 8

Contingent liabilities arise when the payment of a liability depends on uncertain future events, such as the result of a lawsuit.

Current accounting practice requires that when the payment for a contingent liability is probable, and the amount can be reasonably estimated, the amount must be recorded in the journal and reported on the financial statements.

Is this practice reasonable, in light of the fact that the liability is not definite and only estimates are used? Does this practice mislead owners regarding the actual state of affairs surrounding liabilities? Discuss.

Chapter 14

PARTNERSHIPS

LEARNING OBJECTIVES

LO 1	Describe the characteristics, advantages and disadvantages of a partnership
LO 2	Describe different types of partnerships
LO 3	Record the formation of a partnership
LO 4	Record the division of income or loss

LO 5	Record partners' withdrawals
LO 6	Prepare financial statements for a partnership
LO 7	Account for the addition or withdrawal of a partner
LO 8	Record the liquidation of a partnership

AMEENGAGE *Access **ameengage.com** for integrated resources including tutorials, practice exercises, the digital textbook and more.*

Assessment Questions

AS-1 LO 1

What is a partnership?

_____

_____

AS-2 LO 1

List two advantages of organizing a business as a partnership over a proprietorship.

_____

_____

AS-3 LO 1

Compare and contrast the characteristics of proprietorships and general partnerships.

Characteristic	Proprietorship	General Partnership
Amount of capital that can be raised		
Control		
Dissolution		
Liability		
Number of owners		
Profits		
Set Up		
Skills		
Taxation		

AS-4 `LO 3`

What methods may partners choose to pay themselves, other than straight division of profits?

_____

_____

_____

AS-5 `LO 1`

What does mutual agency mean in the context of partnership?

_____

_____

AS-6 `LO 2`

In a limited partnership, what is the difference between a general partner and a limited partner?

_____

_____

AS-7 `LO 2`

What is a limited liability partnership? How is it different from a limited partnership?

_____

_____

_____

_____

AS-8 `LO 2`

Which aspect of a limited liability company is similar to a partnership? Which aspect of a limited liability company is similar to a corporation?

_____

_____

_____

_____

AS-9 `LO 2`

What is an S corporation?

_____

_____

_____

AS-10 `LO 3`

What is a partnership agreement?

_____

_____

_____

AS-11 LO 4

List different ways in which a partnership's profits may be divided.

_____

_____

_____

_____

AS-12 LO 4

Explain the closing of the income summary account for partnerships.

_____

_____

AS-13 LO 5

During the year, partners may withdraw cash or other assets. What account is used to accumulate these withdrawals?

_____

_____

AS-14 LO 5

What happens to partners' withdrawals at year end?

_____

_____

AS-15 LO 7

When a partner is added or removed from the partnership, what happens to the partnership agreement?

_____

_____

AS-16 LO 7

What are the two different ways withdrawal of a partner can take place?

_____

_____

AS-17 LO 7

What happens to a general partnership when a partner passes away?

_____

_____

_____

_____

AS-18 LO 8

In liquidating a partnership, what happens if assets are sold for amounts other than their book values?

_____

_____

AS-19 LO 8

What does capital deficiency mean in the context of partnership liquidation? How is capital deficiency dealt with in the partnership's books?

_____

_____

_____

_____

Application Questions Group A

AP-1A [LO 3]

Chandra Heesch and Allie Owenby have decided to form a general partnership on January 1, 2018. Each partner has agreed to contribute $10,000. Write the journal entry to record the formation of the partnership.

Date	Account Title and Explanation	Debit	Credit

AP-2A [LO 3]

On May 1, 2018, Nataliya, Sam and Seechi form a limited partnership and open a small convenience store. All the partners invest $10,000 cash, and Nataliya also invests equipment worth $5,000.

Required

a) Calculate the total contribution of each partner.

	Nataliya	Sam	Seechi

b) Prepare a journal entry to set up the partnership, and to record the additional investment of equipment.

Date	Account Title and Explanation	Debit	Credit

AP-3A [LO 3]

The following four people started a limited liability partnership and brought the assets and liabilities listed into the new business.

Bianca Lee	
Cash	$14,000
Accounts Receivable	5,000
Allowance for Doubtful Accounts	800
Notes Payable	2,500

Bob Fire	
Cash	$55,000
Equipment	11,000
Accumulated Depreciation	1,000
Notes Payable	8,000

Larry Lenkman	
Cash	$28,000
Building	240,000

Freeda Redgrave	
Cash	$60,000

Note: An independent appraiser determined that the allowance for doubtful accounts should be $600 and the equipment's fair market value is $10,000. All other assets are recorded at their fair market values.

Required

a)   When the partnership is formed, show the account balances that will be listed in the company's books.

Account Title	DR	CR

b)   Earnings are equally divided among the partners. During 2018, the company earned a net income of $360,000. Prepare a journal entry on December 31, 2018 to close the income summary account at year end.

Date	Account Title and Explanation	Debit	Credit

c)   Independent of part b), suppose it was decided that Bianca Lee will receive 10%, Bob Fire will receive 25%, Larry Lenkman will receive 40%, and Freeda Redgrave will receive 25% of the profits. During 2018, the company had a net loss of $15,000. Prepare the journal entry on December 31, 2018 to close the income summary account at year end.

Date	Account Title and Explanation	Debit	Credit

d)   Independent of parts b) and c), suppose it was decided that the earnings will be divided based on each partner's capital contribution. During 2018, the company earned a net income of $86,000. Prepare the journal entry on December 31, 2018 to close the income summary account at year end.

Date	Account Title and Explanation	Debit	Credit

AP-4A  **4**

Mallory Longshore, Lakisha Laffey and Avis Hemsley set up a limited liability company at the beginning of 2018. Mallory contributed $10,000 in cash. Lakisha contributed a van worth $20,000. Avis contributed equipment worth $15,000. The LLC made $9,000 net income for the year. According to the operating agreement, profits are divided in the ratio of members' initial contributions.

Required

a) Record the entry for the division of the profits on December 31, 2018. Assume that revenues and expenses have already been closed to the income summary account.

Date	Account Title and Explanation	Debit	Credit

b) Assume that the LLC recorded a loss of $4,500. Record the entry for the division of the loss. Assume that revenues and expenses have already been closed to the income summary account.

Date	Account Title and Explanation	Debit	Credit

AP-5A **LO** **4**

Brian, Miley and Adriana operate a business as a limited liability company. It was decided that Brian, Miley and Adriana will receive salaries of $65,000, $70,000 and $55,000 respectively. The remaining profits will be equally divided among the members. During the year 2018, the company made a net income of $160,000. Calculate the amount of net income each member will receive.

	Total	Brian	Miley	Adriana
Net Income				
Salaries				
Remainder				
Less: Excess of Allowance over Net Income, Brian				
Less: Excess of Allowance over Net Income, Miley				
Less: Excess of Allowance over Net Income, Adriana				
Transferred to Partners' Capital Accounts				

AP-6A LO 4

Anna, Peter and Jackson formed a limited liability partnership in 2017. In 2019, the beginning capital balance of each partner was $25,000, $35,000 and $30,000 respectively. During 2019, the company earned a net income of $63,000, and Anna withdrew $25,000 while Peter and Jackson withdrew $40,000 and $35,000 respectively.

Required

a) Calculate the amount of net income each partner will receive based on the following independent scenarios.

   (i)   the earnings are divided equally
   (ii)   Anna receives 30%, Peter receives 40%, and Jackson receives 30% of the earnings
   (iii) the earnings are divided based on the partner's capital balance at the beginning of the year

	(i)	(ii)	(iii)
Anna			
Peter			
Jackson			

b) Calculate the ending capital balance of each partner, assuming that method (ii) is used to divide earnings.

	Anna	Peter	Jackson
Beginning Capital Balance			
Add: Additional Contribution			
Share of Net Income			
Subtotal			
Less: Withdrawals			
Ending Capital Balance			

c) Anna, Peter and Jackson decide to receive a salary of $40,000, $55,000 and $45,000 respectively. The remaining earnings will be divided among each partner equally. During 2020, the company earned a net income of $149,000. Calculate the amount of net income that each partner will receive.

	Total	Anna	Peter	Jackson
Net Income				
Salaries				
Remainder				
Share of Profits to Anna				
Share of Profits to Peter				
Share of Profits to Jackson				
Transferred to Partners' Capital Accounts				

d) During 2020, Anna, Peter and Jackson withdrew $10,000, $15,000 and $12,000 respectively. Prepare the journal entries to record the withdrawals.

Date	Account Title and Explanation	Debit	Credit

e) Using the values from parts c) and d), calculate the ending capital balance of each partner. The beginning balance for 2020 is the ending value calculated in part b).

AP-7A LO 3 4 5 6 7

On January 1, 2018, Bob, Mike and Amy form a limited liability partnership to start a small public accounting firm. Bob, Mike and Amy have invested $64,000, $55,000 and $80,000 in cash, respectively. Mike has also invested equipment worth $2,000. During the first year of operations in 2018, the firm earned a net income of $280,000. All earnings are to be divided according to the initial capital contribution of each partner. In addition, Bob and Amy withdrew $5,000 and $7,000 cash from the business. During the second year of operations on January 1, 2019, a new partner (Mia) was added to the firm. Mia purchased 80% of Amy's investment and 10% of Mike's investment (equity) in the business.

Required

a) Assuming year end is on December 31, prepare the journal entries to set up the partnership, record the withdrawals and distribute the income for 2018. Also, prepare any additional closing or adjusting entries.

Date	Account Title and Explanation	Debit	Credit

b)   Prepare the journal entry to record the admission of Mia.

Date	Account Title and Explanation	Debit	Credit

c)   Calculate the ending capital balance of each partner after the addition of Mia on January 1, 2019.

	Bob	Mike	Amy	Mia

AP-8A LO 7

Sylvia, Sonia and Sana are all partners who operate a beauty salon called S3 Beauty. On January 1, 2018, Sylvia, Sonia and Sana had a capital balance of $320,000, $215,000 and $360,000 respectively. Due to the successful growth of the business, the original partners have agreed to add an additional partner, Sharon. Sharon will be investing $300,000 cash in the business.

Required

a)   Calculate the new capital balance for each partner after Sharon has been added to the partnership.

	Sylvia	Sonia	Sana	Sharon	Total

b)   Prepare the journal entry to record the admission of Sharon from part a).

Date	Account Title and Explanation	Debit	Credit

c)   Consider this independent scenario. S3 Beauty has made a good reputation for itself in the market and has a large base of loyal customers. Since the company has a higher market value, Sharon has agreed to invest $390,000 into the business and receive a $300,000 share of the business' book value. Any difference is split equally among the original partners. Calculate the new capital balance for each partner after Sharon has been added to the partnership.

	Sylvia	Sonia	Sana	Sharon	Total

d) Prepare the journal entry to record the admission of Sharon from part c).

Date	Account Title and Explanation	Debit	Credit

e) Consider this independent scenario. S3 Beauty has made a good reputation for itself in the market and has a large base of loyal customers. Since a partnership with Sharon will be very beneficial for S3 Beauty, S3 Beauty will provide Sharon with a $300,000 share of the business' book value for a $285,000 investment. Any difference is split equally among the original partners. Calculate the new capital balance for each partner after Sharon has been added to the partnership.

	Sylvia	Sonia	Sana	Sharon	Total

f) Prepare the journal entry to record the admission of Sharon from part e).

Date	Account Title and Explanation	Debit	Credit

Analysis

Whenever an admission or withdrawal takes place in a partnership, is it necessary to change the name of the partnership to reflect the changes? Explain.

AP-9A LO 5

Tanisha Vanscyoc and Kurt Vicini operate a limited liability company that produces custom-made furniture. On April 12, 2018, Tanisha withdrew $50,000 in cash. On April 15, Kurt removed a couch and chairs worth $30,000 for use in his own home.

Required

a) Write the journal entry to record these transactions.

Date	Account Title and Explanation	Debit	Credit

b)   Write the journal entry to close the withdrawal accounts on December 31, 2018.

Date	Account Title and Explanation	Debit	Credit

AP-10A LO 8

Patricia, Karla, and Nathan operate a small law firm under a limited liability partnership. However, due to some internal conflicts, all the partners have agreed to end the partnership. The following items remain in the balance sheet on June 30, 2018 after all the assets have been liquidated.

Cash	$450,000
Patricia, Capital	188,000
Karla, Capital	82,000
Nathan, Capital	210,000

Prepare the journal entries to allocate any profits or losses on the sale of assets, and to record cash distribution.

Date	Account Title and Explanation	Debit	Credit

AP-11A LO 8

Twenty years ago, three brothers formed a limited liability company, which now has to end due to their increasing conflicts. Before the liquidation, the LLC had cash valued at $10,000, noncash assets valued at $500,000 and liabilities valued at $300,000. The members' equity balances were $60,000 for Brother A, $70,000 for Brother B and $80,000 for Brother C. The brothers sold the noncash assets for $530,000 and paid off the liabilities. Note that any profits or losses are distributed equally among the members according to the terms of their membership agreement. Prepare journal entries on December 31, 2018 for the following transactions.

- The sale of net assets
- The allocation of the gain or loss on the sale of net assets
- The cash distribution to the three brothers

Date	Account Title and Explanation	Debit	Credit

AP-12A LO 7

Thomas, Helen, and Ahmed formed a limited liability company in 2018 to make furniture for commercial projects. On January 1, 2019, the members had the following capital account balances: Thomas—$25,000, Helen—$35,000 and Ahmed—$50,000. On January 1, 2019, Helen decided to withdraw from the LLC. Helen sold 40% of her portion of equity to Thomas and the remaining 60% to Ahmed. Prepare a journal entry to record the transaction and calculate the balance of the member equity accounts after the withdrawal of Helen.

Date	Account Title and Explanation	Debit	Credit

	Thomas	Helen	Ahmed	Total

Application Questions Group B

AP-1B LO 8

Ted Coverdale and Julio Kadlec set up a new limited liability company on March 10, 2018. Ted contributes a warehouse and land worth a combined $1,000,000. The market value of the warehouse is $300,000. Julio contributes $1,000,000 in cash. Write the journal entry to record the contributions to the LLC.

Date	Account Title and Explanation	Debit	Credit

AP-2B LO 1 3

Andrew Watson and Fred Baker formed a general partnership on January 1, 2018 to supply bottled water to businesses. Andrew contributed $10,000 cash and a vehicle with a book value of $6,000. Fred brought $6,000 cash and equipment with a book value of $10,000. An independent appraiser determined that the vehicle is valued at $5,500 and the equipment is valued at $8,800.

Required

a) Prepare a journal entry to record formation of the business.

Date	Account Title and Explanation	Debit	Credit

b) On May 1, 2018, Baker invested an additional $4,000 in cash into the business. Record the journal entry.

Date	Account Title and Explanation	Debit	Credit

Analysis

What are some of the advantages of Andrew and Fred forming a partnership?

_____

_____

_____

_____

AP-3B LO 4

Selena Hagerty, Cody Dawes and Lenore Raap operate their business as a general partnership. According to their partnership agreement, Selena and Lenore split 51% of the profits equally. The remainder of the profits goes to Cody. Record the entry for the division of profits of $100,000 on December 31, 2018. Assume that revenues and expenses have already been closed to the income summary account.

Date	Account Title and Explanation	Debit	Credit

Analysis

Selena is not happy about how the profits are allocated. She is working twice as much as the other partners. What can the other partners do to resolve this issue?

_____

_____

AP-4B LO 4

Noemi Loop, Lilia Hopkin and Guy Scoggin perform in a band operating as a general partnership. According to the partnership agreement, Noemi receives a salary of $22,000, Lilia receives a salary of $30,000, and Guy receives a salary of $28,000. They are also to receive nominal interest of 5% on the capital at the end of the preceding year (Noemi's capital—$1,000, Lilia's capital—$10,000, Guy's capital—$20,000). The remainder is divided equally. During the year the partners withdrew $22,000 each as an advance on their share of partnership earnings. The band made $100,000 after paying all other expenses.

Required

a) Prepare a schedule showing changes in the partners' capital during the year.

b)   Assume that the net income remaining is distributed on the ratio of the opening balance of capital. Prepare the
     schedule showing the changes in capital.

c)   Based on the division of profits calculated in part b), prepare the journal entry to record the distribution of profits and
     close the withdrawals accounts on December 31. Assume that revenues and expenses have already been closed to
     the income summary account.

Date	Account Title and Explanation	Debit	Credit

AP-5B LO 4

Mathew, Henry and Tom formed a limited partnership to open a grocery store in 2018. Each partner contributed $30,000
cash. In addition, Henry brought some furniture worth $3,000 and Tom brought a vehicle worth $8,000. An independent
appraiser determined the vehicle should be valued at $7,000.

Required

a)   During 2018, the business earned a net income of $90,000. The partners decided to divide the profits equally. Prepare
     a journal entry to close the income summary account at year end.

Date	Account Title and Explanation	Debit	Credit

b) Assume instead that Mathew will receive 25%, Henry will receive 30% and Tom will receive 45% of the profits. During the year the business made a loss of $30,000. Prepare a journal entry to close the income summary account at year end.

Date	Account Title and Explanation	Debit	Credit

c) Assume instead that profits will be divided based on each partner's capital contribution. During the year, the business made a net income of $60,000. Prepare a journal entry to close the income summary account at year end.

Date	Account Title and Explanation	Debit	Credit

AP-6B LO 4

Chloe, Chen and Yang are in a general partnership. According to the partnership agreement, Chloe and Chen receive a salary of $5,000 each. Each partner is also entitled to receive 3% interest on his or her capital account balance at the beginning of the year. Any profits or losses are to be shared in the ratio 3:2:1 to Chloe, Chen and Yang, respectively. Capital account balances are Chloe—$25,000, Chen—$20,000 and Yang—$10,000. During 2018, the business earned a net income of $65,000. Calculate the amount of net income each partner will receive.

AP-7B LO 3 4 5 6 7

The following table shows the summary of amounts contributed by each partner to a new limited partnership called Dev, Patel and Forbes on January 1, 2018.

Karthik Dev

Cash	$20,000
Accounts Receivable	5,000
Allowance for Doubtful Accounts	900
Note Payable	3,000

Harish Patel

Cash	$15,000
Notes Payable	6,000
Equipment	9,000
Accumulated Depreciation	1,000

John Forbes

Cash	$18,000
Building	100,000
Vehicle	15,000
Accumulated Depreciation	3,000

An independent appraiser determined the following values for some of the items. All other items are listed at their fair market value.

- Allowance for doubtful accounts should be $1,500
- Equipment should be $10,000
- Vehicle should be $6,000

Required

a) Prepare a trial balance with the account balances.

b) During 2018 the business earned a net income of $150,000. Karthik, Harish and John withdrew $10,000, $8,000, and $15,000 respectively. Karthik and Harish are entitled to a salary of $10,000 each. Partners are also entitled to receive 5% interest on capital (beginning balance). Remaining earnings are divided among the partners in the ratio 1:4:5 to Karthik, Harish and John, respectively. Prepare a statement showing the division of profits.

c)   Prepare a statement of changes in partners' equity.

d)   On January 1, 2019, Karthik decided to withdraw from the partnership. Harish and John have decided to buy out Karthik's interest in equal portions. Prepare the journal entry to record the transaction and calculate the balance of the partners' capital accounts after Karthik leaves.

Date	Account Title and Explanation	Debit	Credit

e)   Independent of part d), assume instead that the partners have decided to pay off Karthik using partnership assets. Prepare the journal entry to record the transaction and calculate the balance of partners' capital accounts after Karthik leaves.

Date	Account Title and Explanation	Debit	Credit

Analysis

Compare the impact on the assets of the partnership in parts d) and e).

_____

_____

_____

AP-8B LO 7

Jack, John, and Joe have been operating a business as a limited liability partnership for several years. On January 1, 2018, Jack, John and Joe had a capital balance of $255,000, $180,000 and $132,000 respectively. However, due to a business conflict, Joe decided to withdraw from the partnership. Jack and John decided to pay off Joe using the partnership's cash.

Required

a) Calculate the new capital balance for each partner after the withdrawal of Joe.

b) Prepare the journal entry to record the withdrawal of Joe.

Date	Account Title and Explanation	Debit	Credit

c) After Joe left, Jack and John added Jim to the partnership on January 1, 2018. A partnership with Jim will considerably increase the value of the business. Therefore, Jim receives a $100,000 share of the business' book value for an $80,000 investment. Any bonus will be split evenly between Jack and John. Calculate the new capital balance for each partner after Joe has been withdrawn and Jim has been added to the partnership.

d) Prepare the journal entry to record the admission of Jim from part c).

Date	Account Title and Explanation	Debit	Credit

e) Independent of part c), assume that Jim will receive a $100,000 share of the business' book value for a $130,000 investment. Calculate the new capital balance for each partner after Joe has been withdrawn and Jim has been added to the partnership.

f) Prepare the journal entry to record the admission of Jim from part e).

Date	Account Title and Explanation	Debit	Credit

g) Independent of part a), assume that when Joe leaves, Joe is going to sell his portion of the partnership to Jim. Jim is also going to purchase 20% of Jack's share in the partnership. The cash transaction will be a private matter between Jim and the two partners; however, the capital amounts must be transferred to Jim in the partnership records. Calculate the new capital balances for each partner

h) Prepare the journal entry to record the admission of Jim and the withdrawal of Joe from part g).

Date	Account Title and Explanation	Debit	Credit

AP-9B LO 6

Bryan Willow and Jason Barfoot are in a limited partnership selling cell phones. On May 1, 2018, Jason took a cell phone worth $800 from the business for his personal use. On December 31, 2018, Bryan withdrew $5,000 cash and Jason withdrew $3,000 cash for personal use.

Required

a) Write the journal entries to record the withdrawal transactions.

Date	Account Title and Explanation	Debit	Credit

b) Write the journal entry to close the withdrawal accounts on December 31, 2018.

Date	Account Title and Explanation	Debit	Credit

AP-10B LO 8

Lindeman LLC has to be terminated after consecutive years of losses. After the liquidation, the following items remained in the balance sheet.

Lindeman LLC	
Balance Sheet	
As at March 31, 2018	
Cash	$150,000
Member Equity	
A. Armstrong	30,000
B. Broderick	55,000
C. Carson	20,000
D. Donaldson	45,000
Total	**$150,000**

Prepare the journal entries to record cash distribution. Assume that the assets were sold at their book value.

Date	Account Title and Explanation	Debit	Credit

AP-11B LO 8

Chong general partnership was terminated on December 31, 2018 due to a dispute between the partners. Before liquidation, cash was valued at $10,000, noncash assets were valued at $600,000 and total liabilities were valued at $250,000. The partners' equity balances were as follows: Xi—$70,000, Yang—$90,000 and Zhou—$200,000. Noncash assets were sold for $570,000 and all the liabilities were paid off. The partnership agreement states profits and losses are to be shared in the ratio 2:3:3 between Xi, Yang and Zhou, respectively. Prepare the journal entries to record the liquidation of the business.

Date	Account Title and Explanation	Debit	Credit

Analysis

What are the reasons a general partnership would decide to liquidate?

_____

_____

_____

_____

_____

_____

AP-12B LO 7

Cooper, Amy and Jacob formed a limited liability partnership in 2018. On January 1, 2019, the partners had the following capital account balances: Cooper—$35,000, Amy—$60,000 and Jacob—$50,000. On January 1, 2019, Jacob decided to withdraw from the partnership due to unresolved disputes. The withdrawal of Jacob was paid from the partnership's assets. Prepare the journal entry to record the transaction and calculate the balance of the partners' capital accounts after the withdrawal of Jacob.

Date	Account Title and Explanation	Debit	Credit

Case Study

CS-1 LO 4 5 6

For the year ended December 31, 2018, a general partnership had sales of $500,000 and expenses of $400,000 before allocating partners' salaries, interest on capital and charges for equipment.

There are two partners who own the business. Each partner will receive earnings based on four factors.

- Each partner will receive a salary of $40,000.
- Each partner will receive interest on capital contributions, which amounts to $2,000 for Partner A, and $1,000 for Partner B.
- Partner B brought equipment into the business and receives $2,000 "rent" on the equipment each year.
- Remaining profits are divided equally.

The opening balances of capital were $200,000 for Partner A and $100,000 for Partner B. During the year, the partners withdrew $30,000 as advances on their annual salary.

Required

a) Calculate the net income of the partnership.

b) Show the calculation of the share of income to be distributed to each partner.

c) Prepare journal entries to record the distribution of income, withdrawals and closing entries.

Date	Account Title and Explanation	Debit	Credit

Date	Account Title and Explanation	Debit	Credit

d) Explain why salaries, interest and rental of equipment are not included in the closing entries.

_____

_____

_____

_____

_____

_____

_____

_____

_____

_____

_____

_____

_____

_____

_____

_____

e) Prepare the statement of partners' equity for the year ended December 31, 2018.

Critical Thinking

CT-1 LO 1 2

Sometimes a person simply wants to invest in a business as an owner, rather than actively participate in the business. This is simple when the business is organized as a corporation. However, if the investor participates in a general partnership, the investor assumes unlimited liability for the general partnership.

Required

a)　Is it wise to invest in a partnership if one does not want to actively participate in the general partnership?

b)　Are there any steps an investor could take to limit liability? Discuss.

Chapter 15

CORPORATIONS: STOCK AND DIVIDENDS

LEARNING OBJECTIVES

LO 1   Describe the characteristics of corporations

LO 2   Describe differences between public and private corporations

LO 3   Explain stockholders' equity

LO 4   Record the issuance of stock

LO 5   Record the payment of cash dividends

LO 6   Record stock splits and stock dividends

LO 7   Record treasury stock

LO 8   Record income tax expense

LO 9   Explain the importance of ethics for corporate reporting

AMEENGAGE   Access **ameengage.com** for integrated resources including tutorials, practice exercises, the digital textbook and more.

Assessment Questions

AS-1 LO 1

What is a common term used to call an owner of a corporation?

AS-2 LO 1

What does it mean when a corporation is considered a going concern?

AS-3 LO 1

Why is tax paid twice on earnings from a corporation? What is this phenomenon called?

AS-4 LO 1

List some advantages and disadvantages of the corporate form of organization.

Advantages

_____

_____

_____

Disadvantages

_____

_____

_____

AS-5 LO 1

What is a nonprofit corporation? How is it different from a for-profit corporation?

_____

_____

AS-6 LO 2

Explain the main difference between a public corporation and a private corporation.

_____

_____

AS-7 LO 2

From which two accounting standards can a private corporation choose?

_____

AS-8 LO 2

Which accounting standard must a US SEC registrant follow?

_____

_____

AS-9 LO 2

What are non-US SEC registrants? Which accounting standards must non-US SEC registrants follow?

_____

_____

AS-10 LO 3

Which portion of stockholders' equity relates to contributions by stockholders? Which relates to accumulated earnings?

_____

_____

AS-11 LO 3

Name the two sub-categories of paid-in capital.

_____

_____

AS-12 LO 3

You are preparing the financial statements for a corporation. You must disclose the number of shares authorized. Where would you find this information?

_____

_____

AS-13 LO 3

What is meant by "authorized shares"?

_____

_____

AS-14 LO 3

What is meant by "outstanding shares"?

_____

_____

AS-15 LO 3

What is meant by "issued shares"? Why is the number of shares outstanding sometimes lower than the number of shares issued?

_____

_____

_____

_____

AS-16 LO 3

Define "market value" of a stock.

_____

_____

_____

AS-17 LO 3

What are some differences between common stockholders and preferred stockholders?

_____

_____

_____

_____

AS-18 LO 3

List some characteristics of common stock.

_____

_____

_____

_____

_____

_____

AS-19 LO 3

List some characteristics of preferred stock.

_____

_____

_____

_____

AS-20 LO 3

Which feature of preferred shares gives stockholders the right to receive dividends in arrears?

_____

_____

_____

_____

AS-21 LO 3

Explain the difference between participating preferred stock and nonparticipating preferred stock.

_____

_____

_____

_____

AS-22 LO 3

Explain the difference between no-par value stock and par value stock. How is the par value of stock related to the company's minimum legal capital?

_____

_____

_____

_____

AS-23 LO 3

What is a stated value of stock? What is the purpose of assigning a stated value?

_____

_____

_____

AS-24 LO 3

What may shares be issued for?

_____

_____

AS-25 LO 4

When stock of a corporation is issued in exchange for assets or services, how is the stock valued in the corporation's books?

_____

_____

_____

_____

AS-26 LO 6

List and describe the three dates associated with accounting for dividends.

_____

_____

_____

_____

AS-27 LO 5 6

Who decides the amount of a dividend to be paid to stockholders?

_____

_____

AS-28 LO 5

What is a liquidating dividend? How is it recorded in a journal entry?

_____

_____

AS-29 LO 6

Explain a stock split and a reverse stock split.

_____

_____

AS-30 LO 6

What is a stock dividend? At which values are small and large stock dividends recorded in the journal entries?

_____

_____

_____

AS-31 LO 6

Provide a few possible reasons why a company's retained earnings may be restricted. Where are restrictions on retained earnings disclosed?

_____

_____

_____

AS-32 LO 7

What is treasury stock?

_____

_____

AS-33 LO 7

Provide a few possible reasons why a company may want to reacquire its stock.

_____

_____

_____

_____

_____

_____

AS-34 LO 7

What effect does a stock reacquisition transaction have on a company's assets, liabilities and stockholders' equity?

_____

_____

AS-35 LO 8

What is corporate income tax?

_____

_____

AS-36 LO 8

What is a deferred income tax liability?

_____

_____

AS-37 LO 8

How is the ending balance of retained earnings calculated?

_____

_____

AS-38 LO 9

What is insider trading? Is it ethical? Why or why not?

_____

_____

_____

_____

_____

Application Questions Group A

AP-1A LO 8

At year end on December 31, 2018, Shuster Home Decor Inc. has accounting income (before income tax expense calculation) of $102,000. Write the journal entry to record the income tax expense in 2018, which will be paid in 2019. Assume that the tax rate is 30% and that the income tax amount calculated under GAAP is the same as the amount calculated under tax laws.

Date	Account Title and Explanation	Debit	Credit

AP-2A LO 1

On April 13, 2018, a group of eight friends started a private corporation called Lucky8 Corporation. They paid $2,000 cash for incorporation and legal fees to form and register the corporation. Write the journal entry to record the organization expenses.

Date	Account Title and Explanation	Debit	Credit

AP-3A LO 5

On February 1, 2018, Adam Enterprises declared a cash dividend of $4,800 to common stockholders of record on the company's books as of February 28. The dividend was paid on March 14. Record the journal entries for these transactions. Adam Enterprises used the cash dividends account to record declaration of cash dividends.

Date	Account Title and Explanation	Debit	Credit

AP-4A LO 3

The stockholders' equity section of Thomas Inc.'s balance sheet at March 31, 2018 is shown below.

Additional Information
- The preferred stock has an average issue price of $5.00 per share.
- The common stock has an average issue price of $3.00 per share.

Fill in the gray areas in the table below with the correct numbers.

Thomas Inc. Balance Sheet (partial) As at March 31, 2018	
Stockholders' Equity	
Paid-In Capital	
Preferred stock, 15% cumulative, $5 par value, 280,000 shares authorized,	
23,000 shares issued and outstanding	
Common stock, $1 par value, unlimited shares authorized,	
120,000 shares issued and outstanding	
Additional Paid-In Capital	
Total Paid-In Capital	475,000
Retained Earnings	
Total Stockholders' Equity	533,675

Analysis

A corporation has the choice to issue only common stock or issue mainly preferred stock. (All corporations must have at least one class of common stock outstanding). If you were a director on the board of a newly incorporated, fast-growing corporation, which is planning to issue stock to the general public, what type of stock would you suggest the management to issue?

_____

_____

_____

_____

AP-5A LO 4

Earnestine, Kepplinger & Co. began a new public corporation. The corporation's common stock has no par value or stated value. During the first month of operations, it had the following stock transactions.

Required

a) Earnestine, Kepplinger & Co. issued 10,000 common shares for $100,000 on May 1, 2018. Write the journal entry to record the transaction.

Date	Account Title and Explanation	Debit	Credit

b) On May 1, 2018, Earnestine, Kepplinger & Co. issued an additional 10,000 common shares in exchange for land and a building. The land was valued at $60,000 and the building was valued at $50,000. Record the transaction.

Date	Account Title and Explanation	Debit	Credit

c) The lawyer that handled the issue of shares has sent a bill for $5,000. The lawyer has agreed to accept 500 common shares instead of cash. Record the transaction on May 10, 2018.

Date	Account Title and Explanation	Debit	Credit

Analysis

In the case of non-monetary exchanges of assets and services for issued stock, a corporation can choose to evaluate the fair value of stock issued with two options.

Option 1: Fair value of assets or services received
Option 2: Fair value of the stock issued

Think of a scenario when option 1 is preferred over option 2 by accountants and explain why.

_____

_____

_____

AP-6A LO 4

Swan River Inc. was formed on January 1, 2018. Its common stock has no par value or stated value. During 2018, the following stock transactions occurred.

Jan 1	Issued 10,000 common shares for $2 per share
May 15	Issued 4,500 common shares for $2.75 per share
Jul 1	Issued 5,000 common shares in exchange for equipment with a fair value of $14,500
Sep 26	Issued 2,800 common shares for $2.50 per share

Required

a) Prepare the journal entries to record the above transactions.

Date	Account Title and Explanation	Debit	Credit

b) Determine the total number and value of common stock issued and outstanding as at December 31, 2018 by completing the following table.

Date	# of Shares Issued	$ per Share	Total
Jan 1	10,000	$2.00	
May 15	4,500	$2.75	
Jul 1	5,000		$14,500
Sep 26	2,800	$2.50	
Total Dec 31, 2018			

Analysis

Suppose that Joe, the president of Swan River Inc., owns 14,500 of the outstanding shares. What percentage ownership does Joe have?

_____

_____

AP-7A LO 5

a) On July 1, 2018, Jonus Enterprises declared a cash dividend of $5,000 to common stockholders on record on July 4, 2018. Record the journal entry associated with this transaction. Jonus Enterprises uses the retained earnings account to record dividends.

Date	Account Title and Explanation	Debit	Credit

b) Record the journal entry when Jonus Enterprises paid out the dividend on August 15, 2018.

Date	Account Title and Explanation	Debit	Credit

Analysis

Both the cash dividend and retained earnings methods are acceptable accounting methods that produce the same result in recording cash dividend payouts. Why do you think some corporations prefer to use the cash dividends method, despite the fact it needs more entries than the other method? What advantages does that method offer to the corporation that chooses to use it?

_____

_____

_____

_____

AP-8A LO 5

On November 1, 2018, Mistry Inc. declared $850,000 of cash dividends to stockholders on record on December 15, 2018. Cash is paid to the stockholders on January 15, 2019. Outstanding are 220,000 no-par common shares worth $2,000,000 and 30,000, no-par $4 cumulative preferred shares worth $3,000,000. No new stock was issued during the year and dividends were last declared in 2014. Mistry had retained earnings of $4,500,000 at the beginning of 2018 and earned a net income of $1,200,000 during the year.

Required

a) Calculate how much Mistry Inc. owes the preferred stockholders.

b) Write the journal entries to record the declaration and subsequent payout of the dividends. Mistry uses the cash dividends account to record dividends.

Date	Account Title and Explanation	Debit	Credit

AP-9A LO 6

Bishop Lutz Hockey Paraphernalia Ltd. has 50,000, $5 par value common shares issued. On January 1, 2018 the organization declared a 20% stock dividend. Prepare the journal entry to record the declaration and distribution (on February 1, 2018) of the dividend. The market price on the date of declaration was $15 per share.

Date	Account Title and Explanation	Debit	Credit

AP-10A `LO 5`

Martin Inc. was formed on January 1, 2016. Its stock was all issued during the first year of operations and was comprised as follows: 80,000, $10 par value common shares and 10,000, $2 cumulative, $45 par value preferred shares. Over the past four years, Martin Inc. has declared and paid the following cash dividends.

Year	Total
2016	$30,000
2017	$35,000
2018	$0
2019	$45,000

Calculate the amount of dividends paid to each class of stockholders for each year.

Class of Shares	# of Shares	2016	2017	2018	2019
Preferred Stock—Cumulative	10,000				
Common Stock	80,000				
Total Dividends Paid		$30,000	$35,000	$0	$45,000

AP-11A `LO 3 5`

Given below is the equity section of Lizzy Dizzy Corporation at December 31, 2018. Preferred stock was sold at $100 each. Both preferred stock and common stock have no par value.

Lizzy Dizzy Corporation Balance Sheet (partial) As at December 31, 2018	
Stockholders' Equity	
Paid-In Capital	
Preferred stock, $7 cumulative, 200,000 shares authorized	$20,000,000
Common stock, unlimited shares authorized, 4,000,000 shares issued and outstanding	59,000,000
Total Paid-In Capital	79,000,000
Retained Earnings	64,450,000
Total Stockholders' Equity	143,450,000

Required

From the information provided above, calculate the following.

a) Calculate the number of preferred shares issued.

_____

b) Calculate the total amount of annual dividend payable to preferred stockholders.

_____

c) Calculate the average issuance price per common share.

_____

d) Calculate the amount due to preferred stockholders if the company last declared dividends in 2014.

_____

e) Suppose that the company declared to pay $25,000,000 as dividend on December 31, 2018 and paid dividends on January 10, 2019. The company last declared dividends in 2014. Prepare journal entries to record the declaration and payment of dividends assuming the company uses the cash dividends account.

Date	Account Title and Explanation	Debit	Credit

AP-12A LO 5

On May 1, 2018, Crackle Canine Inc. declared $196,000 of dividends payable to stockholders on June 3, 2018. There are 24,800, $5 par value common shares and 14,700, 10%, $10 par value, $1 cumulative preferred shares. Dividends were last paid in 2014. Write the journal entry to record the declaration and subsequent payout of the dividends. Assume the company uses the cash dividends account to record dividends.

Date	Account Title and Explanation	Debit	Credit

AP-13A LO 5

The stockholders' equity section of Khan Corporation's balance sheet as at January 1, 2018 was as follows. Both preferred stock and common stock have no par or stated value.

Khan Corporation Balance Sheet (partial) As at January 1, 2018	
Stockholders' Equity	
Paid-In Capital	
Preferred stock, $3 noncumulative, 200,000 shares authorized, 2,000 shares issued and outstanding	$200,000
Common stock, unlimited shares authorized, 32,000 shares issued and outstanding	1,200,000
Total Paid-In Capital	1,400,000
Retained Earnings	320,000
Total Stockholders' Equity	1,720,000

No dividend was declared for common stockholders. However, on December 15, 2018, the directors decided to pay dividends to preferred stockholders. The dividend payment date was December 28, 2018. Income before income tax for the year was $220,000. Income tax expense for the year was $40,000. The company uses the retained earnings account to record dividends.

Required

a) Calculate the amount of dividend to be paid to preferred stockholders.

_____

_____

b) Prepare the journal entries for the declaration and payment of the preferred dividend.

Date	Account Title and Explanation	Debit	Credit

c) Calculate the ending balance of retained earnings for the year ended December 31, 2018.

Calculation of Retained Earnings	
For the Year Ended December 31, 2018	

AP-14A LO 6

Tross Co. was incorporated and began operations on January 1, 2016. Tross Co. presented the following information at the end of the 2018 fiscal year. Tross' common stock does not have a par value or a stated value.

Common Stock, unlimited shares authorized, 75,000 shares issued and outstanding	$225,000
Retained Earnings	148,000

Tross Co. declared a 15% stock dividend on December 31, 2018. The common stock was issued in 2016 for $3.00 each, but the current market price is $5.20 per share. The date of payment is January 5, 2019.

Prepare the journal entries to record the declaration and payment of the dividend.
The company uses the retained earnings account to record dividends.

Date	Account Title and Explanation	Debit	Credit

AP-15A LO 5 6

Enigma Inc. is reaching the end of its fiscal year and has declared the following dividends.
- $20,000 cash dividend
- 10% stock dividend (on common shares)

The following information is also available.
- There are 10,000, $1 par value common shares outstanding, issued for $12 per share
- There are 1,000, 5%, $100 par value noncumulative preferred shares outstanding
- Common stock is currently trading for $10 per share
- For both dividends, the date of declaration is May 21, 2018 and the date of payment is May 31, 2018
- Enigma Inc. had income before income tax of $55,000 and income tax expense of $10,000 during the year
- The balance of retained earnings at the beginning of the year was $123,500

Required

a) Prepare the journal entries to record the declaration and payment of the dividends. The company uses the cash dividends account to record cash dividends and uses the retained earnings account to record stock dividends.

Date	Account Title and Explanation	Debit	Credit

b) Calculate the ending balance of retained earnings for the year.

Calculation of Retained Earnings	
For the Year Ended May 31, 2018	

Analysis

Identify where each of the following accounts would be found on the balance sheet. The first one has been done as an example.

Cash	Current Assets
Common Stock	
Dividends Payable	
Retained Earnings	
Common Stock Dividends Distributable	

AP-16A LO 5

The stockholders' equity section of Genghis Corporation's balance sheet as at January 1, 2018 was as follows.

Genghis Corporation Balance Sheet (partial) As at January 1, 2018	
Stockholders' Equity	
Paid-In Capital	
Preferred stock, 5% noncumulative, $100 par value, 200,000 shares authorized	
1,000 shares issued and outstanding	$100,000
Common stock, $10 par value, unlimited shares authorized,	
35,000 shares issued and outstanding	350,000
Additional Paid-In Capital	845,000
Total Paid-In Capital	1,295,000
Retained Earnings	253,000
Total Stockholders' Equity	1,548,000

No dividend was declared for common stockholders. However on December 15, 2018 the directors decided to pay dividends to preferred stockholders. The dividend payment date was December 28, 2018. For the year 2018, income before income tax was $300,000 and income tax expense was $60,000. The company uses the cash dividends account to record dividends.

Required

a) Calculate the amount of the dividend to be paid to preferred stockholders.

_____

_____

b) Prepare the journal entry for the declaration and payment of the preferred dividend.

Date	Account Title and Explanation	Debit	Credit

c) Calculate the ending balance of retained earnings for the year ended December 31, 2018.

Calculation of Retained Earnings	
For the Month Ended December 31, 2018	

AP-17A LO 1 4 5 8

In 2018, Elizabeth and some of her friends invested money to start a company named FRIENDZ Corporation. The following transactions occurred during 2018.

Jan 1   The corporate charter authorized 70,000 shares of 5%, $100 par value cumulative preferred stock and unlimited shares of $10 par value common stock.

Jan 6   Issued 200,000 common shares at $16 per share to Elizabeth and other investors

Jan 7   Issued another 500 common shares to Elizabeth in exchange for her services in organizing the corporation. The stockholders agreed that the services were worth $8,000.

Jan 12   Issued 3,500 preferred shares for $350,000

Jan 14   Issued 10,000 common shares in exchange for equipment. The fair market value of the equipment could not be readily determined, but the market price of the common stock on this date was $16 per share.

Nov 15   The first annual cash dividend on preferred stock was declared

Dec 20   Paid the dividends declared on preferred stock

Dec 31   Estimated income tax expense of $38,000. However, the actual amount of income tax due for this period based on tax laws is determined to be $34,000.

FRIENDZ Corporation generated a $125,000 net income (after income tax) during the year. The company uses the retained earnings account to record dividends.

Required

a)   Prepare the journal entries to record the above transactions in 2018.

Date	Account Title and Explanation	Debit	Credit

b) Calculate the ending balance of retained earnings for the year ended December 31, 2018.

Calculation of Retained Earnings	
For the Year Ended December 31, 2018	

c) Prepare the stockholders' equity section of the balance sheet as at December 31, 2018.

AP-18A LO 1 4 5 8

In 2018, Joanna and some of her friends invested money to start a company named BUDZ Corporation. The following transactions occurred during 2018.

Jan 1   The corporate charter authorized 76,000 shares of 8%, $50 par value cumulative preferred stock and unlimited shares of $10 par value common stock.

Jan 6   Issued 231,000 common shares at $15 per share to Joanna and other investors.

Jan 7   Issued another 450 common shares to Joanna in exchange for her services in setting up the corporation. The stockholders agreed that the services were worth $6,750.

Jan 12   Issued 3,900 preferred shares for $321,000

Jan 14   Issued 10,000 common shares in exchange for equipment acquired. The fair market value of the equipment could not be readily determined, but the market price of the common stock on this date was $19 per share.

Nov 15   The first annual dividend on preferred stock was declared

Dec 20   Paid the dividends declared on preferred stock

Dec 31   Estimated income tax expense of $45,000. However, the actual amount of income tax due for this period based on tax laws is determined to be $43,500.

BUDZ Corporation generated a $147,000 net income (after income tax) during the year. Assume the company uses the retained earnings account to record dividends.

Required

a) Prepare the journal entries to record the above transactions.

Date	Account Title and Explanation	Debit	Credit

b) Calculate the ending balance of retained earnings for the year ended December 31, 2018.

Calculation of Retained Earnings	
For the Year Ended December 31, 2018	

c)   Prepare the stockholders' equity section of the balance sheet as at December 31, 2018.

AP-19A LO 5 6 8

The stockholders' equity section of East West Corporation's balance sheet as at January 1, 2018 was as follows.

East West Corporation Balance Sheet (partial) As at January 1, 2018	
Stockholders' Equity	
Paid-In Capital	
Preferred stock, 5% noncumulative, $100 par value, 200,000 shares authorized, 1,000 shares issued and outstanding	$100,000
Common stock, $50 par value, unlimited shares authorized, 30,000 shares issued and outstanding	1,500,000
Total Paid-In Capital	1,600,000
Retained Earnings	1,970,000
Total Stockholders' Equity	3,570,000

The following transactions occurred in 2018.

Jan 15	The Board decided to declare a total cash dividend of $120,000 to common and preferred stockholders
Jan 28	Date of record of dividend
Feb 10	Paid the cash dividend declared on January 15
Nov 30	Declared a 20% stock dividend to common stockholders; current market price was $55
Dec 12	Distributed the stock dividends
Dec 31	Estimated income tax expense of $320,000. However, the actual amount of income tax due for this period based on tax laws is determined to be $300,000.

East West Corporation generated a $980,000 net income (after income tax) during the year. The company uses the cash and stock dividends accounts to record dividends.

Required

a) Prepare the journal entries to record the above transactions in 2018. Also prepare the journal entry to close the cash dividends and stock dividends accounts on December 31, 2018.

Date	Account Title and Explanation	Debit	Credit

b) Calculate the ending balance of retained earnings for the year ended December 31, 2018.

Calculation of Retained Earnings	
For the Year Ended December 31, 2018	

c) Prepare the stockholders' equity section of the balance sheet as at December 31, 2018.

AP-20A LO 7

On March 31, 2018, Darred Inc. had 500,000 outstanding common shares. Its balance sheet on March 31, 2018 shows a common stock balance of $500,000 and a paid-in capital, treasury stock balance of zero. The following are the only changes to Darred's common stock that occurred between March 31, 2018 and March 31, 2019.

On April 1, 2018, Darred paid $30,000 cash to reacquire 15,000 of its own common stock.
On August 1, 2018, Darred sold 5,000 shares of its treasury stock for $3 per share.
On March 31, 2019, Darred sold the remaining 10,000 shares of its treasury stock for $1 per share.

Required

a) Record the share reacquisition journal entry on April 1, 2018.

Date	Account Title and Explanation	Debit	Credit

b) Record the treasury stock re-issuance journal entry on August 1, 2018.

Date	Account Title and Explanation	Debit	Credit

c) Record the treasury stock re-issuance journal entry on March 31, 2019.

Date	Account Title and Explanation	Debit	Credit

AP-21A LO 7

Chadwick Corporation's stockholders' equity section of the balance sheet as at September 30, 2018 is as follows.

Chadwick Corporation **Balance Sheet (partial)** **As at September 30, 2018**	
Stockholders' Equity	
Paid-In Capital	
Common stock, $1 par value, unlimited shares authorized,	
50,000 shares issued, 45,000 shares outstanding	$50,000
Paid-In Capital in Excess of Par, Common Stock	100,000
Total Paid-In Capital	150,000
Retained Earnings, $20,000 restricted by purchase of treasury stock	
Total Paid-In Capital and Retained Earnings	100,000
	250,000
Less: Treasury Stock (5,000 shares at cost)	20,000
Total Stockholders' Equity	230,000

Required

Journalize the following transactions that happened between October 1, 2018 and September 30, 2019.

a) On October 15, 2018, Chadwick sold 3,000 shares of treasury stock at $3.50 per share.

Date	Account Title and Explanation	Debit	Credit

b) On May 30, 2019, Chadwick retired the remaining 2,000 shares of treasury stock.

Date	Account Title and Explanation	Debit	Credit

Application Questions Group B

AP-1B `LO` `8`

At year end on December 31, 2018, F'Brae Cheerleading Inc. calculates the fourth-quarter income tax expense based on GAAP to be $63,000. Based on tax laws, the company determines that the actual amount of income tax for this period to be paid on March 15, 2019 is $60,000.

a) Write the journal entry to record the income tax expense on December 31, 2018.

Date	Account Title and Explanation	Debit	Credit

b) Write the journal entry to record the income tax payment on March 15, 2019.

Date	Account Title and Explanation	Debit	Credit

AP-2B `LO` `1` `3`

Chamni Corporation was formed on July 21, 2018. On this date, the corporation raised $120,000 cash by issuing 10,000 shares of $5 par value common stock. It also paid $2,300 cash for incorporation and legal fees to form and register the corporation. Write the journal entries to record the stock issuance and organization expenses.

Date	Account Title and Explanation	Debit	Credit

AP-3B `LO` `5`

On October 10, 2018, Bonzin Corporation's board of directors declared a cash dividend of $278,000 to all stockholders who hold common stock as of October 27, 2018. The cash dividend was paid on November 20, 2018. Record the journal entries associated with the transactions. Bonzin Corporation uses the retained earnings account to record declaration of cash dividends.

Date	Account Title and Explanation	Debit	Credit

AP-4B LO 3

The stockholders' equity section of Sharp Ltd.'s balance sheet as at December 31, 2018 is as follows.

Additional Information

- The preferred stock has an average issue price of $55 per share.
- The common stock has an average issue price of $40 per share.
- Retained earnings as at January 1, 2018 was $187,000, income before tax was $85,450, income tax expense was $20,000, and $9,800 of dividends were declared, payable on January 10, 2019.

Fill in the gray areas in the table below with the correct numbers.

Sharp Ltd. Balance Sheet (partial) As at December 31, 2018	
Stockholders' Equity	
Paid-In Capital	
Preferred stock, 5% cumulative, $50 par value, 5,000 shares authorized	
1,000 shares issued and outstanding	
Common stock, $10 par value, 30,000 shares authorized,	
6,500 shares issued and outstanding	
Additional Paid-In Capital	
Total Paid-In Capital	
Retained Earnings	
Total Stockholders' Equity	

Analysis

Some corporations prefer to issue mainly preferred stock to their stockholders instead of common stock. Discuss reasons that might motivate a corporation to issue mainly preferred stock instead of common stock.

_____

_____

_____

AP-5B LO 4

Sherm & Co. issued 12,100, $1 par value common shares for $91,000 on June 3, 2018.

Required

a) Write the journal entry to record the transaction.

Date	Account Title and Explanation	Debit	Credit

b) In addition to stock issued for cash, on June 3, 2018, Sherm & Co. issued an additional 13,600 common shares in exchange for machinery and a truck. The machinery was valued at $61,000 and the truck was valued at $101,000. The company could not readily determine the fair value of the shares. Record the transaction.

Date	Account Title and Explanation	Debit	Credit

c) The accountant that handled the issue of stock for Sherm & Co. has sent a bill for $5,600. The accountant has agreed to accept 550 common shares instead of cash. The company could not readily determine the fair value of the shares. Record the transaction on June 9, 2018.

Date	Account Title and Explanation	Debit	Credit

Analysis

In the case of non-monetary exchanges, in which assets or services are exchanged for issued stock, a corporation can choose to evaluate the fair value of stock issued with two options.

Option 1: Fair value of assets or services received
Option 2: Fair value of the stock issued

Think of a scenario when option 2 is preferred by accountants over option 1 and explain why.

_____

_____

_____

_____

_____

_____

AP-6B LO 4

Flanders Inc. was formed on March 1, 2018. Upon formation, it issued 8,000, $5 par value common shares for $22 each and 5,500, $10 par value noncumulative preferred shares for $30 each. In addition to the initial stock issuance, the following stock transaction occurred during the fiscal year.

Jun 7   Issued 1,000 common shares for $25 per share

Aug 31   Issued 800 preferred shares for $33 per share

Dec 9   Issued 2,500 common shares for $24 per share and 300 preferred shares for $32 per share

Required

a) Prepare the journal entries to record the above transactions (including the entries to record the formation of Flanders Inc.).

Date	Account Title and Explanation	Debit	Credit

b) Determine the total number of shares and value of common stock, preferred stock, and additional paid-in capital as at December 31, 2018, by filling in the gray shaded areas in the partial balance sheet below.

Flanders Inc. Balance Sheet (partial) As at December 31, 2018	
Stockholders' Equity	
Paid-In Capital	
Preferred stock, 5% noncumulative, $10 par value, 50,000 shares authorized	
_____ shares issued and outstanding	
Common stock, $5 par value, 200,000 shares authorized,	
_____ shares issued and outstanding	
Additional Paid-In Capital	
Total Paid-In Capital	
Retained Earnings	85,000
Total Stockholders' Equity	

Analysis

Suppose that Ned, the president of Flanders Inc., owns 990 shares of the outstanding preferred stock and 6,000 shares of the common stock. What percentage of voting rights in a corporation does Ned have?

AP-7B LO 5

On February 1, 2018, Adam Enterprises declares a cash dividend of $4,800 to common stockholders to be paid on February 4.

Required

a) Record the journal entry associated with this transaction. Assume the company uses the cash dividends account to record dividends.

Date	Account Title and Explanation	Debit	Credit

b) Record the journal entry when Adam Enterprises pays out the dividend on February 4.

Date	Account Title and Explanation	Debit	Credit

Analysis

While a corporation is using the cash dividend method to record dividend payouts, cash dividend amounts are usually debited to the cash dividends account and credited to the dividends payable account on the date of declaration. When cash dividends are paid on the date of payment, the dividends payable account is debited. However, after the date of payment, there will still be debit balances in the cash dividends account. Record the journal entry that Adam Enterprises will have to make at year end to close the cash dividends account.

Date	Account Title and Explanation	Debit	Credit

AP-8B LO 5

On December 1, 2018, Fickle Feline Inc. declared $200,000 of dividends payable to stockholders on the record on December 15, 2018. There are 20,000, $5 par value common shares and 10,000, 5%, $10 par value cumulative preferred shares. No new stock was issued during the year and dividends were last declared in 2015. Fickle Feline had retained earnings of $2,500,000 at the beginning of 2018 and earned a net income of $650,000 during the year.

Required

a) Calculate how much Fickle Feline Inc. owes the preferred stockholders.

b) Write the journal entries to record the declaration of dividends on December 1, 2018 and the payment of dividends on January 3, 2019. Fickle Feline uses the cash dividends account to record dividends.

Date	Account Title and Explanation	Debit	Credit

AP-9B LO 6

Silang Vayman Ltd. is a travel agency that specializes in tours to the Philippines and Russia. It has 75,000, $10 par value common shares issued and outstanding. On March 15, 2018, the organization declared a 45% stock dividend. Prepare the journal entries to record the declaration and distribution (on April 1, 2018) of the dividend. The market price on the date of declaration was $25 per share.

Date	Account Title and Explanation	Debit	Credit

AP-10B `LO 5`

Tilda Inc. was formed on January 1, 2017. Its stock was all issued during the first year of operations as follows: 10,000, $5 par value common shares; 7,000, 4%, $100 par value cumulative preferred shares; and 4,000, 6%, $50 par value noncumulative preferred shares. Over the past four years Tilda Inc. has declared and paid the following cash dividends.

Year	Total
2017	$60,000
2018	0
2019	100,000
2020	70,000

Calculate the amount of dividends paid to each class of stockholders for each year.

Class of Shares	# of Shares	2017	2018	2019	2020
4%, $100 par value preferred—cumulative	7,000				
6%, $50 par value preferred—noncumulative	4,000				
Common	10,000				
Total Dividends Paid		$60,000	$0	$100,000	$70,000

AP-11B `LO 3 5`

The paid-in capital section of Hudson Corporation's balance sheet as at December 31, 2018 is as follows.

Hudson Corporation Balance Sheet (partial) As at December 31, 2018	
Paid-In Capital	
Preferred stock, 12% noncumulative, $100 par value, 100,000 shares authorized, 8,000 shares issued and outstanding	$800,000
Preferred stock, 9% cumulative, $100 par value, 100,000 shares authorized, 20,000 shares issued and outstanding	2,000,000
Common stock, $50 par value, unlimited shares authorized, 40,000 shares issued and outstanding	2,000,000
Total Paid-In Capital	4,800,000

Assume that no dividends were paid in 2016 or 2017. On December 31, 2018, Hudson Corporation declared a total cash dividend of $736,000.

Required

a) Calculate the amount of cash dividend paid to each of the three classes of paid-in capital.

b) Calculate the dividend paid per share for each of the three classes of paid-in capital.

	Common Stock	Cumulative Preferred Stock	Noncumulative Preferred Stock
Total Dividends			
Number of Shares			
Dividend Paid per Share			

c) Prepare the journal entry to record the declaration of dividends on December 31 using the cash dividends account.

Date	Account Title and Explanation	Debit	Credit

AP-12B LO 5

Tea Time Inc. is a distributor of fine artisan tea and has a June 30 year end. Due to several years of poor financial performance, dividends were last paid in 2015. On June 30, 2018, the company declared $100,000 of dividends to all stockholders on record as of July 5. The dividends will be paid on August 5, 2018. As at June 30 and July 5, 2018, the following shares were outstanding: 90,000, $5 par value common shares; 40,000, 3%, $10 par value cumulative preferred shares; and 35,000, 2%, $10 par value noncumulative preferred shares.

Required

a) Calculate how much Tea Time Inc. owes in dividends to each of the stockholders as at June 30, 2018.

	Annual Dividend Paid per Share	# of Shares	# of Years in Arrears	Dividends
Total Dividend Paid				
Cumulative Preferred Stock				
Noncumulative Preferred Stock				
Common Stock				

b) Prepare the journal entries to record the declaration and subsequent payout of the dividends in 2018. Assume the company uses the cash dividend account to record dividends.

Date	Account Title and Explanation	Debit	Credit

AP-13B LO 5

On November 1, 2018, the financial records of Sam Inc. showed the following balances.

Sam Inc. Balance Sheet (partial) As at November 1, 2018	
Stockholders' Equity	
Paid-In Capital	
Preferred stock, 5% cumulative, $100 par value, 200,000 shares authorized, 2,000 shares issued and outstanding	$200,000
Common stock, $10 par value, unlimited shares authorized, 130,000 shares issued and outstanding	1,300,000
Total Paid-In Capital	1,500,000
Retained Earnings	620,000
Total Stockholders' Equity	2,120,000

On November 15, 2018, Sam Inc. declared $320,000 of dividends payable to stockholders. Dividends were last declared in 2015. The declared dividend was paid on December 5, 2018.

During the period November 1 to December 31, 2018, the company earned an income before income tax of $75,000. Income tax expense for the year was $25,000.

Required

a) Calculate how much Sam Inc. owes the preferred stockholders.

b) Prepare the journal entries to record the declaration and payment of dividends. The company uses the cash dividends account to record dividends.

Date	Account Title and Explanation	Debit	Credit

c) Calculate the ending balance of retained earnings for the two-month period of November 1 to December 31, 2018.

Calculation of Retained Earnings	
For the Two Months Ended December 31, 2018	

AP-14B LO 6

On May 31, 2018, Red Synapse Corporation's stockholders' equity section shows the following balances.

Red Synapse Corporation Balance Sheet (partial) As at May 31, 2018	
Stockholders' Equity	
Paid-In Capital	
Common stock, $6 par value, unlimited shares authorized,	
30,000 shares issued and outstanding	$180,000
Additional Paid-In Capital	270,000
Total Paid-In Capital	450,000
Retained Earnings	370,000
Total Stockholders' Equity	820,000

Scenario 1

May 31   After preparing the stockholders' equity section shown above, the company declared and immediately distributed a 100% stock dividend. The market price on the date of declaration was $10. The company recorded the stock dividends by debiting retained earnings.

Required

a)   Calculate the ending balance of retained earnings after the stock dividend.

_____

_____

_____

_____

_____

b)   Prepare the stockholders' equity section of the balance sheet as at May 31, 2018 (after the stock dividend has been distributed).

Scenario 2

May 31   After preparing the stockholders' equity section shown at the beginning of this question (excluding Scenario 1), the company implemented a 2-for-1 stock split.

c) Calculate the number of outstanding shares.

---

d) Prepare the stockholders' equity section of the balance sheet as at May 31, 2018 (after the stock split).

AP-15B LO 5 6

At the end of Pataya Inc.'s third fiscal quarter in 2018, the stockholders' equity section of the balance sheet was as follows. Pataya Inc.'s common stock does not have a par value or a stated value.

Pataya Inc. Balance Sheet (partial) As at September 30, 2018	
Stockholders' Equity	
Common stock, unlimited shares authorized, 60,000 shares issued and outstanding	$960,000
Retained Earnings	580,000
Total Stockholders' Equity	1,540,000

In the fourth quarter of 2018, the following entries related to its equity accounts were recorded.

Date	Account Title and Explanation	Debit	Credit
Oct 2	Retained Earnings	110,000	
	Dividends Payable		110,000
Oct 25	Dividends Payable	110,000	
	Cash		110,000
Oct 31	Retained Earnings	140,000	
	Common Stock Dividends Distributable		140,000
Nov 5	Common Stock Dividends Distributable	140,000	
	Common Stock		140,000

Required

a) Explain each journal entry.

_____

_____

_____

_____

b) Complete the following table showing the equity balances at each indicated date.

	October 2	October 25	October 31	November 5
Common Stock				
Common Stock Dividends Distributable				
Retained Earnings				
Total Stockholders' Equity				

AP-16B LO 4 5

Vitamin Corporation was incorporated and began operations on May 1, 2014. Vitamin presented the following information on April 30, 2018. Vitamin Corporation's preferred stock and common stock do not have a par value or a stated value.

Preferred stock, $3 noncumulative, 300,000 shares authorized, 5,000 shares issued and outstanding	$14,500
Common stock, unlimited shares authorized, 40,000 shares issued and outstanding	280,000
Retained Earnings	645,000

Dividends were last paid out in the 2016 fiscal year. The following transactions relating to stockholders' equity occurred during the 2018 to 2019 fiscal year.

May 1   Issued 60,000 common shares for $8 per share and 15,000 preferred shares for $3 per share

Jun 2   Issued 5,000 common shares in exchange for $30,000 in legal services provided by the lawyer when setting up the corporation

Aug 4   Issued 40,000 common shares in exchange for machinery valued at $250,000. The fair value of the shares could not be readily determined

Nov 15   Issued 10,000 common shares for $8.50 each and 5,000 preferred shares for $3.25 each

Apr 30   Income before income tax was $120,000 and income tax expense for the year was $22,800. Dividends of $165,000 were declared and are payable on May 5, 2018. The company uses the cash dividends account to record dividends.

Required

a) Prepare the journal entries to record the above transactions.

Date	Account Title and Explanation	Debit	Credit

Date	Account Title and Explanation	Debit	Credit

b)   Calculate the ending balance of retained earnings as at April 30, 2019.

Calculation of Retained Earnings	
For the Year Ended April 30, 2019	

AP-17B LO 4 5 8

Gecko Inc. has the following balances in its stockholders' equity section of the balance sheet.

Gecko Inc. Balance Sheet (partial) As at December 31, 2017	
Stockholders' Equity	
Paid-In Capital	
Preferred stock, 10% noncumulative, $5 par value, 40,000	
shares authorized, 12,000 shares issued and outstanding	$60,000
Common stock, $1 par value, 1,000,000 shares authorized,	
75,000 shares issued and outstanding	75,000
Additional Paid-In Capital	286,500
Total Paid-In Capital	421,500
Retained Earnings	147,525
Total Stockholders' Equity	569,025

The following transactions occurred during the year 2018.

Jan 9   Issued 20,000 common shares for $4.50 per share and 3,000 preferred shares for $7 per share

Jun 7   Issued 4,000 preferred shares in exchange for equipment valued at $26,000. The fair value of the stock could not be readily determined.

Sep 8   Issued 12,000 common shares for $4.75 per share

Oct 13   Declared $25,000 of cash dividends. The company uses the cash dividends account to record dividends.

Dec 13   Paid the dividends declared on October 13

Dec 31   Estimated income tax expense of $31,000. However, the actual amount of income tax due for this period based on tax laws is determined to be $29,000. Net income after income tax was $89,000.

Required

a) Prepare the journal entries to record the above transactions for 2018.

Date	Account Title and Explanation	Debit	Credit

b) Calculate the ending balance of retained earnings for the year 2018.

Calculation of Retained Earnings	
For the Year Ended December 31, 2018	

c) Prepare the stockholders' equity section of the balance sheet as at December 31, 2018.

AP-18B LO 3 4 5

Ping Pong Inc. began operations on January 1, 2017. The following transactions relating to stockholders' equity occurred in 2017, the first year of the company's operations.

Jan 1   The corporate charter authorized the issuance of unlimited common shares and 200,000, $3 noncumulative preferred shares. Both common stock and preferred stock do not have a par value or a stated value.

Jan 2   Issued 400,000 common shares for $11 per share

Jan 3   Issued 200,000 common shares in exchange for equipment valued at $750,000 and merchandise inventory valued at $320,000

Jan 4   Instead of paying a $40,000 fee in cash, the company offered the accountant 400, $3 preferred shares

Jan 5   Issued 15,000, $3 preferred shares for $100 cash per share

For the year ended December 31, 2017, the newly incorporated company had an income before income tax of $1,250,000 and income tax expense of $300,000. At the directors' meeting on January 15, 2018, the company decided to pay out 20% of net income as cash dividends to preferred and common stockholders. The date of record of the dividends is January 30, 2018. The company uses the cash dividend account to record cash dividends.

The dividend payment date is February 28, 2018.

Ping Pong Inc. had the following transaction during the year ended December 31, 2018.

Jun 4   Issued 100,000 common shares for $15 per share

For the year ended December 31, 2018, the company had an income before income tax of $2,000,000 and income tax expense of $460,000. At the board of directors' meeting held on January 15, 2019, the company decided to pay out 25% of net income as cash dividends to preferred and common stockholders. The date of record of dividend is January 31, 2019.

The dividend is to be paid on February 28, 2019.

During the period January 1 to February 28, 2019, the company had a net income of $250,000.

Required

a)   Prepare journal entries to record the above transactions. Do not record the income tax expense transactions.

Date	Account Title and Explanation	Debit	Credit

Date	Account Title and Explanation	Debit	Credit

b) Calculate the ending balance of retained earnings for the year 2017.

Calculation of Retained Earnings	
For the Year Ended December 31, 2017	

c) Calculate the ending balance of retained earnings for the year 2018.

Calculation of Retained Earnings	
For the Year Ended December 31, 2018	

d) Prepare the stockholders' equity section of the balance sheet as at December 31, 2017 and December 31, 2018.

AP-19B LO 5 6 8

At the beginning of 2018, Mystery Corporation had the following balances.

Paid-In Capital	
Common stock, $10 par value, 1,000,000 shares authorized; 200,000 shares issued and outstanding	$2,000,000
Retained Earnings	925,000

The following transactions occurred during 2018.

Jan 10	The Board decided to declare $40,000 dividends to common stockholders
Feb 15	Paid the cash dividend declared on January 10
Nov 30	Declared a 40% stock dividend. The market value was $12 per share
Dec 15	Distributed the stock dividend declared on November 30
Dec 31	Estimated income tax expense of $80,000. However, the actual amount of income tax due for this period based on tax laws is determined to be $75,000.

Mystery Corporation generated a $250,000 net income (after income tax) during the year. The company uses the retained earnings account to record cash and stock dividends.

Required

a) Prepare journal entries to record the above transactions.

Date	Account Title and Explanation	Debit	Credit

b) Calculate the ending balance of retained earnings for the year ended December 31, 2018.

Calculation of Retained Earnings	
For the Year Ended December 31, 2018	

c) Prepare the stockholders' equity section of the balance sheet as at December 31, 2018.

AP-20B LO 7

On June 30, 2018, Choibok Corp. had 350,000 outstanding common shares. Its balance sheet on June 30, 2018 shows a common stock balance of $875,000 and a paid-in capital, treasury stock balance of zero. The following are the only changes to Choibok Corp.'s common stock that occurred after June 30, 2018.

On July 1, 2018, Choibok Corp. paid $150,000 cash to reacquire 20,000 of its own common shares.
On October 1, 2018, Choibok Corp. sold 15,000 shares of its treasury stock for $105,000 cash.
On December 1, 2018, Choibok Corp. sold the remaining 5,000 shares of its treasury stock for $45,000 cash.

Required

a) Record the share reacquisition journal entry on July 1, 2018.

Date	Account Title and Explanation	Debit	Credit

b) Record the treasury stock re-issuance journal entry on October 1, 2018.

Date	Account Title and Explanation	Debit	Credit

c)   Record the treasury stock re-issuance journal entry on December 1, 2018.

Date	Account Title and Explanation	Debit	Credit

AP-21B LO 1 4 5 6 7 8

Prakun Corporation was formed on January 1, 2018. The corporate charter authorized the issuance of 10%, $80 par value, 200,000 cumulative preferred shares and unlimited $5 par value common shares. The following transactions occurred between January 1, 2018 and December 31, 2018.

Jan 1   Issued 6,400 shares of common stock in exchange for organizational expenses of $2,000 and $30,000 cash

Jan 3   Issued 100,000 shares of common stock in return for $800,000 cash

Jan 4   Issued 4,000 shares of preferred stock in return for $400,000 cash

Feb 20   Purchased 10,000 shares of its own common stock for $10 per share

Mar 31   Declared cash dividends of $50,000 to the owners of preferred and common stock as of April 30. The company uses the cash dividends account to record cash dividends.

May 30   Paid the cash dividends declared on March 31

Jun 20   Declared 10% common stock dividends to the owners of common stock as of July 20. The market price of common stock on this date is $12 per share. The company uses the retained earnings account to record stock dividends.

Aug20   Distributed the stock dividends declared on June 20

Sep 9   Sold 2,000 shares of treasury stock for $11 per share

Oct 25   Sold 3,000 shares of treasury stock for $9 per share

Dec 31   Estimated income tax expense of $120,000. However, the actual amount of income tax due for this period based on tax laws is determined to be $100,000.

Required

a)   Journalize the entries to record all the transactions.

Date	Account Title and Explanation	Debit	Credit

Date	Account Title and Explanation	Debit	Credit

b) Fill in the missing numbers (gray shaded areas) of shares and account balances in the stockholders' equity section of the balance sheet as at December 31, 2018.

Prakun Corporation **Balance Sheet (partial)** **As at December 31, 2018**	
Stockholders' Equity	
Paid-In Capital	
Preferred stock, 10% cumulative, $80 par value, 200,000 shares authorized,	
_____ shares issued and outstanding	
Common stock, $5 par value, unlimited shares authorized,	
_____ shares issued, 111,040 outstanding	
Additional Paid-In Capital	
Total Paid-In Capital	
Retained Earnings, $50,000 restricted by purchase of treasury stock	163,320
Total Paid-In Capital and Retained Earnings	
Less: Treasury Stock (5,000 shares at cost)	
Total Stockholders' Equity	

Case Study

CS-1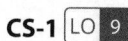

McIntosh Pharmaceutical develops and manufactures cancer-related drugs. For the last 10 years, it has been developing a unique chemical that has been shown to reduce the risk of breast cancer in middle-aged women. Unfortunately, just before going into mass production, scientists within McIntosh uncovered harmful side effects of the drug and strongly recommended to management that mass production be delayed for another five years to better study the drug. McIntosh management decided to delay mass production and announced the news to the public three days after the decision was made. Following the announcement, McIntosh's share price dropped 40%. During the three days of meetings, however, many managers decided to sell their shares in McIntosh.

Was their decision to sell shares ethically sound? Explain.

Critical Thinking

CT-1 LO 5

John Maynard Nash, a budding economist, noticed that the market price of stock seemed to decline after the date of record of a cash dividend. Can you suggest why this might be the case?

Notes

Chapter 16

CORPORATIONS: THE FINANCIAL STATEMENTS

LEARNING OBJECTIVES

LO 1 Explain the different requirements under US GAAP and IFRS when presenting financial statements

LO 2 Prepare an income statement and a statement of comprehensive income

LO 3 Prepare a statement of retained earnings and a statement of changes in equity

LO 4 Record and report on prior period adjustments

LO 5 Prepare a balance sheet and a statement of financial position

LO 6 Calculate and explain earnings per share

LO 7 Calculate ratios used to evaluate earnings and dividend performance

AMEENGAGE Access *ameengage.com* for integrated resources including tutorials, practice exercises, the digital textbook and more.

Assessment Questions

AS-1 LO 1

Describe the differences between users of corporate financial statements and users of a sole proprietorship's financial statements.

AS-2 LO 1

Is a public corporation allowed to adopt US GAAP or IFRS in the United States?

AS-3 LO 2

Define a business segment. How does a business segment relate to discontinued operations?

AS-4 LO 2

Define discontinued operations and briefly discuss the reporting requirements for discontinued operations under US GAAP and IFRS.

_____

_____

_____

_____

_____

_____

AS-5 LO 2

Define other comprehensive income.

_____

_____

_____

AS-6 LO 2

How should other comprehensive income (OCI) be reported under US GAAP and IFRS? Provide specific examples of OCI.

_____

_____

_____

_____

_____

_____

AS-7 LO 2

IFRS requires that expenses on the statement of comprehensive income be presented either by function or by nature. Briefly describe each of the two methods.

_____

_____

_____

_____

_____

_____

_____

_____

AS-8 LO 3

True or False: Where IFRS has been adopted, when a company sells additional common stock to the public, it must report the changes in the value of common stock on its statement of changes in equity. Explain.

_____

_____

_____

AS-9 `LO` `3`

Briefly discuss the major differences between the statement of retained earnings under US GAAP and the statement of changes in equity under IFRS.

_____

_____

_____

AS-10 `LO` `4`

What is the main reason for accounting changes that warrant a prior period adjustment? Why is it important that these are corrected?

_____

_____

AS-11 `LO` `4`

What is the accounting treatment for correcting prior period errors?

_____

_____

_____

AS-12 `LO` `5`

How are assets typically listed on the statement of financial position under IFRS?

_____

_____

AS-13 `LO` `5`

What order is typically used to list assets on the balance sheet under US GAAP?

_____

_____

AS-14 `LO` `6`

Name a key profitability indicator that is required to be presented on the statement of comprehensive income by a public company under both US GAAP and IFRS and provide the formula to arrive at this indicator.

_____

_____

AS-15 `LO` `6`

Why is the weighted average number of shares outstanding used as a denominator when calculating earnings per share? How is the weighted average number of shares calculated?

_____

_____

_____

AS-16 LO 6

Briefly describe the difference between a basic earnings per share calculation and a fully diluted earnings per share calculation.

_____

_____

_____

_____

_____

_____

_____

_____

_____

AS-17 LO 7

Explain what the book value per common share ratio indicates and provide a formula to calculate this ratio.

_____

_____

_____

_____

AS-18 LO 7

Why would investors be interested to know the dividend yield of a given corporation and how would they arrive at this figure?

_____

_____

_____

_____

AS-19 LO 7

What does a high price-earnings ratio usually indicate?

_____

_____

_____

_____

_____

_____

AS-20 LO 2

Name at least three items that are often included in the other income or expenses section of the income statement under US GAAP.

_____

_____

_____

_____

AS-21 LO 2

List two common items that are usually included in the discontinued operations section of the income statement under US GAAP.

_____

_____

_____

_____

_____

_____

_____

_____

_____

_____

_____

_____

_____

_____

_____

_____

_____

_____

_____

_____

_____

_____

_____

_____

_____

_____

Application Questions Group A

AP-1A LO 2

Green Light Emissions Everyday (otherwise known as GLEE Corporation) has sales of $400,000 and COGS of $120,000 for the year ended December 31, 2018. It also has selling expenses of $80,000 and administrative expenses of $20,000. Prepare an income statement under US GAAP taking into account income tax expense. Assume a tax rate of 30%. Exclude the presentation of earnings per share in this question.

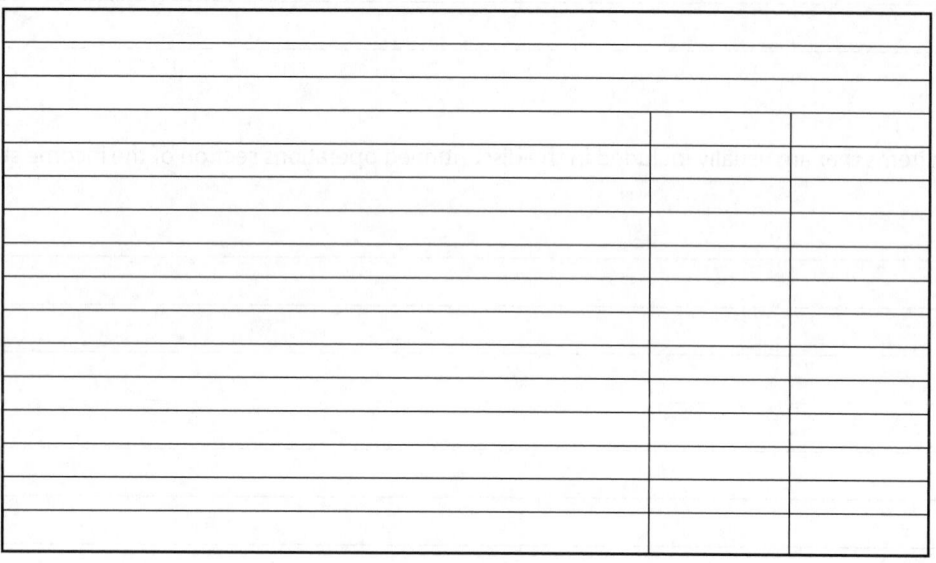

AP-2A LO 2

Budokan Company, a corporation with a December 31 year end, has sales of $530,000, COGS of $120,000, selling expenses of $70,000, administrative expenses of $200,000, interest expense of $6,000 and income tax expense of $40,000 in 2018. Exclude the presentation of earnings per share in this question.

Required

a)   Prepare an income statement under US GAAP for the year ended December 31, 2018.

b) Prepare a statement of comprehensive income (by function) under IFRS for the year ended December 31, 2018.

AP-3A LO 2

Nacho Libray Inc. follows US GAAP and has income from operations of $200,000. Its total other expenses amounted to $100,000 and the income tax expense was $40,000. Calculate the net income for the year.

AP-4A LO 3

The following information was taken from the accounting records of Montana Inc. at May 31, 2018. Montana Inc. prepares statements according to US GAAP.

Assume a tax rate of 37%. During the year, no shares were issued or redeemed.

Line Item	Amount
Total dividends paid	$61,000
Retained earnings, June 1, 2017	110,000
Net income	156,000

Prepare a statement of retained earnings for Montana Inc. for the year ended May 31, 2018.

AP-5A LO 3

Top Cuisine Inc. has a March 31 year end. Retained earnings at March 31, 2017 had a credit balance of $54,700. During the 2018 fiscal year, net income was $24,615 and dividends of $12,600 were declared and paid. During the 2019 fiscal year, Top Cuisine had a net loss of $16,680 and dividends of $10,400 were declared but not yet paid.

Prepare statements of retained earnings for Top Cuisine Inc. as at March 31, 2018 and March 31, 2019.

AP-6A LO 4

On March 17, 2018, the bookkeeper for GIFT Inc. noticed that she made an error when recording a $44,000 expenditure in the prior fiscal year. She posted the amount to the Repairs and Maintenance expense account instead of posting to the Equipment account. Write the journal entry that should be recorded to correct the Equipment account. Ignore the impact of depreciation. Assume the tax rate is 30%.

Date	Account Title and Explanation	Debit	Credit

AP-7A LO 4

On April 4, 2018, an auditor noticed that TFK Inc. accidently recorded an insurance expenditure of $50,000 as an expense instead of as prepaid. The insurance purchase was made on the last day of the 2017 fiscal period. Write the journal entry that should be recorded in the 2018 fiscal period to correct the Prepaid Insurance account. Assume that the insurance covers the period of May 1, 2018 to April 30, 2019 and that the tax rate is 30%.

Date	Account Title and Explanation	Debit	Credit

AP-8A LO 2 3

Below is the adjusted trial balance for Simple Town Corporation. The balance of retained earnings represents the balance at the beginning of the fiscal year. The company decided not to pay dividends this year. Exclude the presentation of earnings per share in this question.

Account Title	Debit	Credit
Simple Town Corporation		
Adjusted Trial Balance		
June 30, 2018		
Cash	$113,000	
Accounts Receivable	93,000	
Prepaid Rent	7,800	
Merchandise Inventory	195,000	
Equipment	120,000	
Accumulated Depreciation—Equipment		$42,000
Accounts Payable		24,000
Unearned Revenue		22,500
Salaries Payable		18,000
Preferred Stock		25,800
Common Stock		191,800
Retained Earnings (beginning balance)		171,290
Sales Revenue		300,000
Unrealized Gain on Trading Investments		2,800
Sales Returns & Allowances	12,000	
Cost of Goods Sold	60,000	
Depreciation Expense—Office Equipment	8,500	
Depreciation Expense—Retail Equipment	4,100	
Office Salaries Expense	42,000	
Sales Salaries Expense	27,000	
Rent Expense—Office	10,000	
Rent Expense—Retail	6,500	
Utilities Expense—Office	8,000	
Utilities Expense—Retail	11,500	
Insurance Expense	23,400	
Supplies Expense	36,000	
Income Tax Expense	17,990	
Loss on Disposal of Equipment	2,400	
Total	**$798,190**	**$798,190**

Required

a)   Prepare an income statement under US GAAP for the year ended June 30, 2018.

b) Prepare the statement of retained earnings for Simple Town Corporation.

AP-9A LO 2 3

Spader Inc. had the following account balances at the end of the year. Assume a tax rate of 20%. Exclude the presentation of earnings per share in this question.

Account Title	Balance
Advertising Expense	$6,200
Cost of Goods Sold	234,000
Income from Operating Discontinued Operations	16,800
Interest Expense	2,700
Loss on Foreign Currency Translation Adjustments	600
Loss on Sale of Discontinued Operations	5,700
Office Salaries Expense	42,500
Rent Expense—Office	12,000
Rent Expense—Retail	20,000
Sales Returns & Allowances	3,900
Sales Revenue	520,000
Sales Salaries Expense	45,000
Supplies Expense	3,800
Utilities Expense—Office	4,100
Utilities Expense—Retail	6,300

Required

a) Prepare a statement of comprehensive income under US GAAP for the year ended December 31, 2018.

b) Prepare a statement of stockholders' equity under US GAAP for the year ended December 31, 2018. The beginning balances of the retained earnings and accumulated other income accounts are $90,000 and $1,000, respectively. Spader Inc.'s common stock balance is $400,000 and remained unchanged throughout 2018. The company declared and paid $30,000 in dividends during the year.

AP-10A LO 5

Below is the adjusted trial balance for Home Care Solutions Inc.

Home Care Solutions Inc. Adjusted Trial Balance June 30, 2018		
Account Title	**Debit**	**Credit**
Accounts Payable		$10,600
Accounts Receivable	$80,000	
Accumulated Depreciation		28,000
Additional Paid-In Capital		8,100
Cash	63,850	
Common Stock		3,000
Cost of Goods Sold	96,000	
Depreciation Expense	35,200	
Income Tax Expense	36,000	
Interest Expense	21,120	
Interest Payable		14,960
Merchandise Inventory	90,000	
Notes Payable		268,800
Preferred Stock		6,500
Prepaid Rent	28,000	
Property, Plant and Equipment	176,000	
Rent Expense	66,000	
Retained Earnings (after Dividends)		40,810
Salaries Expense	72,000	
Salaries Payable		34,000
Sales Returns	12,000	
Sales Revenue		400,000
Unearned Revenue		17,400
Utilities Expense	56,000	
Total	$832,170	$832,170

Additional Information

- Net income for the year was $5,680 and the retained earnings at July 1, 2017 was $44,960. Dividends of $4,150 were declared and paid in the year.
- Home Care Solutions has a note payable due in eight years. The principal payments are $2,800 per month.
- The preferred stock pays a dividend of 10% of its $5 par value. The company issued 1,300 cumulative preferred shares and 15,000 have been authorized. The company issued 3,000, $1 par value common shares and 45,000 have been authorized.

Required

a) Prepare a classified balance sheet as at June 30, 2018 under US GAAP.

b) If the company has accumulated other comprehensive income with a credit balance, how would it appear on the company's balance sheet? Explain.

_____

_____

_____

AP-11A [LO 5]

Sigmund Corporation has the following account balances. Using this information, prepare a classified balance sheet as at December 31, 2018 under US GAAP.

Account Title	Balance
Accounts Payable	$56,000
Accounts Receivable	47,500
Accumulated Depreciation	8,600
Cash	17,000
Common Stock	42,000
Merchandise Inventory	65,500
Notes Payable	110,000
Preferred Stock	50,000
Prepaid Rent	12,000
Property, Plant and Equipment	220,000
Retained Earnings	91,900
Unearned Revenue	3,500

Notes

Both preferred stock and common stock have no par value.

Unlimited common shares are authorized and 2,000 have been issued and are currently outstanding.

For preferred stock, 10,000 shares are authorized and 5,000 have been issued and are currently outstanding. Each share pays a cumulative dividend of $5 annually.

The notes payable is payable over four years and $27,500 will be paid by December 31, 2019.

AP-12A LO 7

The statement of retained earnings for Netting Industries, which follows US GAAP, is shown below.

Netting Industries Statement of Retained Earnings (in thousands) For the Year Ended December 31, 2018	
Retained Earnings, January 1, 2018	$477,820
Net Income	122,280
Less: Cash Dividends	31,061
Retained Earnings, December 31, 2018	$539,039

In 2018, Netting Industries had 30,000 shares of common stock outstanding and did not have any preferred stock outstanding for the whole year. Netting Industries' stock price on December 31, 2018 was $73.50. Calculate the dividend yield and discuss. Compare Netting Industries' dividend yield against the industry average dividend yield of 4%.

_____

_____

_____

_____

_____

_____

AP-13A LO 7

The following data is available for two companies, Sam Corporation and Tally Corporation for the year ended December 31, 2018.

	Sam Corporation	Tally Corporation
Income from continuing operations (net of tax)	$710,000	$510,000
Income from discontinued operations (net of tax)	120,000	60,000
Net income	830,000	570,000
Common stock*	800,000	450,000
Beginning retained earnings	2,070,000	1,580,000
Current liabilities	560,000	420,000
Long-term liabilities	980,000	760,000
Market price per share	14	11
Total dividends paid	200,000	120,000

*Sam has 100,000 shares and Tally has 50,000 shares outstanding throughout the whole year. Both companies' common stock does not have a par value. Both companies do not have preferred stock.

Required

a) Calculate the following ratios for both companies.

1. EPS Ratio

	Sam Corporation	Tally Corporation
EPS Ratio		

2. Dividend Yield

	Sam Corporation	Tally Corporation
Dividend Yield		

3. Price-Earnings Ratio

	Sam Corporation	Tally Corporation
Price-Earnings Ratio		

b) Compare the performance and position of the two companies by interpreting the ratios calculated in part a).

_____

_____

_____

_____

_____

_____

_____

_____

_____

_____

_____

_____

_____

_____

_____

_____

_____

_____

_____

_____

_____

_____

_____

_____

AP-14A LO 2 3 5

Below is a list of accounts and balances for FlipFlop Inc. for the year ending June 30, 2018. All balances are in thousands of dollars. FlipFlop Inc. follows US GAAP. Assume a tax rate of 20%. Exclude the presentation of earnings per share for this question.

Account Title	Balance
Accounts Payable	$8,900
Accounts Receivable	6,100
Accumulated Depreciation	1,200
Advertising Expense	590
Cash	19,000
Cash Dividends	3,500
Common Stock	10,000
Cost of Goods Sold	13,500
Depreciation Expense—Office Equipment	90
Depreciation Expense—Store Equipment	700
Gain on Foreign Currency Translation Adjustments	280
Gain on Sale of Discontinued Operations	2,000
Income from Operating Discontinued Operations	8,000
Interest Expense	120
Merchandise Inventory	18,000
Miscellaneous Administrative Expenses	260
Notes Payable	21,000
Office Salaries Expense	1,400
Prepaid Insurance	3,250
Property, Plant and Equipment	25,000
Rent Expense—Office	600
Rent Expense—Retail	1,000
Retained Earnings (beginning balance)	17,986
Sales Salaries Expense	2,500
Sales Discounts	1,100
Sales Returns & Allowances	840
Sales Revenue	30,000
Unearned Revenue	1,700

Notes

Unlimited common shares are authorized and 2,000 shares have been issued and are currently outstanding. The common stock has no par value. The notes payable is payable over five years and $4,200 of the principal will be paid by June 30, 2019.

Required

a) Prepare a statement of comprehensive income for the year ending June 30, 2018.

b) Prepare a statement of retained earnings for the year ended June 30, 2018.

c) Prepare a classified balance sheet as at June 30, 2018.

d) If the company had followed IFRS, how would the section of assets on the statement of financial position be different?

_____

_____

AP-15A LO 2 3 5

Below is the adjusted trial balance for SandStone Corp. as at September 30, 2018. Assume a tax rate of 40%. Exclude the presentation of earnings per share in this question.

SandStone Corp.		
Adjusted Trial Balance		
September 30, 2018		
Account Title	**Debit**	**Credit**
Accounts Payable		$20,470
Accounts Receivable	$23,000	
Accumulated Depreciation—Equipment		8,050
Additional Paid-In Capital		8,640
Advertising Expense	16,100	
Cash	19,550	
Common Stock		1,000
Cost of Goods Sold	40,250	
Depreciation Expense—Office Equipment	3,000	
Depreciation Expense—Retail Equipment	4,400	
Equipment	50,600	
Gain on Sale of Assets		2,530
Gain on Sale of Discontinued Operations		13,400
Income Tax Benefit		17,028
Interest Expense	5,520	
Interest Payable		3,910
Loss from Operating Discontinued Operations	29,000	
Merchandise Inventory	25,875	
Notes Payable		46,000
Office Salaries Expense	10,120	
Preferred Stock		5,000
Prepaid Insurance	8,050	
Rent Expense—Office	10,350	
Rent Expense—Retail	19,550	
Retained Earnings		35,512
Salaries Payable		9,775
Sales Discounts	11,060	
Sales Salaries Expense	20,700	
Sales Returns & Allowances	3,450	
Sales Revenue		115,000
Unearned Revenue		14,260
Total	**$300,575**	**$300,575**

Required

a) Prepare a multiple-step income statement for the year ended September 30, 2018 under US GAAP.

b) The balance of retained earnings in the adjusted trial balance represents the beginning balance at October 1, 2017. No dividends were declared during the year. Prepare a statement of retained earnings for the year ended September 30, 2018.

c) Prepare a classified balance sheet as at September 30, 2018. Additional information is as follows.
    •   The note payable is due over four years. The principal payments are $1,050 each month.
    •   Preferred stock, 10%, $100 par value, 55,000 shares authorized, 50 shares issued and outstanding
    •   Common stock, $1 par value, 100,000 shares authorized, 1,000 shares issued and outstanding

Application Questions Group B

AP-1B LO 2

Black Light Environment Everyday (otherwise known as BLEE Inc.) has sales of $370,000, COGS of $100,000 and before-tax gain from foreign currency translation adjustments (other comprehensive income) of $4,800 for the year ended June 30, 2018. It also has selling expenses of $75,000 and administrative expenses of $21,000. Prepare a statement of comprehensive income under US GAAP on June 30, 2018 for BLEE, taking into account income tax expense. Assume a tax rate of 31%. Exclude the presentation of earnings per share in this question.

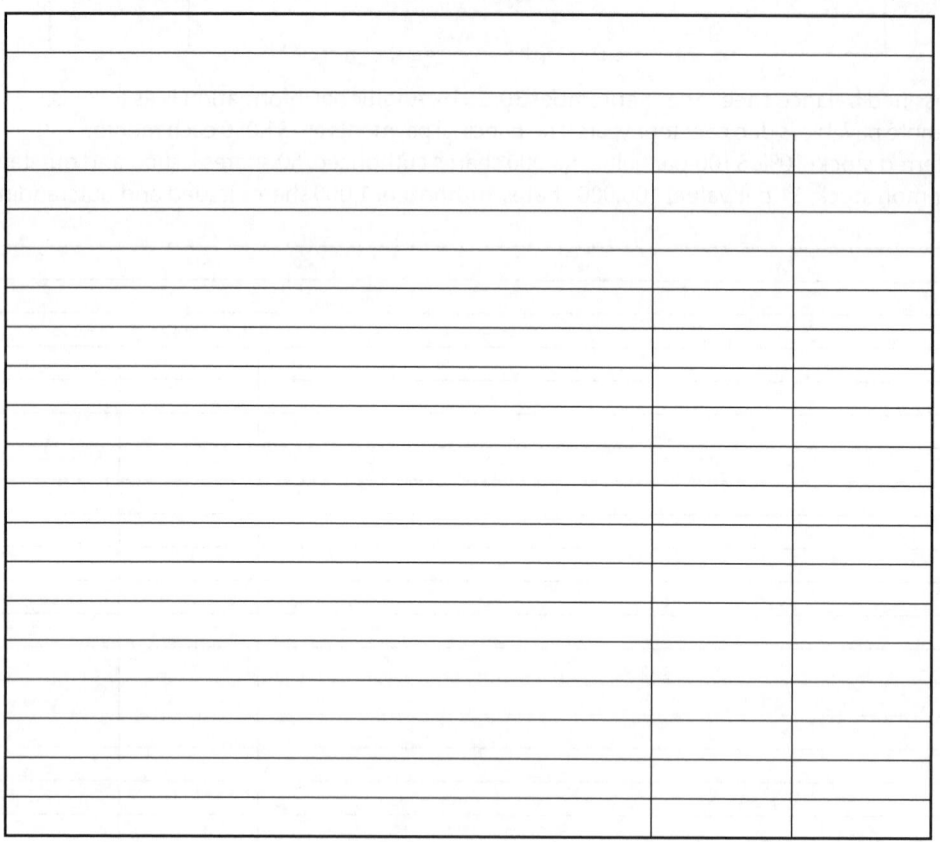

AP-2B LO 2

Venus Space Explorations, a corporation with a June 30, 2018 year end, has sales of $420,000, advertising expense of $12,000, COGS of $200,000, sales salaries expense of $18,000, office salaries expense of $10,000, head office's rent expense of $24,000, office supplies expense of $3,000, interest expense of $7,000, and income expense of $42,000. Exclude the presentation of earnings per share in this question.

Required

a)   Prepare an income statement under US GAAP for Venus for the year ended June 30, 2018.

b) Prepare a statement of comprehensive income (by nature) under IFRS for Venus for the year ended June 30, 2018.

AP-3B LO 2

Gleek the Geek Corporation follows IFRS. In 2018, it has profit for the year from continuing operations (net of income tax expense) of $700,000, profit for the year from discontinued operations (net of income tax expense) of $50,000, and other comprehensive income (net of income tax) of $13,000.

Required

a) Calculate Gleek the Geek's profit for the year for 2018.

_____

_____

b) Calculate Gleek the Geek's total comprehensive income for 2018.

_____

_____

AP-4B LO 3

Below is the adjusted trial balance for Connection Communications Inc. for the month of September 2018. Dividends of $5,800 were declared and paid in the month. There is no change in the common stock and additional paid-in capital accounts in the month of September. Connection Communications Inc. prepares financial statements according to US GAAP.

Connection Communications Inc. Adjusted Trial Balance September 30, 2018		
Account Title	**Debit**	**Credit**
Accounts Payable		$9,676
Accounts Receivable	$12,957	
Accumulated Depreciation—Equipment		11,325
Additional Paid-In Capital		6,600
Cash	16,822	
Common Stock		5,000
Cost of Goods Sold	12,940	
Depreciation Expense	3,395	
Income Tax Expense	5,200	
Interest Expense	1,225	
Interest Payable		2,083
Notes Payable		24,500
Prepaid Insurance	1,850	
Prepaid Rent	7,100	
Property, Plant and Equipment	32,350	
Rent Expense	3,550	
Retained Earnings (after dividends)		23,300
Salaries Expense	6,505	
Salaries Payable		3,882
Sales Revenue		64,700
Supplies	42,055	
Supplies Expense	5,764	
Unearned Revenue		4,852
Utilities Expense	4,205	
Total	**$155,918**	**$155,918**

Required

a)   Prepare a statement of retained earnings for the month ended September 30, 2018.

b)   Prepare a statement of stockholders' equity for the month ended September 30, 2018.

AP-5B LO 3 4

Kensington Corporation has a December 31 year end. Retained earnings as at December 31, 2016 had a debit balance of $15,450. During the 2017 fiscal year net income was $91,550 and dividends of $34,500 were declared and paid. During the 2018 fiscal year Kensington had a net income of $32,100 and dividends of $28,000 were declared and paid. An audit revealed that the 2017 net income was understated because a new engine that was purchased for $5,200 in 2017 was recorded as an expense when it should have been recorded as an asset. Assume the tax rate is 30%. Ignore the effect of depreciation.

Required

a)   Complete Kensington Corporation's statement of retained earnings for 2017.

b)   Complete Kensington Corporation's statement of retained earnings for 2018.

AP-6B LO 4

On January 31, 2018, the bookkeeper for FLAX Inc. noticed that she made an error when recording a $96,000 expenditure in the prior fiscal year. She posted the amount to the Repairs and Maintenance expense account instead of posting to the Equipment account. Write the journal entry that should be recorded to correct the Equipment account. Ignore the impact of depreciation. Assume the tax rate is 30%.

Date	Account Title and Explanation	Debit	Credit

Analysis

What if the error were reversed? Write the journal entry that would have to be made if the $96,000 expense were incorrectly recorded as equipment.

Date	Account Title and Explanation	Debit	Credit

AP-7B LO 4

On January 31, 2018, an auditor noticed that MDK Inc. accidently recorded an insurance expenditure of $60,000 as an expense instead of as prepaid. The insurance purchase was made on the last day of the 2017 fiscal period. Write the journal entry that should be recorded in the 2018 fiscal period to correct the Prepaid Insurance account. Assume that the insurance covers the period of February 1, 2018 to January 31, 2019 and that the tax rate is 30%.

Date	Account Title and Explanation	Debit	Credit

Analysis

US GAAP requires that the correction of an error from a prior period must be included in the statement of retained earnings and not on the income statement. How is this treatment related to the accounting principles for revenue and expense recognition?

_____

_____

_____

_____

_____

_____

_____

_____

_____

_____

AP-8B LO 2 3

Below is the adjusted trial balance for Del Ray Company. Dividends paid during the year were $7,800. Assume a tax rate of 30%. Exclude the presentation of earnings per share in this question.

Del Ray Company Adjusted Trial Balance March 31, 2018		
Account Title	**Debit**	**Credit**
Cash	$33,800	
Accounts Receivable	40,300	
Prepaid Insurance	5,070	
Supplies	4,500	
Property, Plant and Equipment	164,200	
Accumulated Depreciation—Office Equipment		$14,980
Accumulated Depreciation—Retail Equipment		7,770
Accounts Payable		10,400
Unearned Revenue		9,750
Interest Payable		2,250
Notes Payable		25,000
Preferred Stock		14,500
Common Stock		21,700
Retained Earnings (after dividends)		116,110
Sales Revenue		130,000
Foreign Currency Translation Adjustments		5,200
Sales Discounts	650	
Sales Returns & Allowances	1,950	
Cost of Goods Sold	26,000	
Depreciation Expense—Office Equipment	4,850	
Depreciation Expense—Retail Equipment	2,300	
Office Salaries Expense	17,940	
Sales Salaries Expense	11,960	
Rent Expense—Office	2,150	
Rent Expense—Retail	5,000	
Utilities Expense—Office	3,800	
Utilities Expense—Retail	4,650	
Insurance Expense	10,400	
Supplies Expense	15,600	
Interest Expense	1,250	
Income Tax Expense	10,890	
Income from Operating Discontinued Operations		8,100
Gain on Sale of Discontinued Operations		1,500
Total	**$367,260**	**$367,260**

Required

a) Prepare a statement of comprehensive income for the year ended March 31, 2018 under US GAAP.

b) Prepare the statement of retained earnings for Del Ray.

c) If the company adhered to IFRS , there would be no specific rule on how to present the expenses on the statement of comprehensive income. Is that true or false? Explain.

AP-9B LO 2 3

The following information was taken from the accounting records of Splinter Inc. at December 31, 2018. Splinter Inc. follows IFRS. Assume a tax rate of 30%. Exclude the presentation of earnings per share in this question.

Line Item	Amount
Common stock, 50,000 outstanding on January 1, 2018	$350,000
Common stock, 70,000 outstanding on December 31, 2018	470,000
Cost of goods sold	468,000
Dividends paid	50,000
Gain on sale of assets	6,200
Selling expenses	150,000
Administrative expenses	60,000
Interest expense	8,700
Income from operating discontinued operations	7,000
Gain on sale of discontinued operations	55,000
Prior year error—debit to retained earnings	6,000
Retained earnings, January 1, 2018 (prior to adjustment)	410,000
Sales revenue	780,000

Required

a) Prepare the statement of comprehensive income by function for the year ended December 31, 2018.

b) Prepare the statement of changes in equity for the year ended December 31, 2018 showing the changes in contributed capital and retained earnings.

AP-10B  **LO 5**

Below is the adjusted trial balance for Busy Town Inc.

Busy Town Inc. Adjusted Trial Balance December 31, 2018		
Account Title	**Debit**	**Credit**
Accounts Payable		$69,420
Accounts Receivable	$78,000	
Accumulated Depreciation		27,300
Additional Paid-In Capital		56,030
Cash and Cash Equivalents	66,300	
Common Stock		100,000
Cost of Goods Sold	93,600	
Depreciation Expense	34,320	
Goodwill	130,000	
Income Tax Expense	35,100	
Interest Payable		936
Interest Receivable	1,560	
Interest Revenue		10,400
Loss on Sale of Equipment	1,800	
Merchandise Inventory	87,750	
Notes Payable		46,800
Preferred Stock		140,000
Property, Plant and Equipment	171,600	
Rent Expense	64,350	
Retained Earnings		5,784
Salaries Expense	70,200	
Salaries Payable		33,150
Sales Returns	11,700	
Sales Revenue		390,000
Short-Term Investment	27,300	
Unearned Revenue		48,360
Utilities Expense	54,600	
Total	**$928,180**	**$928,180**

Additional Information
- Net income for the year was $34,730 and retained earnings at January 1, 2018 was $70,484. Dividends of $64,700 were declared and paid in the year.
- Busy Town has a long-term notes payable that is due in four years. The principal payments are $975 per month.
- Preferred shares are $100 par value and pay noncumulative dividends of 10%; 95,000 shares have been authorized and 1,400 shares are issued and outstanding. For common stock, 200,000 shares have been authorized and 10,000 shares have been issued.

Prepare a classified balance sheet as at December 31, 2018 under US GAAP.

AP-11B LO 2 3 5

Below is the adjusted trial balance for Excel Network Inc. as at December 31, 2018. Assume a tax rate of 30%.

Excel Network Inc.		
Adjusted Trial Balance		
December 31, 2018		
Account Title	**Debit**	**Credit**
Cash and Cash Equivalents	$84,000	
Accounts Receivable	189,000	
Merchandise Inventory	210,000	
Prepaid Rent	9,240	
Property, Plant and Equipment	43,000	
Accumulated Depreciation		$15,050
Accounts Payable		38,000
Unearned Revenue		35,625
Interest Payable		8,925
Salaries Payable		28,500
Notes Payable		105,000
Preferred Stock		60,000
Common Stock		100,000
Additional Paid-In Capital		20,000
Retained Earnings (after dividends)		115,740
Sales Revenue		475,000
Sales Returns & Allowances	19,000	
Cost of Goods Sold	166,250	
Depreciation Expense—Retail Equipment	3,000	
Depreciation Expense—Office Equipment	1,515	
Sales Salaries Expense	109,250	
Office Salaries Expense	26,125	
Interest Expense	12,935	
Rent Expense—Retail	30,875	
Rent Expense—Office	37,050	
Advertising Expense	57,000	
Income Tax Expense	3,600	
Total	**$1,001,840**	**$1,001,840**

Required

a) Prepare a multiple-step income statement for the year ended December 31, 2018 under US GAAP. Ignore earnings per share.

b) The retained earnings at January 1, 2018 were $164,240 and dividends of $48,500 were declared in the year. Prepare a statement of retained earnings for the year ended December 31, 2018.

c) Prepare a classified balance sheet as at December 31, 2018. Additional information as of December 31, 2018 is as follows.

- The notes payable are due over eight years and nine months. The principal payments are $1,000 for each month.
- Preferred stock: $100 par value, cumulative dividend of 10%, 100,000 shares authorized, 600 shares have been issued and are outstanding
- Common stock: $1 par value, unlimited number of shares authorized, 100,000 shares have been issued and are outstanding

AP-12B LO 6 7

Shown below is a section of the statement of financial position of You Co.

Stockholders' Equity	
Common Stock, unlimited shares authorized, 562,652 shares issued and outstanding	$2,169,856
Retained Earnings	1,733,427
Accumulated Other Comprehensive Income	30,283
Total Stockholders' Equity	3,933,566
Total Liabilities and Stockholders' Equity	$5,511,187

Required

a) Calculate the book value per share for 2018.

Stockholders' Equity	
Shares—End of Year	
Book Value per Share	

b) Calculate the earnings per share for You Co. if it earned $1,293,897 of net income. Assume that the number of common shares remains unchanged throughout the year.

_____

_____

Analysis

In this chapter, you have learned how to calculate earnings per share. Often, a corporation's annual report will report earnings per share as calculated by the corporation. Rarely do the corporation's reported earnings per share agree with a financial analyst's calculation of this number. Discuss why these two calculations may differ.

AP-13B LO 6 7

Marry Inc. provided the following information from its accounting records for the years ending December 31, 2019 and 2018.

	2019	2018
Income from continuing operations (net of tax)	$840,000	$740,000
Income from discontinued operations (net of tax)	150,000	70,000
Net income	990,000	810,000
Each year, 100,000 common shares were outstanding	1,000,000	1,000,000
Beginning retained earnings	1,990,000	1,580,000
Current liabilities	560,000	420,000
Long-term liabilities	980,000	760,000
Market price per share	15	13
Total dividends paid	500,000	400,000

No shares were issued or redeemed during the two years. The company has never issued any preferred stock.

Required

Calculate the following ratios for both years.

a) EPS

	2019	2018
EPS		

b) Dividend Yield

	2019	2018
Dividend Yield		

c) Price-Earnings Ratio

	2019	2018
Price-Earnings Ratio		

d) Book Value per Common Share

	2019	2018
Book Value per Common Share		

Analysis

Price-earnings ratio (or P/E ratio) is generally regarded by many investors as a reliable indicator of a stock's potential growth in the future. One of your clients just told you that a stock he invested in had a significant growth in the P/E ratio, yet the price of that share has not changed. How would you explain to him why the P/E ratio increases without an increase in the share price?

_____

_____

_____

_____

AP-14B LO 2 3 5

Below is the adjusted trial balance for Elements Inc. as at March 31, 2018.

Elements Inc. Adjusted Trial Balance March 31, 2018		
Account Title	**Debit**	**Credit**
Accounts Payable		$19,580
Accounts Receivable	$22,000	
Accumulated Depreciation		7,700
Additional Paid-In Capital		3,800
Cash and Cash Equivalents	18,700	
Common Stock		19,550
Cost of Goods Sold	37,400	
Depreciation Expense—Office Equipment	2,505	
Depreciation Expense—Retail Equipment	3,400	
Income Tax Benefit		810
Interest Payable		660
Interest Receivable	1,320	
Interest Revenue		2,640
Long-Term Investments	33,000	
Loss on Sale of Assets	1,485	
Merchandise Inventory	24,750	
Notes Payable		13,200
Office Salaries Expense	18,150	
Preferred Stock		18,000
Prepaid Insurance	7,700	
Property, Plant and Equipment	49,500	
Rent Expense—Office	9,900	
Rent Expense—Retail	15,400	
Retained Earnings (after dividends)		53,380
Salaries Payable		9,350
Sales Salaries Expense	23,800	
Sales Returns & Allowances	3,300	
Sales Revenue		110,000
Unearned Revenue		13,640
Total	**$272,310**	**$272,310**

a) Prepare a multiple-step income statement for the year ended March 31, 2018 under US GAAP.

b) Retained earnings at April 1, 2017 had a credit balance of $67,530 and dividends of $14,150 were declared and paid in the year. Prepare a statement of retained earnings for the year ended March 31, 2018.

c) Prepare a classified balance sheet as at March 31, 2018. Additional information as of March 31, 2018 is as follows.
  - The notes payable is due over four years. The principal payments are $275 each month.
  - Preferred stock, 5%, $100 par value, noncumulative, 40,000 shares authorized, 180 shares issued and outstanding
  - Common stock: $1 par value, 21,000 shares authorized, 19,550 shares issued and outstanding

d) If the company had followed IFRS, would the statement of retained earnings be the same as part b)? Explain.

_____

_____

_____

AP-15B LO 2 3 6

The following information was taken from the accounting records of Cutler Inc. at December 31, 2018. Cutler Inc. prepares statements according to US GAAP.

Line Item	Amount
Prior-year error—debit to retained earnings	$15,000
Income tax expense	84,000
Total dividends	67,000
Common stock, $10 par value, 1,000,000 shares authorized, 20,100 shares issued	201,000
Sales revenue	605,000
Interest expense	17,000
Income from operating discontinued operations	56,000
Loss due to lawsuit	16,000
Sales discounts	30,000
Selling expenses	10,000
Administrative expenses	13,000
Preferred stock, noncumulative, 10%, $100 par value, 10,000 shares authorized, 600 shares issued	60,000
Retained earnings, January 1, 2018 (prior to adjustment)	135,000
Loss on sale of discontinued operations	25,000
Cost of goods sold	310,000

Assume a tax rate of 35%. During the year, no shares were issued or redeemed. Preferred dividends were paid in full.

Required

a) Prepare an income statement for the year ended December 31, 2018.

b) Prepare a statement of retained earnings for Cutler Inc. for the year ended December 31, 2018.

c) Calculate the EPS ratio.

_____

_____

_____

d) If Cutler Inc. had followed IFRS, what would have been the amount of other comprehensive income for the year?

_____

_____

_____

_____

_____

_____

_____

_____

_____

_____

_____

_____

_____

_____

_____

_____

_____

_____

_____

Case Study

CS-1 LO 2 3 4 5 6 7

Kruma Company sells clothes and fashion accessories through its chain of retail stores. The stockholders' equity section of Kruma Company's statement of financial position as at December 31, 2018 shows the following information.

Kruma Company Statement of Financial Position (partial) As at December 31, 2018	
Stockholders' Equity	
Paid-In Capital	
Preferred stock, noncumulative, 10%, $100 par value, 150,000 shares	
authorized, 12,000 shares issued and outstanding	$1,200,000
Common stock, $1 par value, unlimited shares authorized,	
400,000 shares issued and outstanding	400,000
Additional Paid-In Capital	1,200,000
Total Paid-In Capital	2,800,000
Retained Earnings	1,500,000
Total Stockholders' Equity	4,300,000

On January 28, 2019, Kruma discovered an accounting mistake made in 2018. Accrual of interest revenue was understated by $54,000 because interest receivable and interest revenue of $60,000 were mistakenly recorded as $6,000.

During 2019, Kruma earned and incurred the following revenue and expenses (excluding income tax expenses). Kruma's tax rate is 30%.

Sales Revenue	$1,785,000
Interest Revenue	45,000
Unrealized Gain on Trading Investments	12,000
Gain on Sale of Discontinued Operations	90,000
Loss on Sale of Assets from Continuing Operations	16,000
Loss on Foreign Currency Translation	30,000
Loss from Operating Discontinued Operations	200,000
Cost of Goods Sold	966,000
Selling Expenses	250,000
Administrative Expenses	253,000
Interest Expense	1,000

On October 1, 2019, Kruma issued an additional 20,000 common shares for $100,000. There was no other change in the number of common or preferred shares. Kruma paid $120,000 dividends to preferred stockholders, but no dividend to common stockholders in 2019. The preferred shares are not convertible. The company does not have any outstanding securities that can be converted into common shares.

Required

a) Record the journal entry to correct the mistake related to the understatement of interest receivable and interest revenue in 2018.

Date	Account Title and Explanation	Debit	Credit

b) Prepare a statement of comprehensive income under US GAAP for Kruma for the year ended December 31, 2019. Show detailed calculations of weighted average number of common shares and earnings per share in the space provided on the next page. Present the basic and diluted earnings per share calculated based on net income (loss) at the bottom of the statement of comprehensive income. Do not separate earnings per share into continuing operations and discontinued operations.

Date 2019	Actual Number of Shares	Fraction of Year	Weighted Average Number of Shares

_____

_____

_____

_____

_____

_____

_____

_____

_____

_____

c) Prepare a statement of comprehensive income by function under IFRS for Kruma for the year ended December 31, 2019. Present the basic and diluted earnings per share calculated based on net income (loss) at the bottom of the statement of comprehensive income. Do not separate earnings per share into continuing operations and discontinued operations.

d) Prepare a statement of retained earnings under US GAAP for Kruma for the year ended December 31, 2019.

e) Prepare a statement of changes in equity under IFRS for Kruma for the year ended December 31, 2019.

f) Prepare the stockholders' equity section of Kruma's balance sheet under US GAAP as at December 31, 2019.

g) Prepare the stockholders' equity section of Kruma's statement of financial position under IFRS as at December 31, 2019.

h) In the table below, calculate the given ratios for Kruma's common shares as at December 31, 2019. Assume that the market price of Kruma's common shares on that day is equal to $4.50.

Book Value per Common Share	
Dividend Yield	
Price-Earnings Ratio	

Critical Thinking

CT-1  LO 2 3 5 6 7

One of the most common methods of committing accounting fraud is by manipulating financial statements to overstate revenue (or profit) and understate expenses (or losses). WorldCom is perhaps one of the most famous cases of this type of fraud. In 2003, the company reported that it had overstated earnings and understated expenses for a total value of $74.5 billion.

One of the primary methods it used was to classify regular operating expenses as capital expenditure (also known as capital investment). By doing that, it allowed the company to amortize operating expenses over several financial periods.

Required

a) Discuss the impact this activity would have on the statement of comprehensive income and statement of financial positions, by specifying which item would be overstated or understated. Fill in your answer in the provided table.

Statement Name	Item	Overstated or Understated
Statement of Comprehensive Income	Operational Expenses	
	Depreciation and Amortization Expenses	
	Net Income	
	Tax Expense	
	Earnings Per Share	
Statement of Financial Position	Noncurrent Assets	
	Accumulated Depreciation and Amortization	
	Retained Earnings	

b) Discuss what impact this activity would have on the ratios used to evaluate earnings and dividend performance, by specifying if the ratio would be overstated or understated (assuming all other factors remain unchanged).

_____

_____

_____

_____

_____

_____

_____

_____

_____

_____

_____

_____

_____

_____

_____

_____

_____

Chapter 17

LONG-TERM LIABILITIES

LEARNING OBJECTIVES

LO 1 State the characteristics and different types of bonds

LO 2 Apply the concept of present value

LO 3 Record bonds issued at par

LO 4 Record bonds issued at a discount or a premium

LO 5 Record the retirement of bonds

LO 6 Record installment notes payable

LO 7 Describe how long-term liabilities are analyzed and presented on the balance sheet

LO 8 Apply controls and ethics related to long-term liabilities

Appendix

LO 9 Describe the effective interest amortization method

AMEENGAGE™ *Access **ameengage.com** for integrated resources including tutorials, practice exercises, the digital textbook and more.*

───── Assessment Questions ─────

AS-1 LO 1

Name the typical forms of long-term debt.

_____

_____

AS-2 LO 1

What is a bond?

_____

_____

AS-3 LO 4

An investor pays $83,333 for a bond, but will receive $100,000 when the bond matures. Has the investor bought the bond at a discount or at a premium?

_____

_____

AS-4 LO 3 4

Bonds can be issued at different prices relative to their face value. Name and describe the three types of bonds relative to face value.

_____

_____

_____

AS-5 LO 4

When would a bond be issued at a discount? At a premium?

_____

_____

AS-6 `LO` `4`

A $100,000 bond is issued for $110,000. Is the current market interest rate for bonds above or below the rate stated in the bond contract?

_____

_____

AS-7 `LO` `4 5`

What amount remains in the discount on bonds account or premium on bonds account on the maturity date of the bond?

_____

_____

AS-8 `LO` `1`

What is financial leverage? Does higher financial leverage imply higher or lower risk and return?

_____

_____

_____

_____

AS-9 `LO` `1`

What are some differences between bonds and shares?

_____

_____

_____

_____

AS-10 `LO` `1`

What is a term bond?

_____

_____

AS-11 `LO` `1`

What is the main difference between a debenture and a mortgage bond?

_____

_____

_____

_____

AS-12 `LO` `1`

Define market interest rate.

_____

_____

AS-13 LO 2

If a company keeps money in a bank, the value of its money changes over time even if nothing is done to it. What is this phenomenon called?

_____

_____

AS-14 LO 2

Peter lent $100 to his friend Angela, who promised Peter that the principal would be repaid after two years, with 10% compound interest per annum. Two years later, Peter received $120 from Angela. Did Angela fulfill her promise to Peter? Why or why not?

_____

_____

_____

_____

_____

_____

AS-15 LO 2

A company invested $1,000,000 to buy a property. The appraiser estimated that the property will be worth $1,500,000 in five years. Which amount is the present value of the investment and which is the future value?

_____

_____

AS-16 LO 2

What is an annuity?

_____

AS-17 LO 4

Why should a company issue redeemable bonds?

_____

_____

_____

AS-18 LO 7

What is the condition that a note payable has to meet to be classified as a long-term note payable and where should it be shown on a balance sheet?

_____

_____

_____

AS-19 `LO 6`

What is referred to as an installment in notes payable?

_____

_____

_____

AS-20 `LO 7`

How is debt-to-total-assets ratio calculated? What does it measure?

_____

_____

_____

AS-21 `LO 7`

How is debt-to-equity ratio calculated? What does it measure?

_____

_____

_____

AS-22 `LO 8`

Provide an example of financial measurement that can be applied to control a company's ability to pay off its long-term debt.

_____

_____

_____

AS-23 `LO 9`

How is the effective interest amortization method different from the straight-line amortization method?

_____

_____

_____

_____

_____

_____

_____

_____

_____

_____

_____

Application Questions Group A

Note: Round all calculations and final answers to the nearest whole dollar. When needed, use the present value factors provided in the textbook.

AP-1A LO 2 4

On January 1, 2018, MT Biotech issued $3,500,000, 5% redeemable bonds due in 12 years. At the time of issue, the market interest rate is 6% (interest is due annually). Calculate the discount or premium at which the bonds were issued.

_____

_____

_____

_____

_____

_____

Analysis

If, after the issuance date, the market interest rate increases to 7%, how does this impact the interest expenses? Explain the impact the change in market interest rate has from the perspective of the company and of the investor.

_____

_____

_____

_____

_____

AP-2A LO 3

On September 1, 2018, Delia Company issued $264,000 worth of bonds at par, with an interest rate of 10% per annum. The bonds will mature on August 31, 2021. Interest will be paid annually on August 31. The company has a December 31 year end.

Calculate the accrued interest payable on December 31, 2018.

_____

_____

AP-3A LO 3 5

On April, 1, 2018, Medum Corporation issued a four-year bond worth $421,000 with an interest rate of 5% per annum. The bond was issued at par. Interest is to be paid semi-annually on September 30 and March 31, with a year end on March 31.

Required

a) Prepare the journal entry on April 1, 2018, to issue the bonds.

Date	Account Title and Explanation	Debit	Credit

b) Prepare the journal entry on April 1, 2022, to redeem the bonds at fair value.

Date	Account Title and Explanation	Debit	Credit

AP-4A LO 4

A company issued a $500,000 bond and received $475,000 cash on February 1. Write the journal entry to record the transaction.

Date	Account Title and Explanation	Debit	Credit

AP-5A LO 3

On April 30, 2018, a company issued $600,000 worth of 4% bonds at par. The term of the bonds is 10 years, with interest payable semi-annually on October 31 and April 30. The year end of the company is November 30. Record the journal entries related to interest for 2018 and 2019. Note that interest must be accrued at the end of each year.

Date	Account Title and Explanation	Debit	Credit

AP-6A LO 2 4

On January 1, 2018, Metro Inc. issued a five-year bond with a face value of $700,000. The bond bears an interest rate of 6% per annum, with the interest paid semi-annually. On January 1, 2018, the market interest rate was 8%.

Required

a) Calculate the amount of a bond discount or a bond premium.

b) Prepare the journal entry to record the sale of the bonds.

Date	Account Title and Explanation	Debit	Credit

AP-7A LO 3 5

On February 1, 2018, Smart Water Inc. issued $500,000 worth of bonds with a 7% interest rate. The bonds were issued at par. Interest is payable semi-annually on August 1 and February 1. The bonds mature on February 1, 2028. Smart Water Inc. has a September 30 year end.

Required

Prepare journal entries for the following.

a)   The issuance of the bonds payable on February 1, 2018

b)   The payment of interest on August 1, 2018

c)   The required adjusting entry on September 30, 2018

d)   The payment of interest on February 1, 2019

e)   The maturity of the bond on February 1, 2028 assuming the interest has already been paid.

Date	Account Title	Debit	Credit

AP-8A LO 3 5

On June 1, 2018, Glacier Inc. issued $100,000 worth of bonds with a 6% interest rate. The bonds were issued at par. Interest is payable semi-annually on December 1 and June 1. The bonds mature on June 1, 2038. Glacier Inc. has a December 31 year end.

Required

Prepare journal entries to record the following.

a) The issuance of the bonds on June 1, 2018
b) The payment of interest on December 1, 2018
c) The required adjustment on December 31, 2018
d) The payment of interest on June 1, 2019
e) The maturity of the bonds on June 1, 2038, assuming the interest has already been paid.

Date	Account Title and Explanation	Debit	Credit

AP-9A LO 4 9

A company is issuing $300,000 worth of five-year bonds on January 1, 2018, bearing an interest rate of 4%, payable annually. Assume that the current market rate of interest is 5%.

Required

a) Will the bond be issued at a discount or at a premium?

_____

_____

b) Calculate the value of the resulting discount or premium.

_____

_____

_____

c) Record the journal entry to reflect the sale of bonds and the appropriate discount or premium.

Date	Account Title and Explanation	Debit	Credit

d) Assuming interest is paid annually on December 31, write the journal entry to record payment of interest if the straight-line method for amortization of bond discount or premium is used.

Date	Account Title and Explanation	Debit	Credit

e) Assuming interest is paid annually on December 31, write the journal entry to record payment of interest if the effective interest method for amortizing bond discount or premium is used.

Date	Account Title and Explanation	Debit	Credit

_____

_____

Analysis

If, after the issuance date, the market interest rate increases to 6%, how will this change how the interest expense is recorded?

_____

_____

AP-10A LO 4 9

On April 1, 2018, Hamsar Inc. issued a five-year, 8% bond of $500,000 for the premium price of $542,651. Interest is to be paid semi-annually on October 1 and April 1. The company's year end is December 31. Assume the market rate of interest was 6% on the issuance date.

Required

a) Prepare an amortization schedule for the first four interest periods using the straight-line amortization method.

Semi-Annual Interest Period	A Interest Payment	B Interest Expense	C Premium Amortization	D Bond Amortized Cost

b) Prepare an amortization schedule for the first four interest periods using the effective interest amortization method.

Semi-Annual Interest Period	A Interest Payment	B Interest Expense	C Premium Amortization	D Bond Book Value

Analysis

Would the total cash payment for interest be different from the total interest expenses recorded over the term of the bonds? Explain.

_____

_____

_____

_____

_____

AP-11A LO 4 7 9

Burroughs Corporation (with a December 31 year end) issued $450,000, 9.5% bonds due in eight years on May 1, 2018. Interest is paid semi-annually on November 1 and May 1 of each year. On the issuance date, the market rate of interest was 8.5%, resulting in a price of $475,746 for these bonds.

Note: The premium/discount is amortized using the straight-line method.

a) Is this bond issued at a discount or at a premium? Prepare the journal entry on May 1, 2018, to record the issue of the bonds.

_____

_____

Date	Account Title and Explanation	Debit	Credit

b) Prepare the journal entry on November 1, 2018, to record the first interest payment assuming the straight-line method for amortization of bond discount/premium is used.

Date	Account Title and Explanation	Debit	Credit

c) Prepare the adjusting entry on December 31, 2018 assuming the straight-line method for amortization of bond discount/premium is used.

Date	Account Title and Explanation	Debit	Credit

d) Show the balance sheet presentation of bonds payable and related accounts as at December 31, 2018.

e) If the effective interest method was used, what would be the amounts debited to Interest Expense and Premium on Bonds Payable on November 1, 2018?

AP-12A LO 2 4 5

Fountain Hills Corporation is planning to build a new arena for the community. To complete the project, the company is issuing $3,000,000 worth of five-year, 10% bonds with interest paid semi-annually.

On May 1, 2018, the company completed all the necessary paperwork and is now ready to issue the bonds. The market rate on the date of issuance is 8%. The company uses the straight-line method to amortize any premiums or discounts.

Required

Record journal entries for the following items. Round all amounts to the nearest whole dollar.

a) The issuance of the bonds on May 1, 2018 (Hint: This will require the calculation of the premium/discount.)
b) The payment of interest on October 31, 2018.
c) The necessary adjusting entries at the company's December 31, 2018 year end.
d) The payment of interest on April 30, 2019.
e) The retirement of the bonds on May 1, 2023 (assume interest has already been paid).

Date	Account Title and Explanation	Debit	Credit

AP-13A LO 2 4 5

Wilson Corp. is planning to build a new tennis court for the community. To complete the project, the company is issuing $1,000,000 worth of five-year, 10% bonds with interest paid semi-annually.

On May 1, 2018, the company issued the bonds. The market rate on the date of issuance was 12%.

Required

Record journal entries for the following items. Use the straight-line method to amortize any premiums/discounts. Round all amounts to the nearest whole dollar.

a) The issuance of the bond on May 1, 2018. (Hint: This will require the calculation of the premium/discount.)
b) The payment of interest on October 31, 2018.
c) The necessary adjusting entries at the company's December 31, 2018 year end.
d) The payment of interest on April 30, 2019.
e) The retirement of the bonds on May 1, 2023 (assume interest has already been paid).

Date	Account Title and Explanation	Debit	Credit

AP-14A LO 2 4

On July 1, 2018, Marky Corporation issued $1,500,000 worth of bonds with 9% interest rate. Interest is payable semi-annually on June 30 and December 31. The bonds mature on June 30, 2025. At the time of the bond issuance, the market interest rate was 8%. Any discount or premium resulting from the sale of the bonds will be amortized using the straight-line method. The company's year end is March 31.

Required

a) Calculate the total price of the bonds on the issue date and determine the amount of a bond discount or a bond premium.

b) Prepare the journal entries to record the issuance of the bond and the first interest payment.

Date	Account Title and Explanation	Debit	Credit

c) Prepare the journal entry required on March 31, 2019.

Date	Account Title and Explanation	Debit	Credit

d)   Prepare the journal entry required on June 30, 2019.

Date	Account Title and Explanation	Debit	Credit

e)   Calculate the book value (carrying amount) of bonds payable at December 31, 2018.

AP-15A LO 7

On January 1, 2017, Sedar Co. issued a five-year, 8% installment note payable for $120,000 to finance upgrading its current equipment. The company's year end is December 31. The repayment of $14,795 is done semi-annually on January 1 and July 1.

Required

a)   Assume an equal installment amount of $14,795, fill in the following table and determine the total interest expense incurred over the five-year term.

Interest Period	A Cash Payment	B Interest Expense (D × 8% × 1/2)	C Reduction of Principal (A − B)	D Principal Balance (D − C)

b) Present interest payable and notes payable on the partial balance sheet as at December 31, 2019 using the numbers calculated in part a). Assume that accounts payable balance as at December 31, 2019 is $50,000 and that Sedar has no other liabilities.

c) Assuming Sedar has total assets of $455,000, calculate the debt-to-total-assets ratio and the debt-to-equity ratio for 2019. Comment on the results.

AP-16A LO 6

Evans Ltd. decides to issue a three-year, $150,000 installment note payable on January 1, 2018 to finance the purchase of lab equipment, with an interest rate of 6%. The repayment is done annually on its year-end date of December 31.

Required

a) Calculate the annual installment payments.

b) Show the note's cash payment, interest expense, reduction of principal and principal balance by filling in the table below.

Date	A Cash Payment	B Interest Expense	C Reduction of Principal	D Principal Balance

c) Prepare journal entries to record issuing the note payable and all payments for 2018, 2019 and 2020.

Date	Account Title and Explanation	Debit	Credit

AP-17A LO 6

Aidan's Inc. is looking to replace its old delivery truck, which constantly breaks down. It just happens that one of its suppliers has a slightly used delivery truck for sale. Because Aidan's Inc. has been doing business with this supplier for many years, the supplier offers Aidan's a great deal.

The supplier will sell the truck to Aidan's for $68,000 on January 1, 2018 and issue a five-year installment note payable at 3% interest. Installment payments of $7,374 are made semi-annually.

Prepare a table to calculate the total interest paid over the life of the note.

Round all amounts to the nearest whole dollar.

	A	B	C	D
Date	Cash Payment	Interest Expense	Reduction of Principal	Principal Balance

Application Questions Group B

Note: Round all calculations and final answers to the nearest whole dollar. When needed, use the present value factors provided in the textbook.

AP-1B LO 2 4

On January 1, 2018, Bootic Inc. issued $3,500,000, 6% redeemable bonds due in 12 years. At the time of issue, the market interest rate is 5% (interest is due annually). Calculate the discount or premium at which the bonds were issued. The company's year end is December 31.

AP-2B LO 3

On April 1, 2018, Dixon Company issued $300,000 worth of bonds at par, with the interest rate of 12% per annum. The bonds will mature on March 31, 2025. Interest will be paid semi-annually on September 30 and March 31. The company has a December 31 year end. Calculate the accrued interest payable on December 31, 2019.

AP-3B LO 3

A company issued $502,000 worth of bonds at par on July 4, 2018. Write the journal entry to record the transaction.

Date	Account Title and Explanation	Debit	Credit

AP-4B LO 4

A company issued a $500,000 bond and received $525,000 cash on August 1, 2018. Write the journal entry to record the transaction.

Date	Account Title and Explanation	Debit	Credit

AP-5B LO 3

On April 30, 2018, a company issued $588,000 worth of 9% bonds at par. The term of the bonds is seven years, with interest payable semi-annually on October 31 and April 30. The year end of the company is November 30. Record the journal entries related to interest for 2018 and 2019. Note that interest must be accrued at the end of each year.

Date	Account Title and Explanation	Debit	Credit

AP-6B LO 4

On July 1, 2018, Dilly Company received $562,316 cash for the sale of a 10-year bond with a face value of $500,000. The bond bears an interest rate of 12%, to be paid semi-annually. At the time of the sale, the market interest rate was 10%. The year end is December 31. Prepare a journal entry to record the issuance of bond.

Date	Account Title and Explanation	Debit	Credit

AP-7B LO 3 5

On May 1, 2018, Sweet Lily Flower Inc. issued $30,000 worth of bonds with a 5% interest rate. The bonds were issued at par. Interest is payable semi-annually on November 1 and May 1. The bonds mature on May 1, 2028. Sweet Lily Flower Inc. has a December 31 year end.

Required

Prepare the journal entries to record the following.

a)   The issuance of the bonds payable on May 1, 2018.

b)   The payment of interest on November 1, 2018.

c)   The required adjusting entry on December 31, 2018.

d)   The payment of interest on May 1, 2019.

e)   The maturity of the bond on May 1, 2028 assuming the interest has already been paid.

Date	Account Title and Explanation	Debit	Credit

AP-8B LO 3 5

On November 1, 2018, Breyer Inc. issued $800,000 worth of bonds with a 9% interest rate. The bonds were issued at par. Interest is payable annually on October 31. The bonds mature on October 31, 2028. Breyer Inc. has a December 31 year end.

Required

Prepare the necessary journal entries to record the following.

a)   The issuance of the bonds payable on November 1, 2018.

b)   The required adjustment on December 31, 2018.

c)   The payment of interest on October 31, 2019.

d)   The maturity of the bond on October 31, 2028 with interest.

Date	Account Title and Explanation	Debit	Credit

AP-9B LO 2 3 4

A company issued $1,200,000 worth of 15-year bonds with a 3% interest rate. Interest is to be paid annually. The bond issue date is January 1, 2018 and the company has a year end of December 31.

Required

a) Calculate the bond issue price under each market interest rate.

Market Interest Rate	Bond Price
2%	
3%	
4%	

b)   For each market condition, prepare a journal entry to record the bond issuance.

Market Interest Rate—2%

Date	Account Title and Explanation	Debit	Credit

Market Interest Rate—3%

Date	Account Title and Explanation	Debit	Credit

Market Interest Rate—4%

Date	Account Title and Explanation	Debit	Credit

AP-10B LO 4

On July 1, 2018, Den Inc. issued a seven-year, 10% bond of $500,000 for the discount price of $453,525. Interest is to be paid semi-annually on June 30 and December 31. The company's year end is July 31. Prepare an amortization schedule for the first four interest periods. Assume the market rate of interest was 12% on the issuance date and the discount is amortized using the straight-line method.

Semi-Annual Interest Period	A Interest Payment	B Interest Expense	C Discount Amortization	D Bond Book Value

Analysis

Explain why the total interest expense is greater than the total cash payment for interest.

_____

_____

_____

AP-11B LO 7 9

Sam's Construction is a construction company (with a December 31 year end) that is planning to expand its facilities by constructing a new building and acquiring new equipment. To complete this project, the company has decided to issue $100,000 worth of 10-year bonds at 5% on March 1, 2018. The interest payment is made semi-annually on September 1 and March 1. Just as the company completes all the necessary contracts, and is ready to issue the bonds, the market rate increases to 6%, resulting in a price of $92,564 for these bonds.

Note: The premium/discount is amortized using the effective interest method.

Required

a) Are these bonds issued at a discount or at a premium? Prepare the journal entry for the issuance of bonds on March 1, 2018.

Date	Account Title and Explanation	Debit	Credit

b) Prepare the journal entry for the first payment of interest on September 1, 2018.

Date	Account Title and Explanation	Debit	Credit

c) Prepare the adjusting entry on December 31, 2018.

Date	Account Title and Explanation	Debit	Credit

d) Show the balance sheet presentation of Bonds Payable and related accounts as at December 31, 2018.

AP-12B LO 2 4 5

Phillips Corporation is planning to expand into a new product line. To do this, the company has decided to issue $200,000 worth of five-year, 6% bonds with interest paid annually.

On June 1, 2018, the company completed all the necessary paperwork and is now ready to issue the bonds. The market rate on the date of issuance is 5%. Use the straight-line method to amortize any premiums/discounts.

Required

Record the journal entries for the following items. Round all amounts to the nearest whole dollar.

a) The issuance of the bond on June 1, 2018. (Hint: This will require the calculation of the premium/discount.)
b) The necessary adjusting entries at the company's December 31, 2018 year end.
c) The payment of interest on May 31, 2019.
d) The retirement of the bonds on June 1, 2023 (assume interest has already been paid).

Date	Account Title and Explanation	Debit	Credit

AP-13B LO 2 5 9

Watson Corporation is planning to expand into a new product line. To complete the expansion, the company has decided to issue $200,000 worth of five-year, 3% bonds with interest paid annually.

On June 1, 2018, the company issued the bonds. The market rate on the date of issuance was 4%. Use the effective interest method to amortize any premiums/discounts.

Required

Record the journal entries for the following items. Round all amounts to the nearest whole dollar.

a) The issuance of the bond on June 1, 2018. (Hint: This will require the calculation of the premium/discount.)
b) The necessary adjusting entries at the company's December 31, 2018 year end.
c) The payment of interest on May 31, 2019.
d) The retirement of the bonds on June 1, 2023 (assume interest has already been paid).

Date	Account Title and Explanation	Debit	Credit

AP-14B LO 2 5 9

On May 1, 2018, Ezzy Company issued a six-year bond worth $400,000 with an interest rate of 8% per annum. Interest is to be paid semi-annually on October 31 and April 30. At the time of the issuance, the market interest rate was 6%. Ezzy Company amortizes any premium or discount using the effective interest method.

Required

a) Calculate the bond issue price and the resulting premium or discount.

b) Prepare journal entries to record the following bonds payable transactions.

1) Issuance of bonds on May 1, 2018.
2) Payment of interest and amortization of premium on October 31, 2018.
3) Accrual of interest and amortization of premium on December 31, 2018, which is the company's year end.
4) Payment of interest and amortization of premium on April 30, 2019.
5) Redemption of the bond for $406,000 on May 1, 2023 (one year before maturity).

Date	Account Title and Explanation	Debit	Credit

AP-15B LO 7

On December 31, 2018, Shima Company issued a four-year, 12% installment note payable for $400,000 to finance an additional product line. The company's year end is December 31. The repayment is done quarterly starting from March 31. Present how the current and long-term sections for this note payable would be shown on the partial balance sheet as of December 31, 2019. Assume an equal installment amount of $31,844 is determined per quarter.

Interest Period	A Cash Payment	B Interest Expense $(D \times 12\% \times \frac{1}{4})$	C Reduction of Principal $(A - B)$	D Principal Balance $(D - C)$

Analysis

Shima Company is concerned that it is paying more interest than it should be on its loan. Explain how the interest portion of the blended payment is calculated each period.

AP-16B LO 6

On January 1, 2018, Hala Ltd. issued a three-year, $200,000 installment note payable to finance the purchase of factory equipment, with an interest rate of 5%. The repayment is done annually on December 31.

Required

a)   Calculate the annual installment payments.

b) Show the note's cash payment, interest expense, reduction of principal and principal balance by filling in the table below.

Date	A Cash Payment	B Interest Expense	C Reduction of Principal	D Principal Balance

b) Prepare journal entries from January 1 to December 31, 2018. Assume the company's year end is June 30.

Date	Account Titles and Explanations	Debit	Credit

AP-17B LO 7

Bristol Company has $316,000 in total liabilities and total assets of $855,000. Calculate the debt-to-total-assets and debt-to-equity ratios and explain the meaning of the results.

Case Study

CS-1 LO 1 2 4

You & Us Company issued a redeemable six-year, $1,000,000 bond on December 1, 2015. The interest rate was 4% per year and interest payment would be made semi-annually. In 2015, similar bonds were paying 6% interest on average.

On December 1, 2018, the average market interest rate for similar bonds had decreased to 2%. You & Us Company decided to redeem all the outstanding bonds issued in 2015 and issue new bonds. The new bonds will also have an annual interest rate of 4%. You & Us Company's fiscal year end is on December 31.

In 2015, You & Us Company hired a bookkeeper, who did not have a professional accounting designation. The bookkeeper recorded the journal entries for the issuance of the bond and the two payments of interest in 2016, which are all shown below.

Date	Account Title and Explanation	Debit	Credit
2015			
Dec 1	Cash	900,480	
	Discount on Bonds Payable	99,520	
	Bonds Payable		1,000,000
	To record issuing of $1,000,000 bonds at discount		
Dec 31	No journal entry on issued bonds		
2016			
Jun 1	Interest Expense	20,000	
	Cash		20,000
	To record interest payment on bonds		
Dec 1	Interest Expense	20,000	
	Cash		20,000
	Record interest payment on bonds		
Dec 31	No journal entry on issued bonds		

Required

a) In January 2017, an auditor found errors relating to the bond transactions from 2015 and 2016. What adjustment is required to correct those errors, and what is the correct balance on the discount on bonds account? Assume the company uses the straight-line method to amortize discounts and premiums.

Date	A Cash Payment	B Interest Expense	C Reduction of Principal	D Principal Balance

_____

_____

_____

_____

_____

_____

b) Calculate the value of the new bonds issued on December 1, 2018 to replace the bonds issued in 2015. The new three-year $1,000,000 bonds pay 4% interest annually with semi-annual payments. The current market rate is 2%.

_____

_____

_____

_____

_____

_____

_____

_____

_____

_____

_____

_____

_____

_____

Critical Thinking

CT-1 LO 2 4

When it comes to bonds, IFRS requires using the effective interest method while GAAP allows the straight-line method if the results do not differ significantly. Which method do you recommend for a private company following GAAP? Support your answer.

Notes

Chapter 18

INVESTMENTS

LEARNING OBJECTIVES

LO 1 Describe and classify different types of investments

LO 2 Prepare journal entries for debt investments

LO 3 Prepare journal entries for equity investments

LO 4 Describe how the different types of investments are presented in the financial statements

AMEENGAGE™ Access **ameengage.com** for integrated resources including tutorials, practice exercises, the digital textbook and more.

━━━━━ Assessment Questions ━━━━━

AS-1 LO 1

How is a short-term investment different from a long-term investment? Explain how short-term investments are classified on a balance sheet.

_____

_____

_____

_____

AS-2 LO 1 4

Explain how long-term investments are reported on a balance sheet. Name a few long-term investments.

_____

_____

_____

_____

AS-3 LO 1

Ava Company issues 10-year, $1,000,000 term bonds paying 3% semi-annual interest. Bea Company purchased 20% of these term bonds on the issuance date. Which company is the investor and which company is the investee?

_____

_____

AS-4 LO 1

What is an investment in debt instruments?

_____

_____

AS-5 LO 1

What is an investment in equity instruments?

_____

AS-6 LO 1

Sometimes terms are used such as debt or equity instruments versus debt or equity securities. What is the difference between a security and an instrument?

_____

_____

AS-7 LO 1

What are the three debt investment categories according to GAAP?

_____

_____

AS-8 LO 1

What are the two main categories of equity investments?

_____

_____

AS-9 LO 1

Why may a company want to invest in another corporation for strategic reasons?

_____

_____

_____

AS-10 LO 1

What does an equity investment with a significant influence mean? Which method is used to account for it?

_____

_____

_____

AS-11 LO 1

What does an equity investment with a controlling influence mean? Which method is used to account for it?

_____

_____

_____

AS-12 LO 2

What is a trading investment? Is it a debt or equity investment?

_____

_____

AS-13 LO 2

Why are money market instruments, such as a treasury bill (T-bill), term deposit or money market fund considered short-term debt instruments?

_____

_____

AS-14 `LO` `2`

How are trading securities accounted for and reported?

_____

_____

AS-15 `LO` `3`

On January 1, 2018, Meltam Company purchased 30% of the outstanding shares of common stock of Nitsuga Company at $65 per share. The investment has given Meltam significant influence. At year end, the price has gone up to $67 per share. How should Meltam record this price adjustment?

_____

_____

AS-16 `LO` `2`

How is fair value adjustment recorded and reported on the investor's income statement under the fair value through net income method for a trading security?

_____

_____

_____

_____

_____

AS-17 `LO` `3`

Determine the level of influence that the investor has over the investee at 7%, 21% and 51% of ownership.

Percentage of Ownership by Investor	Investor's Level of Influence on Investee
7%	
21%	
51%	

AS-18 `LO` `2`

Discuss the main difference between the fair value through net income method and the fair value through other comprehensive income method.

_____

_____

_____

AS-19 `LO` `2`

Are held-to-maturity (HTM) investments debt or equity instruments? How are they accounted for?

_____

_____

AS-20 `LO` `3`

Under the equity method, net profit from the investee company is recorded proportionately as part of the investment revenue for the investor. When the investor company receives cash dividend from the investee, which account should be credited?

_____

Application Questions Group A

AP-1A LO 1

Affy Company makes some investments in 2018. Complete the following table for each of the investments.

Investments	Non-Strategic or Strategic Investment	Current or Noncurrent Assets	Accounting Treatment
A one-year treasury bill purchased on November 15, 2018 that Affy plans to hold for interest revenue until maturity.			
A two-year provincial bond purchased on April 1, 2018 that Affy is planning to sell before the year end of December 31, 2018.			
A five-year bond issued by a private business on November 1, 2018 that Affy is planning to hold for longer than a year, but will most likely sell before the maturity date.			
51% of common stock of Smith Company purchased on November 2, 2018 with controlling influence over the investee.			
6% of common stock of John Company purchased on December 2, 2018, which Affy is planning to hold for a short period of time before selling to make a profit.			
45% of common stock of Steve Company, with which Affy has just signed a long-term business alliance agreement.			

AP-2A LO 2

Kaman Company paid $200,000 to purchase a portfolio of debt securities on March 1, 2018. Management's intention is to hold them as available-for-sale securities for shorter than one year. The management does not intend to hold any debt securities until their maturity in this portfolio.

Required

a) What kind of accounting methods should be considered to record this investment?

_____

_____

b) Prepare the journal entry to record the purchase of these debt securities.

Date	Account Title and Explanation	Debit	Credit

c) On March 15, 2018, Kaman received interest of $1,000 from the debt securities in this portfolio. Prepare the journal entry to record the receipt of interest.

Date	Account Title and Explanation	Debit	Credit

d) The fair value of the portfolio at Kaman's year end on March 31, 2018 was $208,000. Prepare the journal entry to record the fair value adjustment.

Date	Account Title and Explanation	Debit	Credit

e) On April 20, 2018, Kaman sold half of the securities in this portfolio for $110,000. Prepare the journal entry to record the sale.

Date	Account Title and Explanation	Debit	Credit

AP-3A LO 1 2

Feng Inc. is planning to purchase $250,000 worth of six-year bonds issued by George Company, a publicly traded company on January 1, 2018 at par. The interest rate of the bonds is 3% annually; payments are made semi-annually on June 30 and December 31 every year. Feng Inc. has a December 31 year end.

Required

a) If Feng's investment goal is to hold the bonds until maturity, which valuation method should be used in recording these bonds?

_____

_____

b) Prepare journal entries for the bonds' acquisition, the first interest payment and retirement of the bonds on January 1, 2024.

Date	Account Title and Explanation	Debit	Credit

AP-4A LO 1 2

Jenny Company, a public company, paid $5,000,000 to purchase a portfolio of debt securities on March 1, 2018. As part of the recent investment strategies, Jenny Company decided to make the best use of its idle cash to earn extra profit. The company purchased these securities for the primary purpose of trading. In other words, the company is hoping to sell the securities quickly for profit. Assume that Jenny Company has a year end date of April 30.

Required

a) Which accounting method is most appropriate to record this investment and why?

_____

b) Prepare journal entries for the purchase of these debt securities.

Date	Account Title and Explanation	Debit	Credit

c) Prepare the journal entry to record fair value adjustment, assuming that the bonds have a fair value of $5,006,000 on April 30, 2018.

Date	Account Title and Explanation	Debit	Credit

d) On July 15, 2018, the company sold the portion of the bonds that originally cost $300,000 for $304,000. Prepare the journal entry to record this sale.

Date	Account Title and Explanation	Debit	Credit

AP-5A LO 1 2

On July 1, 2018, Kabir Company, a public company, decided to buy $240,000, 6% 10-year bonds at par, issued by a private company in the US. The semi-annual payments are made on January 1 and July 1. The company intends to make these bonds available for sale within the next six to nine months. Kabir Company records the bonds using the fair value through other comprehensive income method, in compliance with GAAP. Kabir Company has a year end of September 30.

Required

a) Record the acquisition of the bonds.

Date	Account Title and Explanation	Debit	Credit

b) Assume that on September 30, 2018, the market value of the bonds decreased significantly to $219,000 due to a change of market interest rate. Prepare the journal entry to make the adjustment on this date. You do not need to record the interest accrued for this question.

Date	Account Title and Explanation	Debit	Credit

AP-6A LO 1 2

Midland Company's investment activities from 2018 to 2019 are recorded below. Its year end is on December 31.

1) On January 21, 2018, Midland Company purchased 200 shares of common stock of Marksmen Holding from the New York Stock Exchange at $18.92 per share. This represents a very small percentage of outstanding stock in the company.
2) On June 30, 2018, Midland Company received dividends from Marksmen Holding of $1.50 per share.
3) On December 31, 2018, the trading price of Marksmen Holding went up to $19.00 per share.
4) On January 28, 2019, Midland Company sold 100 Marksmen Holding shares at $19.23 per share.

Record journal entries of the provided investment activities for Midland Company.

Date	Account Title and Explanation	Debit	Credit

AP-7A LO 1 3

To expand further into the market, on January 2, 2018, Oliver Company purchased 150,000 shares of common stock of Provide Company, a public company with 1,000,000 outstanding shares of common stock traded on the New York Stock Exchange.

Required

a) What level of influence does Oliver Company have over Provide Company based on the percentage of ownership? Which accounting method should be considered for recording this investment?

_____

_____

_____

b) At minimum, how many shares need to be acquired by Oliver Company for significant influence to be exercised?

_____

_____

AP-8A LO 1 3

On March 2, 2018, Taxes Holding, a public company, purchased 15% of the 2,000,000 outstanding shares of common stock issued by Utah Holding at a price of $28.75 per share. This investment occurred as part of a business alliance agreement between the two companies. Taxes Holding is planning to hold on to the common stock of Utah Holding for at least 10 years, if not longer.

During 2018, the following activities occurred in regards to this investment.

1) On June 30, 2018, Taxes Holding received a cash dividend from Utah Holding for $1.36 per share.

2) On December 31, 2018, the year end date of Taxes Holding, Utah Holding's shares of common stock were traded at $29.02 per share.

Required

a) Which accounting method should be chosen in this situation and why?

_____

_____

b) Prepare journal entries to record the acquisition of Utah Holding's shares of common stock, receipt of cash dividends and year end adjustments related to Utah Holding's investment in Taxes Holding's books.

Date	Account Title and Explanation	Debit	Credit

AP-9A LO 3

On May 1, 2018, Xiao Company, a public company, acquired 210,000 of the 600,000 outstanding shares of common stock from Zahra Company for a total of $1,680,000. This investment is part of Xiao Company's long-term business diversification plan. Xiao Company's year end is December 31. During 2018, the following investment activities occurred.

1) Zahra Company recorded an annual net income of $908,000 for its 2017–2018 fiscal year end of June 30, 2018.

2) Zahra Company paid a cash dividend of $300,000 on July 30, 2018.

Required

a) Prepare journal entries to record the acquisition of the 210,000 shares of common stock by Xiao Company.

b) Prepare journal entries to record revenue of investment from Zahra Company on June 30, 2018.

c) Prepare journal entries to record the receipt of cash dividends on July 30, 2018.

Date	Account Title and Explanation	Debit	Credit

AP-10A LO 4

On June 2, 2018, Fantasy Company purchased a portfolio filled with stock of three different companies as an investment with insignificant influence. Fantasy plans to sell the entire portfolio by the end of March 2019. The details of this portfolio are as follows.

Investee	Number of Shares Purchased	Cost ($)
Larvetar Inc.	2,000	76,000
Occillery Co.	500	22,500
Pillowdale Corp.	1,400	32,200

The market value per share of each stock in the portfolio as at Fantasy's year end on December 31, 2018 is as follows.

Investee	Market Value per Share on Dec 31
Larvetar Inc.	$40
Occillery Co.	38
Pillowdale Corp.	27

Fantasy did not purchase any additional securities or sell any securities after June 2, 2018.

Required

a) Determine the amount of Fantasy's unrealized gain or loss on these investments in the fiscal year 2018.

b) Present the investment in the asset section of Fantasy's partial balance sheet as at December 31, 2018.

AP-11A LO 4

Different accounting methods of recording investments impact different accounts in either the balance sheet or income statement. From a list of transactions given below, indicate how each account is impacted for the investor. The first one is completed for you as an example.

Item No.	Transaction
1	The $300 interest accrued on a 90-day T-bill that the investor plans to hold to maturity.
2	Interest receipt in cash of $4,800 from a 10-year bond purchased at par and held for trading.
3	Sale of a long-term investment bond for $10,300 cash before maturity, with a book value of $10,900.
4	Accrued interest revenue of $520 for an available-for-sale, long-term bond investment at year end.
5	An adjustment of a market price increase of $900 for a trading bond investment.
6	The $3,000 cash dividend received from an equity investment that has insignificant influence. The investor plans to keep the investment for a few months until it is sold.
7	Fair value increase of an equity investment for $1,500. The investment is valued based on the equity method.
8	The $1,200 cash dividend received for a strategic equity investment using the equity method.
9	A portfolio of bonds, to be sold in two years, is classified as available-for-sale and its fair value has increased by $3,300.
10	Using the equity method, an investee company reported $100,000 of net profit. The investor owns 35% of the investee's common stock.

	Income Statement			Balance Sheet	
	Revenue or Gain	Expense or Loss	OCI	Current Assets	Noncurrent Assets
Item No.					
1	+$300			+$300	
2					
3					
4					
5					
6					
7*					
8					
9					
10					

AP-12A LO 1 2 3

Ian Company, a public company, had the following activities related to its investments over the course of two years. It has a year end of December 31.

1) On January 31, 2018, it acquired 6% of the 1,000,000 outstanding shares of common stock of James Company at $16.00 per share.

2) On December 31, 2018, Ian Company received a cash dividend from James Company of $1.50 per share.

3) On December 31, 2018, James Company's common stock was traded at $16.50 per share on the local stock exchange.

4) On January 1, 2019, Ian Company purchased 25% of the 800,000 Lemon Inc.'s outstanding shares of common stock for a price of $1,100,000. This purchase was enough to give Ian Company significant influence over Lemon Inc.'s operational decisions.

5) On June 30, 2019, Ian Company received a cash dividend payment of $1.50 per share from James Company and $0.50 from Lemon Inc. James Company and Lemon Inc. also reported earnings of $500,000 and $650,000, respectively, for its fiscal year ending June 30, 2019.

Required

a)   Discuss which accounting method should be used by Ian Company for each type of investment.

_____

_____

_____

_____

b)   Prepare journal entries of all activities recorded by Ian Company.

Date	Account Title and Explanation	Debit	Credit

AP-13A LO 2 3 4

The following are investment activities for Koko Company.

1)   On January 31, 2018, Koko Company purchased a $20,000, 10-year bond at par with 5% interest paid annually on December 31. Koko Company is planning to hold this investment until maturity.

2) On February 10, 2018, Koko Company invested $15,000 in Bast Company by purchasing 3,000 shares of common stock. This is an insignificant investment in Bast Company with the intention of selling it within a year.

3) On March 1, 2018, Koko Company made an investment of $62,500 in Engrid Company by acquiring 5% of its 100,000 outstanding shares of common stock. Koko plans to hold on to Engrid's stock for at least a few years.

4) On April 1, 2018, Koko Company received a cash dividend from Bast Company for a total of $900.

5) On April 30, 2018, Koko Company received a cash dividend from Engrid Company for a total of $1,250.

6) On Koko Company's year end of May 31, 2018, Bast Company's common stock was trading at $6.00 per share, and Engrid Company's stock was trading at $12.15 per share.

Required

a) Prepare journal entries using proper accounting methods for all transactions including the year end accrual of the bonds' interest.

Date	Account Title and Explanation	Debit	Credit

b) Describe how valuation allowances for insignificant equity investments are reported on Koko Company's balance sheet as at May 31, 2018.

_____

_____

_____

_____

_____

_____

_____

_____

AP-14A LO 4

On June 1, 2018, PUT Company acquired 5% of the 800,000 outstanding shares of common stock from SIMA Company and paid $3,500,000 in cash. SIMA Company paid cash dividends of $0.68 per share of common stock on July 30, 2018. At PUT Company's year end on December 31, 2018, the market value of SIMA Company's common stock is $90 per share. For the year ended December 31, 2018, PUT Company has income from operations of $1,000,000.

Prepare a partial income statement for PUT Company for the year ended December 31, 2018 that starts from income from operations. Assume that PUT Company pays 30% income tax expense.

AP-15A LO 2 3

Raj Company had the following activities in relation to its investments in 2018. The company has a June 30 year end.

1) On January 1, 2018, Raj purchased 25,000 shares of common stock from Terry Company for $960,000.

2) On March 31, 2018, Raj Company's accountant received financial statements from Terry Company, which reported a net profit of $386,000 for the year ending February 28, 2018.

3) On April 30, 2018, Raj Company received cash dividends from Terry Company of $1.10 per share.

4) On June 30, 2018, Raj Company's year end, Terry Company's stock was traded at $39.20 per share.

Required

a) Prepare journal entries to record the above activities assuming significant influence is **not** achieved, and Raj Company classified the investment in Terry Company as long-term.

Date	Account Title and Explanation	Debit	Credit

b) Prepare journal entries to record the above activities assuming that the 25,000 shares acquired represent 25% of Terry Company's outstanding shares, thus significant influence is achieved.

Date	Account Title and Explanation	Debit	Credit

Analysis

If Raj Company had purchased the common stock of Terry Company with the purpose to sell in a few months, Raj was then NOT allowed to classify the investment as a long-term investment. Why would GAAP enforce this type of restrictions on recording investments?

_____

_____

_____

_____

_____

_____

_____

Application Questions Group B

AP-1B `LO 1`

Betty Company invests in different instruments before the end of 2018. Complete the following table for each of the investments.

Investments	Non-Strategic or Strategic Investment	Current or Noncurrent Assets	Accounting Method
120-day treasury bill purchased on December 31, 2018 that Betty plans to hold for interest revenue until maturity.			
A 3% common stock of a public company purchased on February 1, 2018 that Betty Company is planning on selling before the year end of December 31, 2018.			
A one-year bond issued by a private business on November 1, 2018 that Betty Company is planning to hold until maturity.			
60% of common stock of Tim Company purchased on November 18, 2018. Currently, the company has controlling influence over the investee.			
15% of common stock of Jerry Company purchased on December 24, 2018, which Betty is planning to hold for longer than a year.			
45% of common stock of Sally Company purchased on December 30, 2018, with which Betty Company is trying to acquire more stock to establish control over the investee in the future.			

AP-2B `LO 2`

Quest Company paid $350,000 to purchase a portfolio of debt securities on April 1, 2018. Management's intention is to hold them as available-for-sale securities for longer than one year. The management does not intend to hold any debt securities until their maturity in this portfolio. On June 30, 2018, Quest received cash interest of $500 from the debt securities in this portfolio. The fair value of the portfolio at Quest's year end on December 31, 2018 was $346,000. On May 17, 2019, Quest sold the part of the securities in this portfolio that originally cost $200,000 for $180,000. Prepare the journal entries to record all transactions related to this investment.

Date	Account Title and Explanation	Debit	Credit

AP-3B LO 1 2

To earn some additional interest revenue, Hank Company, a public company, purchased $200,000 worth of 8%, five-year bonds issued by Ivy Company at par on January 1, 2018. Interest payments are made semi-annually on June 30 and December 31. Assume April 30 is the year end for Hank Company.

Prepare journal entries for the acquisition of the bonds, the interest accrual on the first year end, the first cash receipt of interest, and the cash receipt of principal at maturity on January 1, 2023.

Date	Account Title and Explanation	Debit	Credit

Analysis

If the same bonds were traded at a discount in 2019 due to the significant increase of interest rate in the market, should Hank Company change the valuation methods of these bonds? Why or why not?

_____

_____

AP-4B LO 1 2

Jimmy Company, a public company, paid $1,000,000 to purchase a portfolio of debt securities on April 1, 2018. The company purchased these securities for the primary purpose of trading; the company is hoping to sell the securities quickly for profit. Assume that Jimmy Company has a year end date of April 30. The market price of the securities in this portfolio at Jimmy's year end was $990,000.

Assume Jimmy Company sold half of the portfolio for $508,000 on May 30, 2018. Prepare journal entries for the purchase, fair value adjustment at the year end and sale of half of the portfolio.

Date	Account Title and Explanation	Debit	Credit

Date	Account Title and Explanation	Debit	Credit

Analysis

If the management decided to classify these securities as available-for-sale instead of trading, how would this decision affect the company's net income for the year ended April 30, 2018?

_____

_____

_____

_____

_____

_____

_____

AP-5B LO 1 2

On July 1, 2018, Landmark Company, a public company, decided to buy $140,000 worth of 10-year bonds at par with an annual interest rate of 7%, issued by a private company. Interest is paid semi-annually on January 1 and July 1. The company intends to make these bonds available for sale within the next two years. Landmark Company records the bonds using fair value through other comprehensive income method. The company's year end is on November 30.

Required

a) Record acquisition of the bonds.

Date	Account Title and Explanation	Debit	Credit

b) Assume that on November 30, 2018, the market value of the bonds increased to $145,000 due to a change of market interest rate. Prepare journal entries to make the adjustment on this date. You do not need to record the interest accrued for this question.

Date	Account Title and Explanation	Debit	Credit

AP-6B LO 1 2

Norman Company's investment activities from 2018 to 2019 are recorded below. Its year end is on December 31.

1) On January 21, 2018, Norman Company purchased 1,000 shares of common stock of GM Holding from the Nasdaq Stock Market at $92.17 per share. This quantity of stock is less than 2% of the outstanding stock of GM Holding.

2) On June 30, 2018, Norman Company received a dividend from GM Holding of $2.30 per share.

3) On December 31, 2018, the trading price of GM Holding went down to $91.05 per share.

4) On January 19, 2019, Norman Company sold 500 GM Holding shares at $90.05 per share.

Record journal entries of the provided investment activities for Norman Company.

Date	Account Title and Explanation	Debit	Credit

AP-7B LO 1 3

On June 1, 2018, Boxhead Company purchased 150,000 of Supply Company's 600,000 outstanding shares of common stock. Boxhead Company intends to gain control over decisions related to quality assurance made by Supply Company's Board of Directors.

Required

a) What level of influence does Boxhead Company have over Supply Company solely based on the percentage of ownership? Which accounting method should be used for recording this investment?

_____

_____

_____

b) Based on the current ownership percentage, can Boxhead Company control all decisions of quality assurance made by Supply Company?

_____

_____

AP-8B LO 3

On March 16, 2018, Victor Company, a public company, purchased 10% of the 1,000,000 outstanding shares of common stock issued by Water Company at a price of $16 per share. Victor Company is planning to acquire more stock in the future to gradually gain influence over Water Company's operating decisions.

During 2018, the following activities occurred in regards to this investment.

1) On June 30, 2018, Victor Company received a cash dividend from Water Company for $1.08 per share.

2) On December 31, 2018, the year end date of Victor Company, Water's common stock was traded at $15.00 per share.

Prepare journal entries to record the acquisition of common stock, receipt of cash dividends and the year end adjustments related to this investment in Victor Company's books.

Date	Account Title and Explanation	Debit	Credit

AP-9B LO 3

On January 31, 2018, Altona Holding purchased 30% of the 800,000 outstanding shares of common stock from Brain Company and paid $720,000 in cash. Altona Holding is aiming to set up a strategic partnership with Brain Company to explore overseas markets. Altona's year end is on December 31. Altona Holding follows IFRS and the following activities occurred in regards to this investment during 2018.

1) Brain Company recorded a net income of $689,000 for its year ended on October 1, 2018.

2) On December 1, 2018, Brain Company paid cash dividends of $200,000 .

Required

a) Prepare journal entries to record the acquisition of Brain Company's common stock.

b) Prepare journal entries to record revenue of investment from Brain Company on October 1, 2018.

c) Prepare journal entries to record the receipt of cash dividends on December 1, 2018.

Date	Account Title and Explanation	Debit	Credit

d) What would be the balance of the investment on Altona Holding's books on December 31, 2018?

Analysis

Assume by December 2018, Altona's market analyst noticed that Brain Company's common stock is now traded at $8 per share, significantly higher than the original purchase price at the beginning of 2018. Should this change be reflected on Altona Holding's financial statements? Give analysis on whether Altona Holding should make adjustments at its year end to reflect this significant change in value.

AP-10B LO 2

Spera Industries Limited (SIL) began its operations on January 1, 2018. On August 5, 2018, the company purchased a portfolio filled with stock of two companies. SIL plans to hold these securities for a few years. The details of this portfolio are as follows.

Investee	Number of Shares Purchased	Cost ($)
Ursa Inc.	800	34,400
Gliggy Co.	3,000	45,000

SIL has an insignificant influence in both investees. The market value per share of each stock in the portfolio as at SIL's year end on December 31, 2018 is as follows.

Investee	Market Value per Share on Dec 31
Ursa Inc.	$46
Gliggy Co.	9

SIL did not purchase any additional securities or sell any securities after August 5, 2018.

Required

a) Prepare the journal entry to record unrealized gain or loss on investments at SIL's year end.

Date	Account Title and Explanation	Debit	Credit

b) Present the investments in the asset section of SIL's partial balance sheet as at December 31, 2018.

AP-11B LO 1 4

Different accounting methods of recording investments impact different accounts in either the balance sheet or income statement.

Required

a) Indicate which accounting method should be used under GAAP for recording each transaction listed in the table below. The first transaction has been completed as an example.

Item No.	Scenario	Valuation Method
1	Accrued interest of $150 for a 120-day T-bill that the investor intends to hold until maturity for interest revenue.	Amortized Cost
2	Sale of a long-term investment bond for $10,300 cash before maturity. The bond had a book value of $10,000. The original purpose of this investment was for holding to maturity to earn interest revenue.	
3	Received interest payment of $4,000 from a long-term, held-to-maturity bond investment that was purchased at par.	
4	A non-strategic, short-term bond investment accrued interest revenue of $200 at year end. The purpose of this investment was for trading.	
5	The fair value of a non-strategic, short-term bond decreased by $600. The purpose of this investment was for trading.	
6	The fair value of a long-term bond investment increased by $3,600. This bond is invested with the intent of holding to maturity.	
7	An associate company reported $10,000 of net loss. The investor owns 25% of an associate's common stock with significant influence.	
8	A fair value of a long-term, available-for-sale debt investment decreased by $2,000.	

b) Complete the table to show how each transaction from the table above impacts each account for the investor. The first row has been completed as an example.

| | Statement of Comprehensive Income | | | | | | Balance Sheet | | | |
| | Revenue | | Expense | | OCI | | Current Assets | | Noncurrent Assets | |
Item No.	Debit	Credit	Debit	Credit	Debit	Credit	Debit	Credit	Debit	Credit
1										
2										
3										
4										
5										
6										
7										
8										

AP-12B LO 1 2 4

George Company has a year end of December 31. The following activities are related to its investments.

1) On February 2, 2018, George Company acquired 5% of the 1,000,000 outstanding shares of common stock of Helen Company at $17.45 per share. George Company plans to sell the shares quickly to make a profit.

2) On March 16, 2018, George Company purchased 150,000 of 1,000,000 outstanding shares of common stock of Siya Company at $10.00 per share. George Company plans to hold Siya's stock for at least a few years.

3) On June 30, 2018, George Company received a cash dividend of $1.28 per share from Helen Company and $1 per share from Siya Company.

4) On December 31, 2018, Helen Company's common stock was traded for $16.55 per share and Siya Company's common stock was traded for $11 per share on the local stock exchange.

5) On January 31, 2019, George Company sold half of the investment in Helen Company for $450,000 cash.

Required

a) Discuss which accounting method should be used by George Company for each type of investment.

_____

_____

_____

_____

b) Prepare journal entries to record all of George Company's activities.

Date	Account Title and Explanation	Debit	Credit

c) Present the investments in Helen Company and Siya Company in the asset section of George Company's partial balance sheet as at December 31, 2018.

Analysis

Assume in 2020, George Company purchased an additional 100,000 shares from a total of 1,000,0000 outstanding shares of common stock of Siya company. Would this transaction have any impacts on this investment? Explain.

_____

_____

_____

AP-13B LO 2 3

The following are investment activities for Quentin Company. Assume the company has a year end of December 31.

1) On March 1, 2018, Quentin Company made a strategic business investment of $90,000 in Hallow Company, by acquiring 25% of its 100,000 outstanding shares of common stock.

2) On June 30, 2018, Quentin Company received a cash dividend from Hallow Company of $0.18 per share. A total profit of $65,000 was reported on Hallow Company's income statement for the year ended June 30, 2018.

3) On September 1, 2018, Quentin Company spent $20,000 to purchase 6%, 10-year bonds at par. The bond pays interest semi-annually, with the first interest payment on March 1, 2019. Quentin Company is planning to hold the investment until maturity.

4) On December 31, 2018, Quentin Company's accountant accrues interest revenue on bonds and notices that Hallow Company's stock was trading at $4.00 per share.

Prepare journal entries to record the above investment activities.

Date	Account Title and Explanation	Debit	Credit

Analysis

When Quentin Company's accountant noticed the trading price change of Hallow Company on December 31, 2018, the CEO of Quentin Company suggested to make a year end fair value adjustment to "reflect the true market value of the investment." As Quentin Company's accountant, explain if fair value adjustment is needed. Prepare journal entries if necessary.

AP-14B LO 4

Mill Inc. acquired 240,000 shares of common stock from Nixy Company and paid $3,300,000 in cash on January 1, 2018. On July 1, 2018, Nixy Company reported a profit of $900,000 on its annual financial statements, ending June 30, 2018. Nixy paid cash dividends of $0.25 per share, on July 30, 2018. On December 31, 2018, which is Mill Inc.'s year end, the market value of Nixy Company's common stock is $12 per share.

a) Assume that Mill Inc. has an insignificant influence on Nixy Company, and that Mill Inc.'s intention is to hold Nixy Company's stock for at least a few years. Show how Mill Inc. would report the investment in Nixy Company in the asset portion of its balance sheet as at December 31, 2018.

b) Assume instead that Mill Inc.'s acquisition of 240,000 shares represents 30% of all outstanding common stock from Nixy Company. Thus, Mill Inc. has a significant influence in Nixy Company and intends to maintain this influence for multiple years. Show how Mill Inc. would report the investment in Nixy Company in the asset portion of its balance sheet as at December 31, 2018.

AP-15B LO 2 3

Shaw Company had the following activities in relation to its investments in 2018. The company has a June 30 year end.

1) On January 1, 2018, Shaw Company purchased 35,000 shares of common stock from Tang Company for $859,950.

2) On March 31, 2018, Shaw Company's accountant received financial statements from Tang Company, which reported a net loss of $560,000 for the year ending February 28, 2018.

3) On April 30, 2018, Shaw Company received cash dividends from Tang Company of $0.05 per share.

4) On June 30, 2018, Tang Company's stock was traded at $25.25 per share.

Required

a) Prepare journal entries to record the above activities assuming that the 35,000 shares acquired represent 35% of Tang Company's outstanding shares, thus significant influence is achieved.

Date	Account Title and Explanation	Debit	Credit

b) Prepare journal entries to record the above activities assuming significant influence is **not** achieved, and Shaw Company classified the investment in Tang Company as long-term.

Date	Account Title and Explanation	Debit	Credit

Analysis

Can Shaw Company classify its investment in Tang Company as held-to-maturity investment? Explain.

_____

_____

_____

_____

_____

Case Study

CS-1 LO 2 3 4

The following investment transactions happened during the fiscal year ending December 31, 2018 for Dolly Company.

Jan 2	Purchased 30,000 shares of common stock of Vita Company at $10 per share, plus a brokerage fee of $3,000. Dolly Company does not have a significant influence on Vita Company, and classified this investment as long-term.
Feb 26	Purchased 25,000 shares of common stock of Farie Inc. at $38 per share. Because this investment represents 25% of Farie's total outstanding shares, it gives Dolly Company a significant influence over Farie Inc.
Mar 31	Received $12,500 in dividends from Farie Inc.
Apr 19	Received a cash dividend of $2 per share from Vita Company.
May 5	Purchased 1,000 shares of common stock of Tartan Corp. at $22 per share. Dolly Company does not have a significant influence on Tartan Company, and classified this investment as short-term.
Jun 13	Sold 5,000 shares of common stock of Vita Company at $11.50 per share.
Jul 31	Farie Inc. reported a net income of $400,000 for its fiscal year ending July 31, 2018.
Aug 16	Received a cash dividend of $0.50 per share from Tartan Corp.
Sep 24	Sold half of Tartan Corp. shares of common stock at $25 per share.
Oct 31	Purchased $100,000, 15-year, 6% bonds at par value. Dolly Company paid a total of $100,500 for these bonds because the bonds came with $500 accrued interest as of the purchase date. Dolly Company intends to hold these bonds until maturity.
Dec 31	Accrued interest revenue on the bonds purchased on October 31.
Dec 31	The market values for Vita Company and Tartan Corp. shares of common stock are $9 and $24, respectively.

Required

a) Prepare journal entries for the above transactions.

Date	Account Title and Explanation	Debit	Credit

Date	Account Title and Explanation	Debit	Credit

b)   Prepare a partial income statement for Dolly Company for the year ended December 31, 2018 that starts at $700,000 for income from operations. Assume that Dolly Company's income tax rate is 30%.

Chapter 19

THE STATEMENT OF CASH FLOWS

LEARNING OBJECTIVES

LO 1   Classify operating, investing and financing activities

LO 2   Prepare a statement of cash flows using the indirect method

LO 3   Calculate book value and cash received for selling noncurrent assets

LO 4   Explain the concept of free cash flow and its importance for potential investors

LO 5   Discuss ethical issues related to cash flow

Appendix

LO 6   Prepare a statement of cash flows using the direct method

LO 7   Prepare a statement of cash flows in a spreadsheet using the indirect method

AMEENGAGE   *Access **ameengage.com** for integrated resources including tutorials, practice exercises, the digital textbook and more.*

Assessment Questions

AS-1 LO 1

Is the statement of cash flows an optional statement? Explain.

AS-2 LO 1

Identify the three ways a business can generate and use cash.

AS-3 LO 1

What does cash flow from operating activities represent?

AS-4 LO 1

What does cash flow from investing activities represent?

AS-5 LO 1

What does cash flow from financing activities represent?

AS-6 `LO 2`

Which financial statements are required to prepare a statement of cash flows?

_____

_____

AS-7 `LO 2`

Which items appear in the cash flow from operating activities section of the statement of cash flows using the indirect method?

_____

_____

_____

AS-8 `LO 2`

Which items appear in the cash flow from investing activities section of the statement of cash flows?

_____

_____

AS-9 `LO 2`

Which items appear in the cash flow from financing activities section of the statement of cash flows?

_____

_____

AS-10 `LO 3`

What does a gain on the sale of equipment indicate?

_____

_____

AS-11 `LO 3`

How is a gain on sale of equipment shown on the statement of cash flows using the indirect method?

_____

_____

_____

AS-12 `LO 4`

Define free cash flow.

_____

_____

_____

AS-13 `LO 4`

Why would an investor or creditor want to see a company show a positive free cash flow amount?

_____

_____

AS-14 LO 5

What are some actions a company may be tempted to take to unethically and artificially improve its statement of cash flows presentation?

_____

_____

_____

_____

_____

AS-15 LO 6

What is the difference in the presentation of the statement of cash flows between the indirect and the direct methods?

_____

_____

_____

_____

_____

_____

AS-16 LO 6

Using the direct method, how can we calculate the amount of cash spent on inventory?

_____

_____

_____

_____

_____

_____

AS-17 LO 7

When a statement of cash flows is prepared using a work sheet (spreadsheet), how is net income entered into the work sheet?

_____

_____

_____

_____

_____

_____

_____

Application Questions Group A

AP-1A LO 1

For each item listed, indicate how the item will impact cash flow (increase, decrease or no change) using the indirect method.

Item	Effect on Cash
Net Income	
Increase in Accounts Payable	
Decrease in Accounts Receivable	
Purchase of Property, Plant and Equipment	
Payment of Notes Payable	
Increase in Merchandise Inventory	
Pay Dividends	
Increase in Loans	
Increase in Prepaid Insurance	
Gain on Redemption of Bonds	
Issue Stock in Excess of Par Value	

AP-2A LO 2

Indicate the section of the statement of cash flows where each item would be located (operating, investing or financing activities) using the indirect method.

Item	Section
Change in Accounts Payable	
Change in Merchandise Inventory	
Change in Property, Plant and Equipment	
Change in Long-Term Portion of Notes Payable	
Change in Current Portion of Notes Payable	
Change in Prepaid Rent	
Change in Accounts Receivable	
Change in Common Stock	
Gain on Sale of Property, Plant and Equipment	
Change in Paid-In Capital in Excess of Par Value	

AP-3A LO 2

The net income for the year ended on December 31, 2018 for RC Corporation was $120,000. Additional data for the year is provided below.

Loss on retirement of debt	$20,000
Purchase of property, plant and equipment	280,000
Depreciation of property, plant and equipment	14,000
Dividends declared	50,000
Decrease in accounts receivable	29,000
Loss on sale of equipment	13,000
Issue of common stock in excess of par value	10,000

Calculate the net cash provided (used) by operating activities using the indirect method.

___

___

___

___

___

___

___

AP-4A LO 2

Ashe Inc. reported the following data for 2018.

Income Statement		
Net Income		$30,000
Depreciation Expense		4,000
Balance Sheet		
Increase in Accounts Receivable		$9,000
Decrease in Accounts Payable		7,000

Calculate the net cash provided (used) by operating activities.

___

___

___

___

___

___

AP-5A LO 2

The net income for the year ended on August 31, 2018 for Wonderstruck Corporation was $147,000. Additional data for the year is provided below.

Purchase of property, plant and equipment	$257,000
Depreciation of equipment	$11,000
Dividends paid	$42,000
Net increase in accounts receivable	$22,000
Loss on sale of property	$17,000
Gain on retirement of debt	$10,000

Calculate the net cash provided (used) by operating activities.

___

___

___

___

___

AP-6A LO 2

Mellon Incorporated had a net income for 2018 of $320,000. Included on the income statement was a loss on sale of equipment for $5,000, a gain on sale of investments for $15,000, depreciation of $8,000, loss on retirement of debt of $10,000 and interest of $3,000. Calculate the net cash provided (used) by operating activities using the indirect method. Assume that the balances of current assets (except cash) and current liabilities remain the same as last year.

_____

_____

_____

_____

_____

Analysis

Does net income, after being adjusted by the noncash items on the income statement, represent the actual amount of cash received through operating activities by the company during the year?

_____

_____

_____

AP-7A LO 2

The following information pertains to Tree Company for the fiscal year 2018.

Purchase of plant and equipment	$35,000
Purchase of long-term investments	$19,000
Increase in accounts receivable	$7,100
Repayment of bonds payable	$12,000
Depreciation of plant and equipment	$10,000

Calculate the net cash provided (used) by investing activities.

_____

_____

_____

AP-8A LO 2

The Marking Company's cash account decreased by $20,000. Net cash provided by operating activities was $17,000. Net cash used by investing activities was $22,000. Calculate the net cash provided (used) by financing activities.

_____

_____

_____

_____

_____

AP-9A LO 2

The Grading Company's cash account decreased by $14,000. Net cash provided by operating activities was $21,000. Net cash used by investing activities was $22,000. Based on this information, calculate the net cash provided (used) by financing activities.

AP-10A LO 3

Allen Woods has just started working as an accountant for Stickla Supplies. Unfortunately, the company had no proper accounting system in place and Allen had to start everything from scratch. He has been provided with some items from the company's balance sheet and income statement for the end of 2018.

Going through the company's purchase receipts and some other financial documents, Allen realized that Stickla purchased $2,500 worth of equipment in 2018. At the end of 2017, the balance of property, plant and equipment was $11,000 and the balance of accumulated depreciation was $2,900. Accounts payable balance was not affected by any investment activities during 2018.

Accounts	2018
Property, Plant and Equipment	$10,000
Accumulated Depreciation	$3,600
Accounts Payable	$4,000
Notes Payable, Current Portion	$15,000
Retained Earnings	$5,400
Depreciation Expense	$1,200
Loss on Sale of Equipment	$300

Based on the information provided, help Allen fill the missing information in the table below.

Which section of the statement of cash flows is affected?	
How much PPE (book value before deducting accumulated depreciation) was sold in 2018?	
What was the accumulated depreciation for the PPE sold?	
What was the net book value of the PPE sold?	
How much cash was received from the sale?	
How much cash was paid out for the purchase?	
What was the net change in cash resulting from PPE?	

AP-11A LO 2

Balance sheet accounts for Planet Inc. contain the following amounts at the end of 2017 and 2018.

Planet Inc. Balance Sheet As at December 31		
	2018	**2017**
Assets		
Current Assets		
Cash	$7,500	$5,000
Accounts Receivable	21,000	15,000
Prepaid Expenses	2,500	2,000
Merchandise Inventory	37,000	28,000
Total Current Assets	68,000	50,000
Noncurrent Assets		
Equipment	196,000	175,000
Accumulated Depreciation	(41,000)	(32,000)
Total Noncurrent Assets	155,000	143,000
Total Assets	$223,000	$193,000
Liabilities		
Current Liabilities	$33,000	$33,000
Long-Term Liabilities	30,000	35,000
Total Liabilities	63,000	68,000
Stockholders' Equity		
Paid-In Capital		
Preferred Stock	50,000	45,000
Common Stock	20,000	15,000
Additional Paid-In Capital	5,000	0
Total Paid-In Capital	75,000	60,000
Retained Earnings	85,000	65,000
Total Stockholders' Equity	160,000	125,000
Total Liabilities and Stockholders' Equity	$223,000	$193,000

Assume current liabilities include only items from operations (e.g. accounts payable, taxes payable). Long-term liabilities include items from financing (e.g. bonds and other long-term liabilities).

Note that the company did not sell any equipment and did not borrow any additional long-term liabilities throughout the year.

Prepare the statement of cash flows for 2018 using the indirect method. Assume no dividends were declared or paid in 2018.

AP-12A LO 2 6

Breakwater Boats sells boating accessories. At the end of 2018, the income statement and comparative balance sheet were prepared as shown below.

Breakwater Boats Balance Sheet As at December 31		
	2018	**2017**
Assets		
Current Assets		
Cash	$73,870	$62,500
Accounts Receivable	94,800	87,500
Merchandise Inventory	327,000	245,700
Prepaid Expenses	14,500	14,500
Total Current Assets	510,170	410,200
Noncurrent Assets[1]		
Land	0	44,000
Equipment	340,000	340,000
Accumulated Depreciation	(26,200)	(24,500)
Total Noncurrent Assets	313,800	359,500
Total Assets	$823,970	$769,700
Liabilities		
Current Liabilities		
Accounts Payable	$52,600	$45,700
Notes Payable, Current Portion	8,500	8,500
Total Current Liabilities	61,100	54,200
Notes Payable, Long-Term Portion	50,100	58,600
Total Liabilities	111,200	112,800
Stockholders' Equity		
Common Stock	150,000	150,000
Retained Earnings	562,770	506,900
Total Stockholders' Equity	712,770	656,900
Total Liabilities and Stockholders' Equity	$823,970	$769,700

[1] During 2018, land was sold for a gain of $6,000. There was no purchase of equipment throughout the year.

Breakwater Boats	
Income Statement	
For the Year Ended December 31, 2018	
Sales	$562,000
Cost of Goods Sold	365,300
Gross Profit	196,700
Operating Expenses	
Depreciation Expense	1,700
Other Operating Expenses	61,200
Total Operating Expenses	62,900
Income from Operations	133,800
Other Income and Expenses	
Gain on Sale of Land	6,000
Income before Income Tax Expense	139,800
Income Tax Expense	48,930
Net Income	$90,870

Required

a) Prepare the statement of cash flows using the indirect method.

b) Prepare the statement of cash flows using the direct method. Assume accounts payable is only for the purchase of merchandise inventory. Do not show the reconciliation schedule of net income with net cash provided (used) by operating activities at the bottom of the statement of cash flows.

Analysis

Explain the main activities that caused Breakwater Boats' net cash flow to increase or decrease.

_____

_____

AP-13A LO 2 3 6

The balance sheet and income statement for Zooyo Appliance are presented below.

Zooyo Appliance Balance Sheet As at December 31		
	2018	**2017**
Assets		
Cash	$37,580	$15,000
Accounts Receivable	17,000	16,000
Merchandise Inventory	21,000	27,000
Total Current Assets	75,580	58,000
Land	110,000	80,000
Equipment	130,000	160,000
Accumulated Depreciation	(26,500)	(30,000)
Total Assets	$289,080	$268,000
Liabilities		
Current Liabilities		
Accounts Payable	$29,000	$35,000
Taxes Payable	18,000	18,000
Total Current Liabilities	47,000	53,000
Bonds Payable	80,000	65,000
Total Liabilities	127,000	118,000
Stockholders' Equity		
Common Stock	75,000	70,000
Retained Earnings	87,080	80,000
Total Stockholders' Equity	162,080	150,000
Total Liabilities and Stockholders' Equity	$289,080	$268,000

Zooyo Appliance Income Statement For the Year Ended December 31, 2018	
Sales	$142,000
Cost of Goods Sold	92,000
Gross Profit	50,000
Operating Expenses	
Depreciation Expense	4,500
Other Operating Expenses	13,550
Total Operating Expenses	18,050
Income from Operations	31,950
Other Income and Expenses	
Interest Expense	(4,350)
Loss on Sale of Equipment	(3,200)
Income before Income Tax Expense	24,400
Income Tax Expense	7,320
Net Income (Loss)	$17,080

Notes: There was no sale of land or purchase of equipment during the year. The company did not repay any bonds principal during the year. The company declared and paid dividends during the year.

Required

a)   Prepare the statement of cash flows for December 31, 2018 using the indirect method.

b) Prepare the statement of cash flows using the direct method. Assume accounts payable is only for the purchase of merchandise inventory. Do not show the reconciliation schedule of net income with net cash provided (used) by operating activities at the bottom of the statement of cash flows.

AP-14A LO 2 3 6

The balance sheet and income statement for Demgo Inc. are presented below.

Demgo Inc.
Balance Sheet
As at December 31

	2018	2017
Assets		
Cash	$20,140	$21,000
Accounts Receivable	17,000	19,000
Merchandise Inventory	21,000	15,000
Total Current Assets	58,140	55,000
Land	110,000	60,000
Machinery	100,000	140,000
Accumulated Depreciation	(40,500)	(60,000)
Total Assets	$227,640	$195,000
Liabilities		
Current Liabilities		
Accounts Payable	$29,000	$25,000
Taxes Payable	22,000	22,000
Total Current Liabilities	51,000	47,000
Bonds Payable	70,000	65,000
Total Liabilities	121,000	112,000
Stockholders' Equity		
Common Stock	85,000	70,000
Retained Earnings	21,640	13,000
Total Stockholders' Equity	106,640	83,000
Total Liabilities and Stockholders' Equity	$227,640	$195,000

Demgo Inc.
Income Statement
For the Year Ended December 31, 2018

Sales	$130,000
Cost of Goods Sold	72,000
Gross Profit	58,000
Operating Expenses	
Depreciation Expense	20,500
Other Operating Expenses	9,950
Total Operating Expenses	30,450
Income from Operations	27,550
Other Income and Expenses	
Interest Expense	(4,050)
Gain on Sale of Machinery	1,700
Income before Income Tax Expense	25,200
Income Tax Expense	7,560
Net Income (Loss)	$17,640

Notes: There was no sale of land.
Machinery was purchased for an amount of $80,000.
The company did not repay any bonds principal during the year.
The company declared and paid dividends during the year.

Required

a)   Prepare the statement of cash flows for December 31, 2018 using the indirect method.

b)   Prepare the statement of cash flows using the direct method. Assume accounts payable is only for the purchase of merchandise inventory. Do not show the reconciliation schedule of net income with net cash provided (used) by operating activities at the bottom of the statement of cash flows.

AP-15A LO 2 3 6

The balance sheet and income statement for Vispara Company are presented below.

Vispara Company Balance Sheet As at December 31		
	2018	**2017**
Assets		
Cash	$133,400	$75,000
Accounts Receivable	47,000	26,000
Merchandise Inventory	72,000	42,000
Total Current Assets	252,400	143,000
Land	90,000	100,000
Equipment	90,000	130,000
Accumulated Depreciation	(45,000)	(60,000)
Total Assets	$387,400	$313,000
Liabilities		
Current Liabilities		
Accounts Payable	$35,000	$65,000
Taxes Payable	40,000	40,000
Total Current Liabilities	75,000	105,000
Bonds Payable	140,000	95,000
Total Liabilities	215,000	200,000
Stockholders' Equity		
Common Stock	85,000	75,000
Retained Earnings	87,400	38,000
Total Stockholders' Equity	172,400	113,000
Total Liabilities and Stockholders' Equity	$387,400	$313,000

Vispara Company Income Statement For the Year Ended December 31, 2018	
Sales	$380,000
Cost of Goods Sold	247,000
Gross Profit	133,000
Operating Expenses	
Depreciation Expense	5,000
Other Operating Expenses	22,550
Total Operating Expenses	27,550
Income from Operations	105,450
Other Income and Expenses	
Interest Expense	(7,050)
Loss on Sale of Equipment	(5,400)
Gain on Sale of Land	5,000
Income before Income Tax Expense	98,000
Income Tax Expense	29,400
Net Income (Loss)	$68,600

Notes:

The company paid cash dividends during 2018.
The company did not make a bonds payable payment during 2018.
The company did not purchase any equipment during 2018.
The company did not purchase any land during 2018.

Required

a)   Prepare the statement of cash flows for December 31, 2018 using the indirect method.

b) Prepare the statement of cash flows using the direct method. Assume accounts payable is only for the purchase of merchandise inventory. Do not show the reconciliation schedule of net income with net cash provided (used) by operating activities at the bottom of the statement of cash flows.

Analysis

a) Are there any concerns based on the statement of cash flows?

_____

_____

_____

_____

b) Are there any concerns in the cash flow from operating activities section?

_____

_____

_____

_____

AP-16A LO 2

2018 has been a great year for Exany Company, which managed to earn $56,000 of net income. Therefore, the board decided to declare and pay dividends by year end.

Based on the following information, answer the following questions.

Accounts	2018	2017
Retained Earnings	$91,000	$67,000
Common Stock	$120,000	$110,000

a) How much in dividends was paid in 2018?	
b) Which section of the statement of cash flows is affected?	
c) Assuming only the information given impacted the section of the statement of cash flows indicated in b), what is the net change in cash for this section?	

AP-17A LO 1 4

Cleancarpet Vacuums sells vacuum accessories. At the end of 2018, the statement of cash flows below was prepared.

Cleancarpet Vacuums Statement of Cash Flows For the Year Ended December 31, 2018		
Cash Flow from Operating Activities		
Net Income	$83,800	
Adjustments to Reconcile Net Income to Net Cash Provided (Used) by Operating Activities		
Depreciation Expense	4,760	
Gain on Sale of Equipment	(7,200)	
Change in Operating Assets and Liabilities		
Decrease in Accounts Receivable	2,210	
Increase in Merchandise Inventory	(46,800)	
Increase in Accounts Payable	6,000	
Net Cash Provided (Used) by Operating Activities		$42,770
Cash Flow from Investing Activities		
Sale of Equipment	20,300	
Net Cash Provided (Used) by Investing Activities		20,300
Cash Flow from Financing Activities		
Payment of Notes Payable	(19,100)	
Payment of Cash Dividend	(23,700)	
Net Cash Provided (Used) by Financing Activities		(42,800)
Net Increase (Decrease) in Cash		20,270
Cash at the Beginning of the Year		68,300
Cash at the End of the Year		$88,570

Required

a)   How much of the company's cash is from day-to-day operations?

b) Why does the company have positive cash flow from investing activities? Would such positive cash flow from investing activities be sustainable?

_____

_____

_____

_____

_____

c) Calculate Cleancarpet Vacuums' free cash flow in 2018.

_____

_____

Analysis

What could Cleancarpet Vacuums do if selling the equipment was not an action the company could take, yet it still wanted to have a positive net cash flow at the end of the year?

_____

_____

AP-18A LO 7

The balance sheet and income statement for Beyond Lights Company are presented below.

Beyond Lights Company Balance Sheet As at December 31		
	2018	**2017**
Assets		
Cash	$133,400	$75,000
Accounts Receivable	47,000	26,000
Merchandise Inventory	72,000	42,000
Total Current Assets	252,400	143,000
Land	90,000	100,000
Equipment	90,000	130,000
Accumulated Depreciation	(45,000)	(60,000)
Total Assets	$387,400	$313,000
Liabilities		
Current Liabilities		
Accounts Payable	$35,000	$65,000
Notes Payable, Current Portion	40,000	40,000
Total Current Liabilities	75,000	105,000
Notes Payable, Long-Term Portion	140,000	95,000
Total Liabilities	215,000	200,000
Stockholders' Equity		
Common Stock	85,000	75,000
Retained Earnings	87,400	38,000
Total Stockholders' Equity	172,400	113,000
Total Liabilities and Stockholders' Equity	$387,400	$313,000

Beyond Lights Company	
Income Statement	
For the Year Ended December 31, 2018	
Sales	$380,000
Cost of Goods Sold	247,000
Gross Profit	133,000
Operating Expenses	
Depreciation Expense	5,000
Other Operating Expenses	29,600
Total Operating Expenses	34,600
Income from Operations	98,400
Other Income and Expenses	
Loss on Sale of Equipment	(5,400)
Gain on Sale of Land	5,000
Income before Income Tax Expense	98,000
Income Tax Expense	29,400
Net Income (Loss)	$68,600

Notes: The company did not purchase any land or equipment during the year.

Prepare a statement of cash flows using a spreadsheet by means of the indirect method.

	Beyond Lights Company					
	Spreadsheet for Statement of Cash Flows					
	For the Year Ended December 31					
	Balance		**Changes**			**Balance**
	Dec 31, 2017		**Debit**		**Credit**	**Dec 31, 2018**

Application Questions Group B

AP-1B [LO 1]

Indicate which section each item in the table below would appear in a statement of cash flows using the indirect method. Also indicate whether the item would increase or decrease cash using the indirect method.

Item	Section	Effect on Cash
Loss on sale of equipment		
Decrease in accounts payable		
Increase in merchandise inventory		
Depreciation expense		
Gain on sale of investments		
Dividends paid		
Issued shares in the company		
Net income		
Decrease in notes payable		
Sold equipment		
Decrease accounts receivable		
Loss on redemption of bonds		

AP-2B [LO 2]

Bonus Company had the following amounts in its statement of cash flows for the year ended December 31, 2018.

Net decrease in cash from operating activities	$100,000
Net decrease in cash from investing activities	400,000
Net increase in cash from financing activities	350,000
Cash balance, January 1, 2018	600,000

Calculate the cash balance at December 31, 2018.

AP-3B [LO 2]

The net income for the year ended December 31, 2018 for Kersley Company was $73,000. Additional information is shown below.

Interest expense on borrowing	$8,000
Gain on redemption of bonds	10,000
Increase in accounts receivable	10,000
Decrease in prepaid expense	3,000
Decrease in accounts payable	4,000
Dividends paid to common stockholders	14,000

Calculate the net cash provided (used) by operating activities.

_____

_____

_____

_____

_____

_____

AP-4B LO 2

Use the following information to prepare the operating activities section of a statement of cash flows for MNO Co. for 2018 using the indirect method.

Net income	$140,000
Increase in merchandise inventory	30,000
Increase in accounts payable	20,000
Depreciation expense	55,000
Increase in accounts receivable	18,000
Gain on sale of land	25,000

_____

_____

_____

_____

_____

AP-5B LO 2

Danes Company had net income for 2018 of $120,000. Included in net income was a depreciation of $3,000, a gain on sale of land of $5,000, loss on redemption of bonds of $10,000 and income taxes of $30,000. Using the information given, calculate the net cash provided (used) by operating activities using the indirect method. Assume that the balances of current assets (except cash) and current liabilities remain the same as last year.

_____

_____

_____

_____

_____

Analysis

Why are some items from the income statement added back to net income on the statement of cash flows?

_____

_____

_____

_____

758

AP-6B `LO 2`

The following information pertains to Bush Company for the fiscal year 2018.

Purchase of plant and equipment	$33,000
Sale of long-term investments	12,000
Increase in accounts payable	6,000
Repayment of bonds payable	15,000
Depreciation of plant and equipment	7,000
Loss on redemption of bonds	5,000

Calculate the net cash provided (used) by investing activities.

AP-7B `LO 2`

The following events took place during 2018 at Bernard Company. Based on the information given, calculate net cash provided (used) by investing activities.

Gain on sale of investments	$4,000
Sale of investments (including gain)	50,000
Issued company stock	60,000
Paid off notes payable	30,000
Purchased equipment	70,000

AP-8B `LO 2`

The following events took place during 2018 to Shaw Company. Based on the information given, calculate net cash provided (used) by financing activities.

Loss on sale of land	$10,000
Sale of land (including loss)	110,000
Issued company stock	120,000
Paid off notes payable	50,000
Paid dividends	30,000
Depreciation expense	6,000

Analysis

If Shaw Company's net income during 2018 was $25,000, identify a potential concern from the cash flows from financing activities section.

_____

_____

AP-9B LO 2

The following events took place during 2018 to Robinson Company. Based on the information given, calculate the net cash provided (used) by investing activities and financing activities.

Gain on sale of equipment	$2,000
Sale of equipment (including gain)	90,000
Purchase of long-term investments	65,000
Issued company stock	60,000
Issued a note payable	40,000
Paid dividends	20,000
Increase in merchandise inventory	24,000

_____

_____

_____

_____

_____

_____

_____

_____

Analysis

Suppose Robinson Company had a net increase in cash of $50,000. Explain why the company may be in trouble despite having a large increase in cash during the year.

_____

_____

_____

_____

_____

_____

_____

AP-10B LO 3

Factsy Inc. is planning to make the best use out of its cash on hand by purchasing some additional long-term investments. Factsy's long-term investments are held at cost. In January 2018, Factsy bought additional investments. The company also sold part of its investments in November 2018 due to a sudden growth in the value of its holdings. December 31 is its year end.

Below are the data of Factsy Company.

Accounts	2018	2017
Long-Term Investment	$120,000	$110,000
Purchase of Investment	$40,000	
Gain on Sale of Investment	$5,000	

Calculate the net cash provided (used) by investing activities resulting from the long-term investment.

_____

_____

_____

_____

Analysis

Factsy's bookkeeper believes that the net change in cash from the investing activities must be a positive number (a cash inflow) as a result of a big gain on the sale of investment. Do you agree with this comment? Explain.

_____

_____

_____

_____

_____

_____

_____

_____

_____

_____

_____

_____

_____

_____

_____

_____

_____

AP-11B LO 3

Flax Corporation's balance sheet accounts as at December 31, 2018 and 2017 are presented below.

Flax Corp. Balance Sheet As at December 31		
	2018	**2017**
Assets		
Current Assets		
Cash	$460,000	$300,000
Short-Term Investments	600,000	-
Accounts Receivable	1,020,000	1,020,000
Merchandise Inventory	1,360,000	1,200,000
Total Current Assets	3,440,000	2,520,000
Noncurrent Assets		
Long-Term Investments	400,000	800,000
Equipment	3,100,000	2,500,000
Accumulated Depreciation	(900,000)	(600,000)
Total Noncurrent Assets	2,600,000	2,700,000
Total Assets	$6,040,000	$5,220,000
Liabilities		
Current Liabilities	$2,300,000	$2,000,000
Long-Term Liabilities	800,000	700,000
Total Liabilities	3,100,000	2,700,000
Stockholders' Equity		
Common Stock	1,800,000	1,680,000
Retained Earnings	1,140,000	840,000
Total Stockholders' Equity	2,940,000	2,520,000
Total Liabilities and Stockholders' Equity	$6,040,000	$5,220,000

Assume current liabilities include only items from operations (e.g. accounts payable, taxes payable). Long-term liabilities include items from financing (e.g. bonds and other long-term liabilities).

Note that there was no sale of equipment throughout the year.

Prepare the statement of cash flows for 2018 using the indirect method. Assume the net income for 2018 was $300,000.

AP-12B LO 2 6

Vortex Manufacturing makes and sells integrated circuit boards. At the end of 2018, the income statement and comparative balance sheet were prepared as shown below.

Vortex Manufacturing Balance Sheet As at December 31		
	2018	**2017**
Assets		
Current Assets		
Cash	$239,820	$135,640
Accounts Receivable	242,100	265,300
Merchandise Inventory	503,200	465,300
Prepaid Expenses	26,500	26,500
Total Current Assets	1,011,620	892,740
Noncurrent Assets[1]		
Land	0	16,000
Equipment	840,400	840,400
Accumulated Depreciation	(102,300)	(95,600)
Total Noncurrent Assets	738,100	760,800
Total Assets	$1,749,720	$1,653,540
Liabilities		
Current Liabilities		
Accounts Payable	$305,600	$324,500
Notes Payable, Current Portion[2]	32,000	23,000
Total Current Liabilities	337,600	347,500
Notes Payable, Long-Term Portion[2]	205,000	185,000
Total Liabilities	542,600	532,500
Stockholders' Equity		
Common Stock	290,000	260,000
Retained Earnings	917,120	861,040
Total Stockholders' Equity	1,207,120	1,121,040
Total Liabilities and Stockholders' Equity	$1,749,720	$1,653,540

[1] During 2018, land was sold for a loss of $5,000. There was no purchase of equipment throughout the year.

[2] The company did not pay off any amount of the notes payable.

Vortex Manufacturing Income Statement For the Year Ended December 31, 2018	
Sales	$2,650,000
Cost of Goods Sold	1,722,500
Gross Profit	927,500
Operating Expenses	
Depreciation Expense	6,700
Other Operating Expenses	752,600
Total Operating Expenses	759,300
Income from Operations	168,200
Other Income and Expenses	
Loss on Sale of Land	(5,000)
Income before Income Tax Expense	163,200
Income Tax Expense	57,120
Net Income (Loss)	$106,080

Required

a) Prepare the statement of cash flows using the indirect method.

b) Prepare the statement of cash flows using the direct method. Assume accounts payable is only for the purchase of merchandise inventory. Do not show the reconciliation schedule of net income with net cash provided (used) by operating activities at the bottom of the statement of cash flows.

AP-13B `LO 2 3 6`

The balance sheet and income statement for Venus Company are presented below.

Venus Company Balance Sheet As at December 31		
	2018	**2017**
Assets		
Cash	$191,410	$94,000
Accounts Receivable	30,000	34,000
Merchandise Inventory	42,000	50,000
Total Current Assets	263,410	178,000
Land	90,000	100,000
Building	125,000	130,000
Accumulated Depreciation	(62,000)	(60,000)
Total Assets	$416,410	$348,000
Liabilities		
Current Liabilities		
Accounts Payable	$76,000	$65,000
Notes Payable, Current Portion	45,000	40,000
Total Current Liabilities	121,000	105,000
Notes Payable, Long-Term Portion	120,000	95,000
Total Liabilities	241,000	200,000
Stockholders' Equity		
Common Stock	85,000	75,000
Retained Earnings	90,410	73,000
Total Stockholders' Equity	175,410	148,000
Total Liabilities and Stockholders' Equity	$416,410	$348,000

Venus Company Income Statement For the Year Ended December 31, 2018	
Sales	$380,000
Cost of Goods Sold	255,000
Gross Profit	125,000
Operating Expenses	
Depreciation Expense	42,000
Other Operating Expenses	28,500
Total Operating Expenses	70,500
Income from Operations	54,500
Other Income and Expenses	
Loss on Sale of Building	(5,400)
Gain on Sale of Land	3,200
Income before Income Tax Expense	52,300
Income Tax Expense	15,690
Net Income (Loss)	$36,610

Notes: Building and land were purchased for $115,000, and $200,000 respectively.
The company declared and paid dividends during the year.
The company did not pay off any amount of the notes payable.

Required

a)   Prepare the statement of cash flows for December 31, 2018 using the indirect method.

b) Prepare the statement of cash flows using the direct method. Assume accounts payable is only for the purchase of merchandise inventory. Do not show the reconciliation schedule of net income with net cash provided (used) by operating activities at the bottom of the statement of cash flows.

AP-14B LO 2 3 6

The balance sheet and income statement for Twely Inc. are presented below.

Twely Inc. Balance Sheet As at December 31		
	2018	**2017**
Assets		
Cash	$62,927	$56,000
Accounts Receivable	27,000	23,000
Merchandise Inventory	24,500	18,000
Total Current Assets	114,427	97,000
Long-Term Investment	42,000	45,000
Land	119,000	100,000
Equipment	89,000	76,000
Accumulated Depreciation	(28,200)	(24,000)
Total Assets	$336,227	$294,000
Liabilities		
Current Liabilities		
Accounts Payable	$29,000	$25,000
Notes Payable, Current Portion	22,000	22,000
Total Current Liabilities	51,000	47,000
Notes Payable, Long-Term Portion	79,000	65,000
Total Liabilities	130,000	112,000
Stockholders' Equity		
Common Stock	85,000	85,000
Retained Earnings	121,227	97,000
Total Stockholders' Equity	206,227	182,000
Total Liabilities and Stockholders' Equity	$336,227	$294,000

Twely Inc. Income Statement For the Year Ended December 31, 2018	
Sales	$140,000
Cost of Goods Sale	76,000
Gross Profit	64,000
Operating Expenses	
Depreciation Expense	8,200
Other Operating Expenses	14,790
Total Operating Expenses	22,990
Income from Operations	41,010
Other Income and Expenses	
Gain on Sale of Investment	1,100
Gain on Sale of Equipment	2,500
Income before Income Tax Expense	44,610
Income Tax Expense	13,383
Net Income (Loss)	$31,227

Notes: There was no sale of land.

Equipment and long-term investment were purchased for $30,000 and $10,500, respectively.

The long-term investment is held at cost.

The company declared and paid dividends during the year.

The company paid off $22,000 of the notes payable in 2018.

Required

a)   Prepare the statement of cash flows for December 31, 2018 using the indirect method.

b) Prepare the statement of cash flows using the direct method. Assume accounts payable is only for the purchase of merchandise inventory. Do not show the reconciliation schedule of net income with net cash provided (used) by operating activities at the bottom of the statement of cash flows.

AP-15B LO 2 3 6

The balance sheet and income statement for Joe's Fish Hut are presented below.

Joe's Fish Hut Balance Sheet As at December 31, 2018		
	2018	**2017**
Assets		
Cash	$2,100	$23,000
Accounts Receivable	21,000	12,000
Merchandise Inventory	21,000	25,000
Total Current Assets	44,100	60,000
Land	100,000	100,000
Equipment	170,000	150,000
Accumulated Depreciation	(28,600)	(25,000)
Total Assets	$285,500	$285,000
Liabilities		
Current Liabilities		
Accounts Payable	$23,000	$33,000
Notes Payable, Current Portion	12,000	12,000
Total Current Liabilities	35,000	45,000
Notes Payable, Long-Term Portion	48,000	60,000
Total Liabilities	83,000	105,000
Stockholders' Equity		
Paid-In Capital		
Preferred Shares	4,000	0
Common Shares	15,000	15,000
Additional Paid-In Capital	1,000	0
Total Paid-In Capital	20,000	15,000
Retained Earnings	182,500	165,000
Total Stockholders' Equity	202,500	180,000
Total Liabilities and Stockholders' Equity	$285,500	$285,000

Joe's Fish Hut Income Statement For the Year Ended December 31, 2018	
Sales	$161,000
Cost of Goods Sold	112,700
Gross Profit	48,300
Operating Expenses	
Depreciation Expense	3,600
Other Operating Expenses	19,700
Total Operating Expenses	23,300
Income before Income Tax Expense	25,000
Income Tax Expense	7,500
Net Income (Loss)	$17,500

Note:

The company did not sell any equipment during the year. The company did not sign any additional notes payable in 2018.

Required

a) Prepare the statement of cash flows for December 31, 2018 using the indirect method.

b)   Prepare the statement of cash flows using the direct method. Assume accounts payable is only for the purchase of merchandise inventory. Do not show the reconciliation schedule of net income with net cash provided (used) by operating activities at the bottom of the statement of cash flows.

Analysis

a)   Are there any concerns based on the statement of cash flows?

_____

_____

_____

b)   Are there any concerns in the cash flow from the operating activities section?

_____

_____

_____

AP-16B LO 1 2

Carlin Corporation has prepared the following statement of cash flows for the year end.

Carlin Corporation Statement of Cash Flows For the Year Ended December 31, 2018		
Cash Flow from Operating Activities		
Net Income	$56,200	
Adjustments to Reconcile Net Income to Net Cash Provided (Used) by Operating Activities		
Depreciation Expense	3,100	
Changes in Opening Assets and Liabilities		
Increase in Accounts Receivable	(31,000)	
Increase in Merchandise Inventory	(33,000)	
Decrease in Accounts Payable	(26,000)	
Net Cash Provided (Used) by Operating Activities		($30,700)
Cash Flow from Investing Activities		
Purchase of Equipment	(95,000)	
Sale of Land	120,000	
Net Cash Provided (Used) by Investing Activities		25,000
Cash Flow from Financing Activities		
Proceeds from Issuance of Common Stock	10,000	
Proceeds from Notes Payable	45,000	
Dividends Paid	(40,000)	
Net Cash Provided (Used) by Financing Activities		15,000
Net Increase (Decrease) in Cash		9,300
Cash at the Beginning of the Year		12,000
Cash at the End of the Year		$21,300

Required

a) The company had a net income during the year; however, they had a negative cash flow from operations. Identify the problems that led to a negative cash flow from operations.

_____

_____

_____

_____

b) Even though cash flow from operations was negative, total cash increased by $9,300. How did cash increase?

_____

_____

_____

c)   Are there any other concerns regarding the statement of cash flows that have not been covered in parts a) and b)?

_____

_____

_____

AP-17B LO 1 2

Dawson Corporation has prepared the following statement of cash flows for the year end.

Dawson Corporation Statement of Cash Flows For the Year Ended December 31, 2018		
Cash Flow from Operating Activities		
Net Income	$68,000	
Adjustments to Reconcile Net Income to Net Cash		
Provided (Used) by Operating Activities		
Depreciation Expense	3,700	
Gain on Sale of Equipment	(8,000)	
Changes in Operating Assets and Liabilities		
Decrease in Accounts Receivable	15,000	
Increase in Merchandise Inventory	(60,000)	
Decrease in Accounts Payable	(5,000)	
Net Cash Provided (Used) by Operating Activities		$13,700
Cash Flow from Investing Activities		
Sale of Equipment	84,000	
Purchase of Land	(240,000)	
Net Cash Provided (Used) by Investing Activities		(156,000)
Cash Flow from Financing Activities		
Proceeds from Issuance of Common Stock	30,000	
Proceeds from Notes Payable	120,000	
Payment of Dividends	(10,000)	
Net Cash Provided (Used) by Financing Activities		140,000
Net Increase (Decrease) in Cash		(2,300)
Cash at the Beginning of the Year		12,000
Cash at the End of the year		$9,700

Required

a)   The company had a total decrease in cash during the year of $2,300. What is the primary cause of this decrease in cash?

_____

_____

_____

b)   Are there any concerns with operating activities?

_____

_____

Analysis

In a cash flow budgeting meeting, the company's CEO argued that, "we could have taken a larger loan to finance our land purchase in 2018. In fact, instead of borrowing only $120,000, we should have asked for $240,000. That would have put us into a better cash flow situation." Evaluate this comment from the CEO. How would a larger loan affect the cash flow of Dawson Corporation?

_____

_____

_____

_____

_____

_____

_____

_____

_____

AP-18B LO 7

The balance sheet and income statement for Joe's Fish Hut are presented below.

	2018	**2017**
Joe's Fish Hut		
Balance Sheet		
As at December 31		
Assets		
Cash	$2,100	$23,000
Accounts Receivable	21,000	12,000
Merchandise Inventory	21,000	25,000
Total Current Assets	44,100	60,000
Land	100,000	100,000
Equipment	170,000	150,000
Accumulated Depreciation	(28,600)	(25,000)
Total Assets	$285,500	$285,000
Liabilities		
Current Liabilities		
Accounts Payable	$23,000	$33,000
Notes Payable, Current Portion	12,000	12,000
Total Current Liabilities	35,000	45,000
Notes Payable, Long-Term Portion	48,000	60,000
Total Liabilities	83,000	105,000
Stockholders' Equity		
Paid-In Capital		
Preferred Stock	4,000	0
Common Stock	15,000	15,000
Additional Paid-In Capital	1,000	0
Total Paid-In Capital	20,000	15,000
Retained Earnings	182,500	165,000
Total Stockholders' Equity	202,500	180,000
Total Liabilities and Stockholders' Equity	$285,500	$285,000

Joe's Fish Hut	
Income Statement	
For the Year Ended December 31, 2018	
Sales	$161,000
Cost of Goods Sold	112,700
Gross Profit	48,300
Operating Expenses	
Depreciation Expense	3,600
Other Operating Expenses	19,700
Total Operating Expenses	23,300
Income before Income Tax Expense	25,000
Income Tax Expense	7,500
Net Income (Loss)	$17,500

Notes:

The company did not sell any equipment during the year. The company did not sign any additional note payable in 2018.

Prepare a statement of cash flows using a work sheet (spreadsheet) by means of the indirect method.

	Joe's Fish Hut					
	Work Sheet (Spreadsheet) for Statement of Cash Flows					
	For the Year Ended December 31					
	Balance		**Changes**			**Balance**
	Dec 31, 2017		**Debit**		**Credit**	**Dec 31, 2018**

Case Study

CS-1 LO 2

Granite Surfaces specializes in making granite countertops. A new accounting clerk has compiled the following information to prepare the statement of cash flows for the year ended December 31, 2018.

- Net income for the year was $114,140.
- Depreciation expense was $15,300.
- Equipment was sold for a gain of $16,000. Cash proceeds from the sale were $36,000.
- Equipment was purchased for $250,000.
- Dividends of $50,000 were paid.
- Accounts receivable increased by $31,400.
- Merchandise inventory decreased by $38,700.
- Accounts payable increased by $41,100.
- Notes payable increased by $55,000.
- Stock was sold for $50,000 (also its book value).
- Cash balance on January 1, 2018 was $114,800.
- Cash balance on December 31, 2018 was $117,640.

The statement of cash flows the accounting clerk prepared is shown below.

Granite Surfaces Statement of Cash Flows For the Year Ended December 31, 2018		
Cash Flow from Operating Activities		
Net Income	$114,140	
Adjustments to Reconcile Net Income to Net Cash Provided (Used) by Operating Activities		
Depreciation Expense	15,300	
Changes in Operating Assets and Liabilities		
Increase in Accounts Receivable	31,400	
Decrease in Merchandise Inventory	(38,700)	
Increase in Accounts Payable	41,100	
Sale of Equipment	36,000	
Purchase of Equipment	(250,000)	
Net Cash Provided (Used) by Operating Activities		($50,760)
Cash Flow from Investing Activities		
Proceeds from Notes Payable	55,000	
Net Cash Provided (Used) by Investing Activities		55,000
Cash Flow from Financing Activities		
Payment of Cash Dividend	(50,000)	
Proceeds from Issuance of Common Stock	50,000	
Net Cash Provided (Used) by Financing Activities		0
Net Increase (Decrease) in Cash		4,240
Cash at the Beginning of the Year		114,800
Cash at the End of the Year		$119,040

Required

a) Identify the problems with the statement of cash flows that the accounting clerk prepared.

_____

_____

_____

_____

_____

_____

b) Prepare a corrected statement of cash flows.

Notes

Chapter 20

FINANCIAL STATEMENT ANALYSIS

LEARNING OBJECTIVES

LO 1 Explain the importance of analyzing financial statements

LO 2 Conduct a horizontal and vertical analysis of financial statements

LO 3 Calculate and apply liquidity ratios

LO 4 Calculate and apply profitability ratios

LO 5 Calculate and apply operations management and solvency ratios

LO 6 Calculate and apply capital market ratios

LO 7 Identify the limitations of financial statement analysis

AMEENGAGE™ *Access **ameengage.com** for integrated resources including tutorials, practice exercises, the digital textbook and more.*

─────────────── **Assessment Questions** ───────────────

AS-1 LO 1

What is financial analysis?

AS-2 LO 1

What is the Management's Discussion and Analysis (MD&A) section in a company's annual report?

AS-3 LO 4

What is the formula for gross profit margin?

AS-4 LO 4

What does gross profit margin tell us?

AS-5 LO 5

What is the formula for the times interest earned ratio?

AS-6 `LO 5`

Is it more preferable to have a higher or lower interest coverage ratio? Explain.

_____

_____

AS-7 `LO 4`

How do you calculate net profit margin?

_____

_____

AS-8 `LO 4`

What is the formula for return on equity?

_____

_____

AS-9 `LO 4`

For a particular company, if net income increased significantly from one year to the next, does this guarantee that the return on equity will also increase? Explain.

_____

_____

_____

AS-10 `LO 4`

What is the formula for return on assets?

_____

_____

AS-11 `LO 4`

What are some possible reasons why return on assets may have decreased from one period to the next?

_____

_____

AS-12 `LO 4`

Suppose that Company A and Company B generate the same level of net income each period. However, Company A is more capital-intensive than Company B. Which company will likely have the higher return on assets?

_____

_____

AS-13 `LO 3`

What is the formula for the current ratio?

_____

_____

AS-14 LO 3

What does the current ratio tell you?

_____

_____

AS-15 LO 3

If current assets stay constant from one period to the next, but current liabilities increase, what will happen to the current ratio?

_____

_____

AS-16 LO 3

What is the formula for the quick ratio?

_____

_____

AS-17 LO 5

What is the formula for the debt-to-equity ratio?

_____

_____

AS-18 LO 5

What is the formula for days' sales outstanding?

_____

_____

AS-19 LO 5

What does days' sales outstanding tell you?

_____

_____

_____

AS-20 LO 5

How do you calculate accounts receivable turnover?

_____

_____

AS-21 LO 5

How is days' sales in inventory calculated?

_____

_____

AS-22 LO 5

What is the formula for the inventory turnover ratio?

_____

_____

AS-23 LO 7

Why is it necessary to compare a company's calculated ratios with industry benchmarks?

_____

_____

_____

_____

AS-24 LO 6

How is book value per common share calculated?

_____

_____

AS-25 LO 6

What does book value per common share tell us?

_____

_____

_____

_____

_____

AS-26 LO 6

How is earnings per share calculated? And what does it tell us?

_____

_____

_____

AS-27 LO 2

How does the base-year differ from the base-figure?

_____

_____

_____

_____

Application Questions Group A

AP-1A LO 4

Simply Mullet Company reported the following.
- Sales: $1,000,000
- Cost of Goods Sold: $700,000
- Operating Expenses: $400,000
- Income Tax Rate: 20%

Calculate the gross profit margin. Differentiate between gross profit margin and gross profit.

_____

_____

_____

_____

_____

_____

_____

AP-2A LO 4 5

Trooper Nova Company reported the following.

Sales	$2,000,000
Cost of Goods Sold	700,000
Operating Expenses	400,000
Interest Expense included in Operating Expenses	50,000
Income Taxes	40% of income before tax
Stockholders' Equity (Average)	$20,000,000

Required
a) Calculate net income.

_____

_____

_____

b) Calculate the net profit margin.

_____

_____

_____

c) Calculate the times interest earned

_____

_____

_____

d) Calculate the return on equity. Banks are currently paying interest of 4% on deposits invested for two or more years. Comment on the ratio.

_____

_____

_____

_____

_____

AP-3A `LO 3`

All-You-Can-Buy Company reports current assets of $6,572, and current liabilities of $2,786. Calculate the current ratio and the working capital.

_____

_____

_____

AP-4A `LO 3`

Total current liabilities for Nicholson Restoration Company are $2,786. If cash is $2,000, short-term investments are $3,000, long-term investments are $1,000 and accounts receivable is $1,200, calculate the quick ratio.

_____

_____

AP-5A `LO 4`

The income statement of Ellen Corporation for the years 2017 and 2018 showed the following gross profit.

	2018	2017
Net Sales	$97,200	$80,000
Cost of Goods Sold	72,000	50,000
Gross Profit	$25,200	$30,000

Required

a) Calculate the gross profit margins for both years.

_____

_____

_____

_____

b) In which year does Ellen Corporation have a better gross profit margin? Explain.

_____

_____

_____

_____

AP-6A LO 5

Kingston Company sells on credit, with the balance due in 30 days. The company's DSO ratio has changed from 60 days last year to 42 days this year. Are things getting better or worse? Explain the relationship between the sales terms and DSO.

_____

_____

_____

AP-7A LO 4 5

Presented below is the comparative income statement of Newton Company for 2018 and 2017.

Newton Company Income Statement For the Year Ended December 31		
	2018	**2017**
Sales	$194,890	$108,345
Cost of Goods Sold	116,934	65,007
Gross Profit	77,956	43,338
Operating Expenses		
Administrative Expense	12,000	8,000
Selling Expense Expense	22,540	13,627
Total Operating Expenses	34,540	21,627
Other Income and Expenses		
Interest Expense	1,248	580
Income before Income Tax Expense	42,168	21,131
Income Tax Expense	12,650	6,339
Net Income	**$29,518**	**$14,792**

Required

a) Calculate the following ratios for both years.

	2018	2017
Net Profit Margin		
Times Interest Earned Ratio		

b) In which year does the company have a better performance with respect to the ratios calculated in part a)? Explain.

_____

_____

_____

_____

AP-8A `LO 5`

At the beginning of 2018, Acatela Corp. had inventory of $350,000. During the year, it purchased $220,000 worth of raw materials and sold $500,000 worth of inventory. Determine the inventory turnover ratio and the days' sales in inventory.

_____

_____

_____

_____

_____

_____

_____

AP-9A `LO 5`

At the end of 2018, accounts receivable amounted to $200,000. At the beginning of the year, it was $165,000. Net credit sales for the year amounted to $813,000 and net income was calculated to be $229,000.

Determine the days' sales outstanding ratio and the accounts receivable turnover ratio. Comment on the ability of the company to enforce its credit policy of 60 days.

_____

_____

_____

_____

AP-10A `LO 3`

Selected financial data from Crew Company is provided below.

	As at December 31, 2018
Cash	$75,000
Accounts Receivable	$225,000
Merchandise Inventory	$270,000
Short-Term Investments	$40,000
Land and Building	$500,000
Current Portion of Long-Term Debt	$30,000
Accounts Payable	$120,000

Required

a) Calculate the quick ratio.

_____

_____

_____

_____

b) What does Crew Company's quick ratio suggest about the company's performance?

_____

_____

AP-11A `LO 5`

Bo Kyung Company had a debt-to-equity ratio last year of 1.46. This year, the ratio is 2.0. Are things getting better or worse? Explain your answer.

_____

_____

_____

AP-12A `LO 4 5`

Presented below are select figures from the balance sheet of Edison Company for 2018 and 2017.

Edison Company Balance Sheet As at August 31		
	2018	**2017**
Total Assets	$286,633	$203,311
Total Liabilities	119,006	69,873
Stockholders' Equity	167,627	133,438

In 2018, Edison Company had sales of $413,000 and net income of $46,500. Calculate the ratios for 2018 as indicated below.

Return on Assets
Asset Turnover
Debt-to-Equity
Debt-to-Total-Assets

AP-13A `LO 6`

Testa Inc. had a net income of $158,000 for the year ended December 31, 2018. The company does not have any preferred stock and has 45,000 common shares outstanding for the entire year. During the year, they paid out $20,000 in dividends. Assume the market price of each common share is $24, which happens to be double of the book value per share.

Required

a) Calculate earnings per share.

_____

_____

_____

_____

b) Calculate the dividend yield.

_____

_____

_____

_____

c) Calculate the price-earnings ratio.

_____

_____

_____

_____

AP-14A LO 6

Freebird Inc. had a net income of $358,400 for the year ended September 30, 2018. The company does not have any preferred stock and has 113,000 common shares outstanding for the entire year. During the year, they paid out $60,000 in dividends. Stockholders' equity is valued at $332,000. Assume the market price of each common share at the company's year end is $17 per share.

Required

a) Calculate earnings per share.

b) Calculate the dividend yield.

c) Calculate the price-earnings ratio.

d) Calculate the book value per common share.

Analysis

Book value per common share is rarely equal to the selling price of the share on the stock market. What are some factors that could cause the market value to differ from the book value?

AP-15A LO 4

Below is select financial statement information for Rock Co. and Roll Inc.

	Rock Co.	Roll Inc.
Income Statement		
Sales	$348,500	$465,800
Cost of Goods Sold	106,293	160,701
Gross Profit	242,208	305,099
Expenses		
Salaries Expense	52,275	69,870
Depreciation Expense	34,850	46,580
Advertising Expense	17,425	23,290
Interest Expense	15,683	37,264
Total Expenses	120,233	177,004
Income before Income Tax Expense	121,975	128,095
Income Tax Expense	62,730	83,844
Net Income	$59,245	$44,251
Balance Sheet		
Cash	$14,850	$19,800
Accounts Receivable	25,000	22,500
Merchandise Inventory	34,500	43,125
Equipment	85,800	81,510
Total Assets	$160,150	$166,935
Accounts Payable	$27,500	$24,750
Unearned Revenue	17,800	19,580
Long-Term Liabilities	29,350	62,925
Stockholders' Equity	85,500	59,680
Total Liabilities and Stockholders' Equity	$160,150	$166,935

Required

a) Calculate the profitability ratios shown in the table below. For any ratios that require an average value from the balance sheet accounts, just use the single figure provided for each company.

	Rock Co.	Roll Inc.
Gross Profit Margin		
Net Profit Margin		
Return on Equity (ROE)		
Return on Assets (ROA)		

b) Based on the ratios from part a), which company would an investor be more likely to invest in?

AP-16A LO 3 4 5

Chicken Inc. and Egg Inc. are both in the toy retail business. All sales are on credit. Below is select financial information for the current year.

	Chicken Inc.	Egg Inc.
Income Statement		
Sales	$150,000	$135,000
Cost of Goods Sold	48,750	41,850
Gross Profit	101,250	93,150
Expenses		
Salaries Expense	22,500	27,000
Depreciation Expense	15,000	13,500
Advertising Expense	7,500	6,750
Interest Expense	6,750	5,130
Total Expenses	51,750	52,380
Income before Income Tax Expense	49,500	40,770
Income Tax Expense	26,250	24,300
Net Income	$23,250	$16,470
Balance Sheet		
Cash	$40,850	$24,510
Accounts Receivable	15,000	9,000
Merchandise Inventory	34,500	20,125
Equipment	85,800	51,480
Total Assets	$176,150	$105,115
Accounts Payable	21,000	32,000
Unearned Revenue	27,800	18,670
Long-Term Liabilities	39,350	15,635
Stockholders' Equity	88,000	38,810
Total Liabilities and Stockholders' Equity	$176,150	$105,115

Required

a) Calculate each ratio listed below for each company and indicate which company is better for each one. For any ratios that require an average value from the balance sheet accounts, just use the single figure provided for each company.

	Chicken Inc.	Egg Inc.	Which company is better?
Gross Profit Margin			
Net Profit Margin			
Return on Equity (ROE)			
Return on Assets (ROA)			
Asset Turnover			
Current Ratio			
Quick Ratio			
Debt-to-Equity Ratio			
Debt-to-Total-Assets Ratio			
Days' Sales Outstanding			
Accounts Receivable Turnover			
Days' Sales in Inventory			
Inventory Turnover			

b) Examining all of the ratios, explain which company has a stronger financial position in regards to the following categories.

i. Profitability

ii. Liquidity

iii. Managerial performance

iv. Solvency

AP-17A LO 3 4 5

The bookkeeper for Contigo Corporation has calculated several ratios for the past three fiscal years, shown below.

Required

a) For each of the ratios, indicate whether the ratio is improving or weakening overall from the previous years.

Contigo Corporation				
Ratio	2018	2017	2016	Improving or Weakening?
Gross Profit Margin	32.80%	31.50%	31.10%	
Return on Common Stockholders' Equity	18.04%	17.33%	17.11%	
Times Interest Earned Ratio	11.60	12.10	12.20	
Current Ratio	1.50	1.31	0.97	
Quick Ratio	0.90	0.79	0.73	
Debt-to-Equity Ratio	0.53	0.61	0.86	
Days' Sales Oustanding	31.50	31.20	30.80	
Days' Sales in Inventory	78.10	76.54	73.41	

b) Contigo is looking at applying for a new bank loan. The bank will examine the ratios that focus on the strength of Contigo's cash flow to determine if they should approve the loan. Based on the information in part a), would you recommend the bank to approve the bank loan? Why or why not?

_____

_____

_____

_____

_____

AP-18A LO 2

Perform a horizontal analysis for Groff Inc. Use 2015 as the base year and comment on the results.

Groff Inc. In Millions of Dollars				
	2018	**2017**	**2016**	**2015**
Sales Revenue	500	400	300	200
Net Income	166	158	144	120

Groff Inc. In Millions of Dollars				
	2018	**2017**	**2016**	**2015**
Sales Revenue				
Revenue Ratio				
Net Income				
Net Income Ratio				

_____

_____

AP-19A LO 2

The following financial statements are taken from the records of Abaya Inc.

Abaya Inc. Balance Sheet As at December 31			
	2018	**2017**	**2016**
Current Assets			
Cash	$315,000	$325,000	$210,000
Accounts Receivable	140,000	198,000	92,000
Merchandise Inventory	411,000	397,000	428,000
Short-Term Investments	115,000	100,000	100,000
Total Current Assets	981,000	1,020,000	830,000
Noncurrent Assets	356,000	250,000	403,000
Total Assets	$1,337,000	$1,270,000	$1,233,000
Current Liabilities	214,000	265,000	90,000
Long-Term Liabilities	22,000	150,000	100,000
Total Liabilities	236,000	415,000	190,000
Stockholders' Equity	1,101,000	855,000	1,043,000
Total Liabilities and Stockholders' Equity	$1,337,000	$1,270,000	$1,233,000

Abaya Inc. Income Statement For the Year Ended December 31			
	2018	**2017**	**2016**
Sales	$701,000	$689,000	$514,000
Cost of Goods Sold	379,000	396,000	385,000
Gross Profit	322,000	293,000	129,000
Operating Expenses			
Administrative Expense	28,050	15,780	16,100
Selling Expense	65,000	34,000	30,000
Total Operating Expenses	93,050	49,780	46,100
Other Income and Expenses			
Interest Expense	18,600	12,600	8,500
Income before Income Tax Expense	210,350	230,620	74,400
Income Tax Expense	63,105	69,186	22,320
Net Income	$147,245	$161,434	$52,080

Required

a) Use horizontal analysis techniques to compare the changes between the 2018 and 2017 balance sheet items.

Abaya Inc. Balance Sheet As at December 31				
	2018	**2017**	**$ Change**	**% Change**
Current Assets				
Cash	$315,000	$325,000		
Accounts Receivable	140,000	198,000		
Merchandise Inventory	411,000	397,000		
Short-Term Investments	115,000	100,000		
Total Current Assets	981,000	1,020,000		
Noncurrent Assets	356,000	250,000		
Total Assets	$1,337,000	$1,270,000		
Current Liabilities	214,000	265,000		
Long-Term Liabilities	22,000	150,000		
Total Liabilities	236,000	415,000		
Stockholders' Equity	1,101,000	855,000		
Total Liabilities and Stockholders' Equity	$1,337,000	$1,270,000		

b) Using 2016 as a base year, provide a horizontal analysis of sales, gross profit, operating expenses and net income.

	2018	2017	2016
Sales			
Gross Profit			
Operating Expenses			
Net Income			

_____

_____

_____

c) Perform a vertical analysis of income statement for 2018, 2017 and 2016 and state all of the income statement items as a percentage of net sales.

Abaya Inc.
Income Statement
For the Year Ended December 31

	2018	2017	2016
Sales			
Cost of Goods Sold			
Gross Profit			
Operating Expenses			
Administrative Expense			
Selling Expense			
Total Operating Expenses			
Other Income and Expenses			
Interest Expense			
Income before Income Tax Expense			
Income Tax Expense			
Net Income			

_____

_____

_____

_____

AP-20A LO 2

Perform a vertical analysis (use Sales as the base) for Hiltonia Inc. Comment on the results. Note that figures are in millions of dollars.

Hiltonia Inc.		
	2018	2017
Sales	$210	$250
COGS	150	200
Gross Profit	60	50
Selling Expenses	5	4
Salaries	2	2
Rent	5	5
Total Expenses	12	11
Income before Tax	48	39
Taxes (35%)	16.8	13.65
Net Income	$31.2	$25.35

Hiltonia Inc.				
	2018	**% of Sales**	**2017**	**% of Sales**
Sales				
COGS				
Gross Profit				
Selling Expenses				
Salaries				
Rent				
Total Expenses				
Income before Tax				
Taxes (35%)				
Net Income				

_____

_____

_____

_____

_____

_____

AP-21A `LO 3 4 5 6`

The income statements and balance sheets for Fallon Inc. are shown below for the last three fiscal years.

Fallon Inc. Income Statement For the Year Ended			
	2018	**2017**	**2016**
Sales	$360,000	$324,000	$342,000
Cost of Goods Sold	108,000	89,100	85,500
Gross Profit	252,000	234,900	256,500
Expenses			
Operating Expense	54,000	48,600	51,300
Depreciation Expense	36,000	32,400	34,200
Advertising Expense	18,000	16,200	17,100
Interest Expense	6,800	7,650	8,500
Total Expenses	114,800	104,850	111,100
Income before Income Tax Expense	137,200	130,050	145,400
Income Tax Expense	72,000	64,800	68,400
Net Income	$ 65,200	$65,250	$77,000

Fallon Inc. Balance Sheet At the Year Ended			
	2018	**2017**	**2016**
Cash	$63,650	$39,750	$36,000
Short-Term Investments	11,000	10,000	8,000
Accounts Receivable	48,000	40,000	32,000
Merchandise Inventory	18,000	22,500	27,000
Equipment	110,000	104,500	83,600
Total Assets	$250,650	$216,750	$186,600
Accounts Payable	$52,800	$44,000	$35,200
Current Portion of Long-Term Debt	8,500	8,500	8,500
Long-Term Debt	68,000	76,500	85,000
Common Stock	66,000	57,600	57,000
Retained Earnings	55,350	30,150	900
Total Liabilities and Stockholders' Equity	$250,650	$216,750	$186,600

Other Information

1) Fallon Inc. has an unlimited number of shares authorized. The following number of common shares were outstanding in each year for the entire year: 2018—50,000, 2017—48,000, 2016—47,000.

2) The following dividends were paid: $40,000 in 2018, $36,000 in 2017 and $38,000 in 2016.

Required

a) Calculate the following ratios for Fallon Inc. for 2017 and 2018, and state whether the ratio improved or weakened in 2018.

	2018	2017	Improved or Weakened
Gross Profit Margin			
Times Interest Earned Ratio			
Net Profit Margin			
Return on Equity (ROE)			
Return on Assets (ROA)			
Asset Turnover			
Current Ratio			
Quick Ratio			
Debt-to-Equity Ratio			
Debt-to-Total-Assets Ratio			
Days' Sales Outstanding			
Accounts Receivable Turnover			
Days' Sales in Inventory			
Inventory Turnover			
Book Value per Common Share			
Earnings per Share			

b) Fallon Inc. has a credit policy of 30 days. That is, it expects all customers to pay their bills within 30 days from sale. Comment on the company's ability to enforce this policy.

_____

_____

_____

_____

Analysis

Comment on the company's ability to cover its short-term debt obligations.

_____

_____

_____

_____

_____

AP-22A LO 4

The stockholders' equity section of Adora Corporation's balance sheet as at December 31, 2017 and 2018 is presented below.

	2018	2017
Stockholders' Equity		
Paid-In Capital		
Preferred stock, $7, noncumulative, 10,000 shares authorized,		
1,000 shares issued and outstanding	$100,000	$100,000
Common stock, unlimited shares authorized,		
50,000 shares issued and outstanding	500,000	500,000
Total Paid-In Capital	600,000	600,000
Retained Earnings	338,000	300,000
Total Stockholders' Equity	938,000	900,000

Both preferred and common stock do not have par value. There were no changes in the number of shares of preferred and common stock during 2017 and 2018. Adora announced and paid preferred dividends of $7 per share and common dividends of $0.50 per share in 2018. Its net income in 2018 was $70,000.

Required

a) Calculate Adora's return on equity for 2018. Round your answer to two decimal places.

b) Calculate Adora's return on common stockholders' equity for the year 2018. Round your answer to two decimal places.

Application Questions Group B

AP-1B `LO 4`

Gross profit increased from $300,000 in 2017, to $400,000 in 2018. Gross profit margin decreased from 30% in 2017, to 28% in 2018. Comment on whether or not the company's profitability improved or deteriorated.

AP-2B `LO 4 5`

Sou Heng Company reported the following financial information at the end of 2018.

Sales Revenue	$2,110,000
Cost of Goods Sold	$740,000
Operating Expenses	$394,000
Interest Expense included in Operating Expenses	$53,000
Income Tax Expense	38% of income
Stockholders' Equity (Average)	$18,000,000

Required

a) Calculate net income.

b) Calculate the net profit margin.

c) Calculate the times interest earned.

d) Calculate the return on equity.

AP-3B `LO 3`

Goliath Gardening Services Ltd. reports current assets of $6,261, and current liabilities of $2,925. Calculate the current ratio and the working capital. Comment on the company's ability to cover short-term obligations.

AP-4B LO 3

Selected financial data from Jai Home Company is provided below.

Cash	$85,000
Accounts Receivable	$233,000
Merchandise Inventory	$267,000
Short-Term Investments	$50,000
Land and Building	$464,000
Current Portion of Long-Term Debt	$36,000
Accounts Payable	$117,000

Required

a) Calculate the quick ratio.

b) True or False? The quick ratio calculated in part a) shows that Jai Home Company is likely to meet its short-term cash obligations.

AP-5B LO 4

The income statement for Ellen Corporation for the years 2017 and 2018 showed the following information.

	2018	2017
Sales Revenue	$98,000	$66,000
Cost of Goods Sold	$77,000	$43,000
Gross Profit	$21,000	$23,000

Required

a) Calculate the gross profit margins for both years.

b) In which year does Ellen Corporation have a better gross profit margin?

AP-6B LO 5

At the end of 2018, accounts receivable for Genuine Interiors amounted to $210,000. At the beginning of the year, it was $200,000. Net credit sales for the year amounted to $900,000 and net income was calculated to be $205,000.

Determine the days' sales outstanding ratio and the accounts receivable turnover ratio.

Analysis

Generally, a lower days' sales outstanding (DSO) is desirable, since it means collections are happening faster for the company. Is there any drawback to getting the DSO extremely low, such as to only two or three days?

_____

_____

_____

_____

_____

AP-7B LO 4 5

Presented below is the comparative income statement of JeansWear Company for 2018 and 2017.

JeansWear Company Income Statement For the Year Ended January 31		
	2018	**2017**
Sales	$184,794	$107,933
Cost of Goods Sold	115,550	69,022
Gross Profit	69,244	38,911
Operating Expenses		
Administrative Expense	9,770	4,485
Selling Expense	22,000	16,000
Total Operating Expenses	31,770	20,485
Other Income and Expenses		
Interest Expense	1,343	579
Income before Income Tax Expense	36,131	17,847
Income Tax Expense	10,839	5,354
Net Income	$25,292	$12,493

Required

a) Calculate the following ratios for both years.

	2018	**2017**
Net Profit Margin		
Times Interest Earned Ratio		

b) In which year does the company have a better performance with respect to the net profit margin calculated in part a)?

_____

_____

AP-8B LO 5

At the beginning of 2018, Percolate Corp. had inventory of $337,000. During the year, it purchased $210,000 worth of raw materials and sold $505,000 worth of inventory. Determine the inventory turnover ratio and the days' sales in inventory. Comment on the company's ability to sell its inventory, which has a shelf-life of 90 days.

_____

_____

_____

_____

_____

AP-9B `LO 5 7`

Below is the past annual information for Java Time Inc. All sales are on credit.

	2018	2017	2016	2015
Sales	$44,500	$46,280	$47,900	$55,085
Sales Discounts	2,003	2,083	2,155	2,479
Net Sales	42,498	44,197	45,744	52,606
Accounts Receivable	6,130	5,885	5,649	5,084

Required

a) Calculate the following ratios for 2016, 2017 and 2018.

	2018	2017	2016
Days' Sales Outstanding			
Accounts Receivable Turnover			

b) Are the ratios improving or weakening? What could the company do to better control these ratios?

_____

_____

_____

_____

_____

AP-10B `LO 3`

Information from Silky Company's year-end financial statements is as follows.

	2018	2017
Current Assets	$200,000	$210,000
Current Liabilities	100,000	90,000
Stockholders' Equity	250,000	270,000
Net Sales	830,000	880,000
Cost of Goods Sold	620,000	640,000
Operating Income	50,000	55,000

Required

a) Calculate the current ratio for both years.

_____

_____

_____

_____

b) In which year does Silky Company have a better current ratio? Explain.

_____

_____

_____

AP-11B LO 4

Selected information for the Universal Company is as follows.

| | **December 31** | | |
	2018	**2017**	**2016**
Common Stock	$840,000	$648,000	$550,000
Retained Earnings	370,000	248,000	150,000
Net Income for the Year	240,000	122,000	98,000

Required

a) Calculate the return on equity ratio for 2018 and 2017.

_____

_____

_____

_____

b) Has the Universal Company's performance improved in 2018? Explain using the return on equity ratio.

_____

_____

_____

_____

AP-12B LO 5

Below is selected financial information for Swingline Inc.

	2018	**2017**	**2016**	**2015**
Ending Inventory	4,850	5,626	5,723	6,014
Cost of Goods Sold	68,950	72,398	65,503	71,708

Required

a) Calculate the following ratios for 2018, 2017 and 2016.

	2018	**2017**	**2016**
Days' Sales in Inventory			
Inventory Turnover			

b) Are the ratios improving or weakening? What could the company do to better control these ratios?

_____

_____

_____

_____

_____

AP-13B LO 6

Bluebird Inc. had a net income of $387,400 for the year ended August 31, 2018. The company does not have any preferred stock and has 125,000 shares of common stock outstanding for the entire year. During the year, they paid out $60,000 in dividends. Assume the market price of each common share at the company's year end is $12 per share.

Required

a) Calculate earnings per share.

b) Calculate the dividend yield.

c) Calculate the price-earnings ratio.

AP-14B LO 6

Below is select financial statement information for Beta Corp. and Gamma Inc. in 2018.

	Beta Corp.	Gamma Inc.
Net Income	$157,840	$246,850
Stockholders' Equity		
Preferred Stock	$8,740	$74,055
Common Stock	102,596	160,453
Retained Earnings	7,352	4,355
Total Stockholders' Equity	118,688	238,863
Number of Common Shares Outstanding	10,820	12,400

Both Beta and Gamma declared preferred dividends in 2018. For Beta, the total preferred dividends were equal to 5% of net income; for Gamma, they were equal to 8% of net income.

Required

a) Calculate the following ratios for each company.

	Beta Corp.	Gamma Inc.
Book Value per Common Share		
Earnings per Share (EPS)		

b) Based on the ratios from part a), which company would an investor be more likely to invest in?

_____

_____

_____

_____

AP-15B LO 3 4 5

Below is select financial statement information for Alpha Inc. and Delta Corp.

	Alpha Inc.	Delta Corp.
Income Statement		
Sales	$105,000	$87,000
Cost of Goods Sold	34,125	29,580
Gross Profit	70,875	57,420
Expenses		
Salaries Expense	15,750	13,050
Depreciation Expense	10,500	8,700
Advertising Expense	5,250	4,350
Interest Expense	8,925	4,524
Total Expenses	40,425	30,624
Income before Income Tax Expense	30,450	26,796
Income Tax Expense	18,900	15,660
Net Income	$11,550	$11,136
Balance Sheet		
Cash	$18,525	$24,700
Accounts Receivable	12,300	21,070
Merchandise Inventory	34,500	30,125
Equipment	66,800	63,460
Total Assets	$132,125	$139,355
Accounts Payable	$43,530	$33,177
Unearned Revenue	17,800	29,580
Current Portion of Long-Term Debt	8,304	1,324
Long-Term Debt	27,680	8,825
Stockholders' Equity	34,811	66,449
Total Liabilities and Stockholders' Equity	$132,125	$139,355

Required

a) Calculate the liquidity and solvency ratios as shown in the table below.

	Alpha Inc.	Delta Corp.
Debt-to-Total-Assets Ratio		
Times Interest Earned Ratio		
Current Ratio		
Quick Ratio		
Debt-to-Equity Ratio		

b) Which company has stronger liquidity and solvency ratios? Which company would a bank prefer to provide lending to based on the calculations in part a)?

_____

_____

_____

_____

_____

_____

_____

_____

_____

_____

_____

AP-16B LO 7

The following information is available for three different companies within the same industry.

	Company A	Company B	Company C
Cash	$7,800	$7,020	$10,530
Short-Term Investments	2,000	1,800	4,700
Accounts Receivable	8,250	7,425	13,138
Prepaid Expenses	1,500	1,350	3,025
Merchandise Inventory	9,500	8,550	5,825
Total Current Assets	$29,050	$26,145	$37,218
Accounts Payable	$4,300	$4,515	$4,730
Deferred Revenue	7,500	7,875	8,250
Current Portion of Long-Term Debt	15,800	16,590	17,380
Total Current Liabilities	$27,600	$28,980	$30,360

Required

a) Calculate the current and quick ratios for each company listed below. Which company has the strongest and weakest liquidity?

	Company A	Company B	Company C
Current Ratio			
Quick Ratio			

b) Is the current ratio adequate for each company? Explain.

_____

_____

_____

c) Is the quick ratio adequate for each company? Explain.

_____

_____

_____

_____

_____

Analysis

All three companies are public companies and thus prepare their financial statements in accordance to GAAP. Does this mean that all values on their financial statements can be compared without further investigation into how the values were calculated?

_____

_____

_____

_____

_____

_____

AP-17B LO 3 4 5

The most recent income statements and balance sheets for Midland Company are shown below.

Midland Company Income Statement For the Year Ended		
	2018	**2017**
Sales (on Credit)	$600,000	$540,000
Cost of Goods Sold	252,000	216,000
Gross Profit	348,000	324,000
Expenses		
Salaries Expense	210,000	162,000
Depreciation Expense	48,000	54,000
Advertising Expense	60,000	54,000
Interest Expense	9,000	9,000
Total Expenses	327,000	279,000
Income before Income Tax Expense	21,000	45,000
Income Tax Expense	8,400	18,000
Net Income	$12,600	$27,000

Midland Company Balance Sheet At the Year Ended		
	2018	**2017**
Cash	$76,540	$41,400
Accounts Receivable	37,000	44,400
Merchandise Inventory	73,000	54,750
Equipment	110,000	158,000
Total Assets	$296,540	$298,550
Accounts Payable	$24,050	$28,860
Unearned Revenue	14,000	23,800
Long-Term Debt	60,000	60,000
Common Stock	50,000	50,000
Retained Earnings	148,490	135,890
Total Liabilities and Stockholders' Equity	$296,540	$298,550

Required

a) Calculate the following ratios for Midland Company for its 2018 fiscal year.

	Industry Average	Midland Company
Gross Profit Margin	40.0%	
Net Profit Margin	5.0%	
Return on Equity (ROE)	8.0%	
Return on Assets (ROA)	6.9%	
Quick Ratio	1.2	
Debt-to-Equity Ratio	0.75	
Days' Sales Outstanding	40.0	
Inventory Turnover	6.1	

b) Perform some ratio analysis to determine how Midland Company has performed in 2018 compared to the industry average.

_____

_____

_____

_____

_____

AP-18B LO 2

Perform a horizontal analysis for Mazzic Inc. Use 2015 as the base year.

Mazzic Inc. In Millions of Dollars				
	2018	**2017**	**2016**	**2015**
Revenue	$469	$331	$292	$197
Revenue Percentage of 2015 Base-Year				
Net Income	$258	$223	$178	$84
Net Income Percentage of 2015 Base-Year				

AP-19B LO 2

The following financial statements are taken from the records of Jade Inc.

Required

a) Use horizontal analysis techniques to compare the changes between 2018 and 2017 balance sheet items.

Jade Inc. Balance Sheet As at October 31				
	2018	**2017**	**$ Change**	**% Change**
Current Assets				
Cash	$318,300	$319,400		
Accounts Receivable	150,900	170,100		
Merchandise Inventory	381,200	414,800		
Short-Term Investments	116,500	104,700		
Total Current Assets	966,900	1,009,000		
Noncurrent Assets	527,850	318,900		
Total Assets	$1,494,750	$1,327,900		
Current Liabilities	$258,200	$224,600		
Long-Term Liabilities	126,900	109,500		
Total Liabilities	385,100	334,100		
Stockholders' Equity	1,109,650	993,800		
Total Liabilities and Equity	$1,494,750	$1,327,900		

b) Perform a vertical analysis of the income statement for 2018 and state all the income statement items as a percentage of net sales.

Jade Inc. Income Statement For the Year Ended October 31		
	2018	**2018**
Sales	$700,800	
Cost of Goods Sold	373,800	
Gross Profit	327,000	
Expenses		
Advertising	4,400	
Utilities	8,200	
Rent	4,300	
Salaries and Wages	47,000	
Depreciation	34,530	
Interest	7,620	
Total Expenses	106,050	
Income before Income Tax Expense	220,950	
Income Tax Expense	55,100	
Net Income	$165,850	

Analysis

Analyze the strengths and weaknesses of Jade's financial position based on the above horizontal and vertical analyses.

_____

_____

_____

_____

_____

_____

_____

_____

_____

_____

AP-20B LO 4 7

The financial information at December 31, 2018 for two similar companies is shown below.

	Shaken Inc.		Stirred Inc.	
Balance Sheet				
Average Total Assets		$80,000		$50,000
Average Stockholders' Equity		30,000		45,000
Income Statement				
Sales		100,000		68,000
Cost of Goods Sold		40,000		34,000
Gross Profit		60,000		34,000
Expenses				
Advertising Expense	$20,000		$5,000	
Salaries Expense	15,000		18,000	
Rent Expense	10,000		-	
Depreciation Expense	2,500		1,000	
Interest Expense	1,500		500	
Total Expenses		49,000		24,500
Net Income		$11,000		$9,500

Which company performed better during the year? Use relevant ratios to support your answer.

	Shaken Inc.	Stirred Inc.
Gross Profit Margin		
Net Profit Margin		
Asset Turnover		
Return on Equity		
Return on Assets		

_____

_____

_____

_____

_____

Analysis

The comparison between these two companies assumes they are following the same accounting standards (GAAP or IFRS). What impact, if any, would there be on the comparison if one followed GAAP and the other followed IFRS?

_____

_____

_____

_____

_____

_____

AP-21B LO 3 4 5 6

The income statements and balance sheets for Hathaway Inc. are shown below for the last three fiscal years. All sales are on credit.

Hathaway Inc. Income Statement For the Year Ended	2018	2017	2016
Sales	$800,000	$720,000	$760,000
Cost of Goods Sold	260,000	288,000	266,000
Gross Profit	540,000	432,000	494,000
Expenses			
Operating Expense	320,000	216,000	342,000
Depreciation Expense	64,000	72,000	76,000
Advertising Expense	80,000	72,000	114,000
Interest Expense	10,000	10,000	10,000
Total Expenses	474,000	370,000	542,000
Income (Loss) before Income Tax Expense (Benefit)	66,000	62,000	(48,000)
Income Tax Expense Benefit	29,700	27,900	(21,600)
Net Income (Loss)	$36,300	$34,100	($26,400)

Hathaway Inc. Balance Sheet At the Year Ended	2018	2017	2016
Cash	$234,400	$149,600	$80,000
Accounts Receivable	84,000	70,000	56,000
Merchandise Inventory	136,000	102,000	61,200
Equipment	110,000	174,000	246,000
Total Assets	$564,400	$495,600	$443,200
Accounts Payable	$54,600	$45,500	$36,400
Unearned Revenue	21,000	23,100	18,900
Long-Term Debt	50,000	50,000	50,000
Common Stock	85,500	60,000	55,000
Retained Earnings	353,300	317,000	282,900
Total Liabilities and Stockholders' Equity	$564,400	$495,600	$443,200

Other Information

Hathaway Inc. has an unlimited number of shares authorized; the following common shares were outstanding in each year for the entire year: 2018—60,000, 2017—40,000, 2016—30,000.

Required

a) Calculate the following ratios for Hathaway Inc. for 2017 and 2018, and state whether the ratio improved or weakened in 2018.

	2018	2017	Improved or Weakened
Gross Profit Margin			
Times Interest Earned Ratio			
Net Profit Margin			
Return on Equity (ROE)			
Return on Assets (ROA)			
Current Ratio			
Quick Ratio			
Debt-to-Equity Ratio			
Debt-to-Total-Assets Ratio			
Days' Sales Outstanding			
Accounts Receivable Turnover			
Days' Sales in Inventory			
Inventory Turnover			
Book Value Per Common Share			
Earnings Per Share			

b) The owner of Hathaway Inc. is pleased to see that the company has started generating profits again and assumes that profitability must be improving. Perform some ratio analysis to determine if the owner's assumption is correct or not. Explain.

Analysis

What does the company's inventory turnover ratio indicate/suggest?

AP-22B LO 4

The following information is extracted from the financial statements of Knight Inc. and Emperor Corp.

	Knight	Emperor
Sales Revenue	$600,000	$400,000
Net Income	70,000	35,000
Average Total Assets	1,600,000	1,000,000
Average Total Liabilities	650,000	200,000
Average Total Stockholders' Equity	950,000	800,000
Average Preferred Stock	40,000	150,000
Total preferred dividends declared and paid during the year	3,200	9,000
Total common dividends declared and paid during the year	6,000	4,900

Required

a) Calculate net profit margin for both companies.

_____

_____

_____

_____

b) Calculate return on equity for both companies.

_____

_____

_____

_____

c) Calculate return on common stockholders' equity for both companies.

_____

_____

_____

_____

_____

_____

_____

d) Calculate return on assets for both companies.

_____

_____

_____

_____

e) Based on all the ratios calculated in parts a) to d), which company's common stock is more attractive to potential investors?

_____

_____

_____

_____

_____

_____

_____

_____

_____

_____

_____

Case Study

CS-1 LO 3 4 5

Suppose that you have decided to invest some money in the stock market. After some research online, you come across the financial statements of Yong Wireless Limited. Before you can make a decision to invest in the company, you will need to calculate some key financial ratios and then analyze them. The statements are presented below.

Yong Wireless Limited Consolidated Balance Sheet (in thousands) As at February 28		
	2018	**2017**
Assets		
Cash	$1,550,861	$835,546
Short-Term Investments	360,614	682,666
Accounts Receivable	2,800,115	2,269,845
Merchandise Inventory	621,611	682,400
Other Current Assets	479,455	371,129
Total Current Assets	5,812,656	4,841,586
Long-Term Investment	958,248	720,635
Property, Plant and Equipment	1,956,581	1,334,648
Intangible Assets	1,476,924	1,204,503
Total Assets	$10,204,409	$8,101,372
Liabilities		
Accounts Payable	$615,620	$448,339
Accrued Liabilities	1,638,260	1,238,602
Income Taxes Payable	95,650	361,460
Other Current Liabilities	82,247	66,950
Total Current Liabilities	2,431,777	2,115,351
Long-Term Liabilities	169,969	111,893
Total Liabilities	2,601,746	2,227,244
Stockholders' Equity		
Common Stock	2,113,146	2,208,235
Retained Earnings	5,489,517	3,665,893
Stockholders' Equity	7,602,663	5,874,128
Liabilities and Stockholders' Equity	$10,204,409	$8,101,372

Yong Wireless Limited Consolidated Income Statement (in thousands) For the Year Ended February 28		
	2018	**2017**
Revenue	$14,953,224	$11,065,186
Cost of Sales	8,368,958	5,967,888
Gross Profit	6,584,266	5,097,298
Operating Expenses		
Research and Development	964,841	684,702
Selling, Marketing and Admin	1,907,398	1,495,697
Amortization Expense	310,357	194,803
Litigation Expense	163,800	0
Total Operating Expenses	3,346,396	2,375,202
Income from Operations	3,237,870	2,722,096
Other Income and Expenses		
Investment Income	28,640	78,267
Income before Income Tax Expense	3,266,510	2,800,363
Income Tax Expense	809,366	907,747
Net Income	$2,457,144	$1,892,616

Yong Wireless Limited Summary of the Statement of Cash Flows (in thousands) For the Year Ended February 28		
	2018	**2017**
Net Cash Provided by Operations	$3,034,874	$1,451,845
Net Cash Used by Investing	($1,470,127)	($1,823,523)
Net Cash Used by Financing	($849,432)	$22,826
Net Increase (Decrease) in Cash	$715,315	($348,852)

Required

a) Calculate the following ratios for Yong Wireless Limited for 2018 and 2017. For any ratios that require an average (i.e. ROE), use the closing balance for the year.

	2018	**2017**
Gross Profit Margin		
Net Profit Margin		
Return on Equity		
Return on Assets		
Asset Turnover		
Current Ratio		
Quick Ratio		
Debt-to-Equity Ratio		

b) Based on the figures you calculated, has the company shown improvement in 2018 over 2017? Would you invest in Yong Wireless Limited? Explain.

_____

_____

_____

_____

_____

_____

CS-2 LO 3 4 5

The following information has been taken from the financial statements of Ivory Inc.

Ivory Inc.	
Current Assets, December 31, 2018	$175,000
Total Assets, January 1, 2018	500,000
Total Assets, December 31, 2018	575,000
Current Liabilities, December 31, 2018	75,000
Total Liabilities, December 31, 2018	175,000
Stockholders' Equity, January 1, 2018	300,000
Stockholders' Equity, December 31, 2018	400,000
Net Sales	900,000
Depreciation Expense	10,000
Interest Expense	20,000
Income Tax Expense	25,000
Net Income	40,000

Required

a) Given the data for Ivory Inc., calculate the following ratios for 2018 (round to two decimal places). The company's ratios for 2017 are given for comparison.

	Ratio	2017
i)	Current Ratio	3.5
ii)	Times Interest Earned Ratio	5.40
iii)	Debt-to-Equity	25.00%
iv)	Return on Assets	12.50%
v)	Return on Equity	20.20%
vi)	Net Profit Margin	8.60%

	Ratio	2018
i)		
ii)		
iii)		
iv)		
v)		
vi)		

b) Using 2017 as a comparison, discuss whether the company improved or deteriorated in its ability to (i) pay current liabilities as they come due, (ii) meet its long-term debt obligations and (iii) profitability. Be sure to make reference to specific ratios in your answers.

Critical Thinking

CT-1 LO 7

Financial statement analysis is performed on historical information. Since the past cannot be changed, calculating financial ratios is of no use. What management and investors are really interested in is the future, specifically the future profitability of a company. Discuss.

Notes